Missouri Newspapers:

When and Where

1808 - 1963

Missouri Newspapers:

When and Where
1808 - 1963

Compiled by William H. Taft

School of Journalism

University of Missouri

THE STATE HISTORICAL SOCIETY OF MISSOURI

COLUMBIA, MISSOURI * 1964

Richard S. Brownlee, Director

**Dedicated
to
L. Mitchell White**

Representative of all that is fine

in Missouri Newspaperdom

Foreword

Missouri Newspapers: When and Where is a compilation of nearly six thousand publications that have appeared in the state and where they are located. It is the most thorough that has been prepared for Missouri papers, yet certainly it does not profess to be complete. There are probably dozens of other newspapers that existed, though many for only a brief span. Copies either were not preserved or the publishers failed to earn a more lasting place in the hall of newspaper fame. Too, there are gaps in the foreign-language area. The German-language press has been well covered, through the recent publication of *German-American Newspapers and Periodicals*, a national listing by Karl J. R. Arndt and May E. Olson, published by Quelle and Meyer, Heidelberg. However, the other language papers in Missouri have not been studied adequately, nor have copies been saved as historians would have preferred.

For this study, directories, magazines, newspapers and many other sources have been consulted. All copies of Rowell's *American Newspaper Directory*, published between 1869 and 1908, and Ayer's *Directory of Newspapers and Periodicals*, published since 1880, have been consulted. In addition, other directories with briefer careers were noted, such as Pettengill's *Newspaper Directory and Advertisers' Handbook* and Dauchy's *Newspaper Catalogue*. Winifred Gregory's *American Newspaper, 1821-1936* is another valuable source noting available files, as is the Library of Congress *Newspapers on Microfilm* directory.

The most complete file of Missouri newspapers is in the State Historical Society of Missouri in Columbia. In addition to these holdings, lists of other holdings were obtained from many libraries and historical societies. Not every library, of course, was questioned, although a representative group of the larger ones were. A number of these sources contributed valuable data that aided in verifying starting and ending dates.

Missouri libraries were surveyed and many answered the questionnaires provided by Glenn Davis, a University of Missouri School of Journalism graduate student who assisted in the early phase of this project. Colleges and universities in Missouri were asked to submit lists of their holdings.

Additional material came from the *Missouri Editor*, later named the *Country Editor*, published monthly by Walter Williams and E. W. Stephens in the late 1890's. Since 1933 the Missouri Press Association has published its monthly *Press News* and all copies were reviewed for changes in the newspaper scene. A collection of nameplates helped to prove some starting dates, although in other instances this merely added to the confusion.

Additional sources included Minnie Organ's series on the "History of the County Press in Missouri" that appeared in the *Missouri Historical Review*, April-October 1910, and a thesis by Thomas B. Hammond on more than 1,000 newspapers, with data obtained primarily from county histories.

In numerous cases the compiler has had to make his own decision as to the starting and ending dates. Efforts have been made to verify whenever possible, yet in some cases this could not be done. Publishers have been faithful in "tooting their own horn" to announce the beginning of a newspaper; the silence at the end has been noticeable in its lack of information. Through the publication of this list it is hoped that persons having additional knowledge of Missouri papers will make such data available to the compiler. It is hoped that this project will stimulate additional research and that many of the missing publications will come out of attics, basements, newspaper offices, personal files, and other areas and will be sent to the State Historical Society for microfilming and permanency.

In nearly half of these listings, copies of the papers are available, either at the State Historical Society in Columbia or in one or more of the several hundred sources surveyed.

In indicating source material to justify the listings of each newspaper, frequent notations have been added. These are many, such as "In Rowell 1870-1876, Ayer 1880-1887." In other cases there is a line, "In Ayer 1887 with founding date 1887." This indicates a paper that barely started before the directory was printed. The Ayer directory today, the most complete directory in its field, collects data in late fall for the next year's edition. Thus a paper started in early 1964 may not appear until the 1965 edition.

Many credits are deserved for this project. The co-operation of the State Historical Society of Missouri staff has been most enjoyable, especially that of Kenneth Holmes who has charge of the newspaper reference department. Too, the Society provided the funds necessary for publication of this list. The University of Missouri Research Council furnished a grant for the final typing, a tedious task capably performed by Miss Louise Zimmerly. Historians and librarians across the nation have been encouraging in their contributions of material. The Missouri Press Association, the guiding force behind the founding of the State Historical Society of Missouri, has encouraged this and other studies concerning the state press and has co-operated in providing data. Tom Bell, of the University of Missouri School of Journalism Linotype School, aided in the introductory pages. Special credit must go to those hundreds of publishers since 1808 who have made their printed mark upon the history of Missouri through their newspapers.

William H. Taft

School of Journalism
University of Missouri
January, 1964

Sources

Missouri sources, not counting a number of libraries that only had one or two listings, are included:

MoBoH: Boonville High School, Boonville, Mo.
MoCaT: Southeast State Teachers College,
    Cape Girardeau.
MoCon: Conception Seminary, Conception.
MoHeA: Advertiser-Courier, Hermann.
MoHi: State Historical Society of Missouri, Columbia.
MoJcL: Lincoln University, Jefferson City.
MoKc: Kansas City Public Library, Kansas City.
MoKl: Linda Hall Library, Kansas City.
MoS: St. Louis Public Library, St. Louis.
MoSC: Central Bureau Library, St. Louis
MoSCHi: Concordia Historical Institute, St. Louis.
MoSCon: Concordia Seminary, St. Louis (See MoCon)
MoSHi: Missouri Historical Society, St. Louis.
MoSM: St. Louis Mercantile Library Association,
    St. Louis.
MoSe: Sedalia Public Library, Sedalia.
MoSp: Springfield Public Library, Springfield.
MoSU: St. Louis University, St. Louis.
MoMU: Missouri University Library, Columbia.
MoSW: Washington University Library, St. Louis.
MoSc: St. Charles Public Library, St. Louis.
MoWE: Eden Theological Seminary, Webster Groves.
MoScR: St. Charles Rectory, St. Charles.
MPN: Abbreviation used for *Missouri Press News*.
MHR: Abbreviation used for *Missouri Historical Review*.

The following historical associations and libraries across the nation submitted lists of their holdings:

AzTP: Arizona Pioneers' Historical Society, Tucson, Ariz.
CoD: Denver Public Library, Denver, Colo.
CtY: Yale University, New Haven, Conn.
CL: Los Angeles Public Library, Los Angeles, Calif.
CoU: University of Colorado, Boulder, Colo.
Ct: Connecticut State Library, Hartford, Conn.
CSmH: Henry E. Huntington Library, San Marino, Calif.
DLC: Library of Congress, Washington, D. C.
ICHi: Chicago Historical Society, Chicago, Ill.
IaHi: State Historical Society of Iowa, Iowa City, Iowa.
ICN: Newberry Library, Chicago, Ill.
ICU: University of Chicago Library, Chicago.
IHi: Illinois State Historical Society, Springfield, Ill.
IU: University of Illinois Library, Urbana, Ill.
KHi: Kansas State Historical Society, Topeka, Kansas.
LU: Louisiana State Univerity Library, Baton Rouge, La.
LNT-MA: Tulane University: New Orleans, La.
MnHi: Minnesota Historical Society, Minneapolis, Minn.
MWA: American Antiquarian Society, Worcester, Mass.

NN: New York Public Library, New York, N. Y.
NHi: New York Historical Society, New York, N. Y.
NbHi: Nebraska State Historical Society, Lincoln, Neb.
NcD: Duke University Library, Durham, N. C.
NcU: University of North Carolina, Chapel Hill, N. C.
NmSM: Museum of New Mexico, Santa Fe, N. M.
NjR: Rutgers University Library, New Brunswick, N. J.
OrHi: Oregon Historical Society, Portland, Oregon.
PHi: Historical Society of Pennsylvania, Philadelphia, Pa.
T: Tennessee State Library & Archives, Nashville, Tenn.
USIC: Church of Jesus Christ of Latter-Day Saints,
    Historians' Office Library, Salt Lake City, Utah.
WHi: State Historical Society of Wisconsin,
    Madison, Wis.
WvAr: West Virginia Department of Archives and
    History, Charleston, W. Va.

Miscellaneous Sources

Micro-Photo: Micro Photo Inc., 1700 Shaw Avenue,
    Cleveland 12, Ohio.
Microfilm Service: Microfilm Service & Sales Co.,
    P. O. Box 8066, Dallas, Texas.
Central Microfilm: Central Microfilm Service Corp.,
    2121 Olive Street, St. Louis 3, Mo.

Additional Theses

Ashcraft, James Lee, "Agrarian Reform Newspapers In
    Missouri, 1888-1896," (Master's thesis, University of
    Missouri, 1947).
Brown, Dorothy, "Early Saint Louis Newspapers,
    1808-1850," (Master's thesis, Washington Universi-
    ty, 1931).
Busen, Leonard, "A History of the Newspapers of
    Gasconade County, Missouri From 1843 to 1960,"
    (Master's thesis, University of Missouri, 1960).
Creighton, James H., "A Historical Study of Early
    Boonville Newspapers, 1831-1862," (Master's thesis,
    University of Missouri, 1959).
Rader, Howard A., "Newspaper History of Callaway
    County, Missouri, From 1836 to 1960," (Master's
    thesis, University of Missouri, 1961).
Wilkie, David Lloyd., "Independence, Missouri, News-
    papers, 1832-1900, From Saints to Socialism".
    (Master's thesis, University of Missouri, 1956).

INSTRUCTIONS

This publication has been arranged in alphabetical order according to the communities in Missouri. After each name is given the county. The reader will soon discover that some of these communities have disappeared along with their newspapers.

Newspapers within each community have been listed in alphabetical order. Following the name of each newspaper is the frequency of publication. In many cases this has involved weekly (w), tri-weekly (tw), daily (d), and some irregular publication schedules. Some of the sources listing newspaper holdings did not indicate whether these are weekly, daily, or otherwise. City dailies frequently issued Country editions for rural areas, taking the important items from the dailies and reprinting in weekly or in tri-weekly editions.

An effort has been made here to determine the starting dates as well as the ending dates for these newspapers. However, this has been the most difficut part of this project since much data is missing while other information may provide conflicting dates. The publishers supplied their own copy that appeared in Rowell and Ayer and founding dates varied from time to time. At times this compiler has determined the dates from data not printed here. In many cases, however, it has been necessary to use the question mark (?) to indicate insufficient material to determine an exact date.

In the majority of the listings both the bound and individual copies are indicated, followed by the copies on microfilm. An example to study might be the Alton South Missourian on page 3. In this case the State Historical Society of Missouri (MoHi) has one copy for 1902, plus 1905-1909 copies that are bound. The microfilm copies are available for part of 1898 and 1899. However, MoHi has more copies under a more complete title for this newspaper, the Oregon County South Missourian, for dates listed. In addition, copies are available in at least two other communities, with their dates indicated.

In many cases neither copies nor microfilms are known to be available. In such instances some references are made to the sources used to learn about the paper, as well as other data such as any mergers, sales, changes in names, etc.

The reader is reminded that libraries continue to add to their holdings. Thus it is hoped that a revised edition of this list may be published in five years or so. The cooperation of all who use this list is sought in an effort to add material for future use. The compiler will be happy to supply information on the papers listed here.

W.H.T.

ADRAIN (Bates County)

Advertiser w 1882-1889
    In Rowell 1884-1889, Ayer 1883-1887.

Journal w 1889+
    MoHi: 1919-1944. Film, Aug 14, 1903-1909; 1910 inc; 1911-1918; 1945+

Register w 1885?-1888
    In Rowell, Ayer 1886-1888.

ADVANCE (Stoddard County)

Guard w 1902-1908
    MoHi: Apr 20, 1906-Nov 6, 1908.

New Era w 1911-1919
    MoHi: May 4, 1916-Oct 31, 1918. Film, Apr 17-Dec 4, 1919.

Post w 1901
    In Rowell-Ayer 1902.

Optimist w 1910-1911
    In Ayer 1911.

Stoddard County Journal w 1910-1920?
    In Ayer 1921, founding date 1910.

AFFTON (St. Louis County)

Gravois News w 1946-1948
    In Ayer 1947-1949.

South St. Louis County News w 1947+
    Free paper, first in Ayer 1950.

AGENCY (Buchanan County)

Boomer w 1902-1905?
    In Rowell 1902-1906.

Democrat w 1905-1906?
    In Ayer 1906, Rowell 1907.

Recorder w 1902-1906
    In Rowell 1904-1907, Ayer 1905-1906.

ALBA (Jasper County)

Leader w 1913-1916
    In Ayer 1914-1917.

Review w 1906-1911
    In Rowell 1907, Ayer 1907-1911.

Transcript w 1902
    In Ayer 1903.

ALBANY (Gentry County)

Advance w 1891-1896?
    In Rowell 1892-1897, Ayer 1892-1897.

ALBANY (Continued

Advocate w 1890-1897
   In Rowell, Ayer 1891-1898.

American Freeman w 1874-1884
   See Grand River News. In Rowell 1874-1884, Ayer
   1880-1881.

Argus sw 1904-1905
   In Ayer 1905-1906, Rowell 1906.

Capital w 1890-1957
   MoHi: Aug 2, 1901-1944. Film, 1945-1957.
   Merged with Ledger, Jan 10, 1957.

Courier w 1857-1861
   Mentioned by Organ, Hammond.

Democrat w 1876
   In Rowell 1876, starting date 1876.

Farmer w 1896
   Start noted in Missouri Editor, Feb 1896.

Gentry County Beacon w 1874
   Mentioned in county history.

Gentry County Capital w 1887
   In Rowell-Ayer 1888.

Gentry County Chronicle w 1875-1877?
   Mentioned in county history.

Gentry County News w 1864-1873?
   NHi: w, Apr 9, 1873, which reads "Vol 10, No. 1,
   Established in 1864."

Ledger w 1868+
   MoHi: 1920-1944. Film, Jly 11, 1884-1919; 1945+
   MWA: Oct 5, 1876.
   ICHi: May 18, 1876.

Grand River News w 1864-1873
   Changed to American Freeman, became anti-
   monopoly reform paper, according to Organ.

Memoranda w 1884-1885?
   In Rowell 1885-1886, Dauchy 1885.

Missouri Farmer w 1895-1896
   In Ayer 1897.

Press w 1878?
   In Pettengill 1878.

Republic, or Republican w 1888-1889
   Republican in Ayer 1889, Republic 1890.

Sun w 1880-1882, 1886?
   First Greenback. Second in Rowell 1887.

ALDRICH (Polk County)

Enterprise w 1897
   In Ayer 1898.

Journal w 1911?
   In Ayer 1912.

Record w 1909-1910
   In Ayer 1910-1911.

Register w 1889
   In Ayer 1890.

Times w 1912
   In Ayer 1913.

ALEXANDRIA (Clark County)

Blade w 1867
   W. H. Resor attended editors' meeting 1867.

Commercial w 1869-1880?
   MoHi: Mar 14, Apr 25, May 16, 23, 1872; Jan 23,
      Aug 14, 1873; Sep 4, 1879. Film, Mar 2, 1871-
      Oct 2, 1873.
   IU: 1869-1878.
   ICHi: May 25, 1876.

Delta w 1856-1863
   MoHi: Apr 17, 1861.

Delta Sun w 1905-1911?
   MoHi: Film, May 5, 1905-Apr 27, 1906.

Democrat w 1881-1882?
   MoHi: Aug 15, 1882. In Ayer 1883.

North Missourian w 1854-1855
   MoHi: Feb 20, 1855.

Old Homestead w 1899-1900?
   In Rowell 1900-1901, Ayer 1900.

Reveille w 1850-1859
   Mentioned by Organ.

True Flag w 1864-1866
   MoHi: Feb 16, 1865.

ALLEN DALE (Worth County)

Mineral Springs Chronicle w 1881-1882
   IHi: Jly 21, 1882.

ALMA (Lafayette County)

Courier w 1937-1941.
   In Ayer 1939-1940. Stopped 1941.

ALTAMONT (Daviess County)

Index w 1895-1907?
   In Rowell 1896-1908, Ayer 1896-1906.

Live Wire w 1913-1915?
   In Ayer 1914-1916.

ALTAMONT (continued)

Times   w   1908+
    In Ayer 1910, founding date 1908.

ALTON (Oregon County)

Oregon County Democrat   w   1898-1909
    MoHi: Jly 26, 1901-1905. Became South Missourian-
    Democrat May 6, 1909.

Record   w   1911-1916
    In Ayer 1913-1917.

Republican   w   1908
    In Ayer 1909.

South Missourian-Democrat   w   1871+
    MoHi: May 6, 1909-Nov 1925; Feb 1926-1944.
    Film, 1945+

South Missourian   w   1871-1909
    MoHi: May 1, 1902; Aug 10, 1905-Apr 29, 1909.
    Film, Dec 1, 1898-May 18, 1899. Became
    Oregon County South Missourian May 25, 1899.
    Back to South Missourian Aug 10, 1905. MoHi
    has bound, Jly 18, 1901-Aug 3, 1905. Film,
    May 25, 1899-Jun 7, 1900 of Oregon County
    South Missourian.
    MoSHi: Mar 21, 1889.
    ICHi: Jly 8, 22, 1876.

AMORET (Bates County)

Beacon   w   1899-1902?
    In Rowell 1900-1903, Ayer 1896-1901.

Chief   w   1890-1892
    In Ayer 1890-1891, Rowell 1891-1892.
    KHi: Oct 3, 1890-Dec 30, 1892.

Enterprise   w   1892
    In Ayer 1892, starting date 1892.

Leader   w   1912-1923
    In Ayer 1915-1924.
    KHi: Oct 7, 1915.

Ledger   w   1897
    In Ayer 1898.

News   w   1897-1898
    In Rowell 1898-1899, Ayer 1899.

Post   w   1906-1911
    In Rowell 1907-1908, Ayer 1907-1912.

AMSTERDAM (Bates County)

Argus   w   1895
    Start in Missouri Editor, Sep 1895.

Border Banner   w   1931-1944
    Sold to Butler Times 1944.

AMSTERDAM (continued)

Border Breezes   w   1894-1900
    Last in Rowell 1901.

Border Chief   w   1890-1893
    KHi: Jan 6-Jun 3, 1893.

Clipper   w   1904-1913?
    In Ayer 1914, founding date 1904.

Enterprise   w   1903?-1923?
    MoHi: 1906-Nov 1907; 1909-1910; 1913-Nov 21,
    1918. Film, Jly 9, 1903-1905; Nov 14, 1907-
    1908; 1911-1912.

Enterprise-Leader   w   1902-1923?
    Union List says probably known as Enterprise these
    years.
Local   w   1903-1915
    In Ayer 1916 with 1903 founding date.

Tempest   w   1900-1902
    In Rowell 1901-1905, Ayer 1901-1903.

ANDERSON (McDonald County)

Advocate   w   1896-1898?
    In Rowell 1897-1899, Ayer 1897-1899.

Argus   w   1900-1905
    MoHi: 1901-Dec 8, 1905. Renamed McDonald
    County Republican Jan 1905.

Banner   w   1905
    In Rowell 1906.

Broadax   w   1899-1902
    In Rowell 1902-1903.

Enterprise   w   1927
    In Rowell 1928.

McDonald County Republican   w   1900-1908?
    MoHi: Dec 7, 1906-Sep 6, 1907. See Argus.

Messenger   w   1893-1895
    In Rowell, Ayer 1894-1896.

News   w   1900-1914
    Ayer 1915 refers to News-Review.

News-Review   w   1900+
    MoHi: Film, May 15, 1914-1919; Jly 30, 1959+.
    Formed by merger of News and Review May 1914.

Review   w   1912-1914
    MoHi: Film, Jan 2-May 1, 1914.

ANNAPOLIS (Iron County)

Mountain Echo   w   1937-1944
    MoHi: Film, Aug 29, 1941-Dec 29, 1944. Moved to
    Ironton 1944.

ANNAPOLIS (continued)

    Record   w   1927-1929
        In Ayer 1928-1930.

ANUTT (Dent County)

    West End Booster   w   1911-1913?
        In Ayer 1913-1914.

APPLETON CITY (St. Clair County)

    Argus   w   1871
        In Rowell 1872.

    Courier   w   1879-1881
        See St. Clair County Courier.

    Democrat   w   1875-1876
        MoHi: Film, Nov 2,1875-Jun 1,1876.
        ICHi: Mar 9,1876.

    Democratic Standard   w   1885-1886?
        In Rowell 1886-1887, Ayer 1887.

    Gazette   w   1873-1875
        Became Pilot in 1875, later moved to Osceola.
        Listed in Rowell 1874-1875. Copy dated May 7,
        1873 (Vol 1, No 9) titled St. Clair Gazette.

    Herald   w   1890-1902?
        In Rowell 1895-1903, Ayer 1898-1900.

    Journal   w   1881+
        MoHi: 1903-1904; 1913-Apr 6,1944. Film, Mar
          16-Dec 14,1882; 1883-Jan 1884; Mar 20-Sep
          4,1884; Oct 1884-1885; Feb-Dec 1886; Jan
          20,1887-Nov 15,1888; Dec 1888-Nov 1889;
          1890-1902; 1905-Dec 19,1912; Apr 13,1944+
          Leader established 1878, called Courier 1879-
          1881, Pantagraph Jan 8 to Aug 1881, then Journal.

    Leader   w   1878-1879
        MoHi: Mar 6,1879.

    News   w   1871
        Mentioned by Hammond, short-lived.

    Pantagraph   w   1881
        In Ayer 1881 as founded in 1879.

    Pilot   w   1875-1878?
        ICHi: Apr 19,1876. Moved to Osceola.

    Southwestern Democrat   w   1887-1888
        In Rowell-Ayer 1888.

    Star   w   1891-1894
        In Rowell 1892-1894, Ayer 1892-1895.

    St. Clair County Courier   w   1879-1881
        Also referred to as Courier.

    Tribune   w   1900-1909
        Last listed in Ayer 1910.

APPLETON CITY (continued)

    Voice   w   1878-1881
        To Osceola, became Voice of the People.

ARCADIA (Iron County)

    Prospect   w   1859-1860
        Moved to Ironton 1860, suspended 1861.

ARCHIE (Cass County)

    Advance   w   1897-1898
        In Rowell 1897-1899, Ayer 1898-1899.

    Enterprise   w   1894-1897
        Death noted in Country Editor Feb 1897.

    Herald   w   1884-
        In Dauchy 1884.

    New Era   w   1885
        In Rowell-Ayer 1886.

    News   w   1899-1900
        In Rowell 1900-1901, Ayer 1900.

    Tribune   w   1907-1908
        In Rowell 1908, Ayer 1908-1909.

ARDEOLA (Stoddard County)

    Banner   w   1892
        In Ayer 1892 with 1892 founding date.

    Mineral Avalanche   w   1881-1883?
        Mentioned in county history.

ARMSTRONG (Howard County)

    Autograph   w   1883-1884
        In Ayer 1883, Rowell 1884.

    Herald   w   1888-1960
        MoHi: 1934-1944; Jly 20,1894; Jan 7,1904. Film,
          1888-1921; 1932-1933; 1945-1960.
        MoSHi: Oct 14,1915. Ended Nov 17,1960.

ARROW ROCK (Saline County)

    Democratic Cable   w   1870-1871
        In Rowell 1872.

    Enterprise   w   1891-1893
        MoHi: Film, Jly 24,1891-Oct 6,1893.

    Saline County Herald   w   1856-1861
        Mentioned by Organ.

    Statesman   w   1893-1919
        MoHi: Aug 14,1908; 1917-Apr 25,1919. Film,
          1897-Sep 16,1898; Nov 25,1898-1899; 1900-
          Nov 23,1917.

ARROW ROCK (continued)

Times   w   1881-1890, 1920-1921
MoSHi: Nov 24, 1881
In Rowell 1883-1890, Ayer 1883-1890, 1922.

ASBURY (Jasper County)

News   w   1896
In Ayer 1897.

ASH GROVE (Greene County)

Advance   w   1897-1904
MoHi: Jan-Dec 1903; Feb-Jun 1904.

American   w   1891
People's Party paper, brief career.

Commonwealth   w   1881+
MoHi: Jly-Dec 1904; 1914-1944; Mar 30, 1905;
Jly 16, 1908; Jun 11, Jly 2, 1914. Film, 1945+

Republican   w   1892-1898
In Rowell 1893-1899, Ayer 1892-1898.

Searchlight   w   1901
In Ayer 1902.

ASHLAND (Boone County)

Bugle   w   1877-1941
MoHi: 1910-Aug 1, 1941; Jly 27, 1895. Film, Sep
3, 1903-Dec 19, 1907. Suspended Aug 1, 1941.

ASHBURN (Pike County)

Willow Bark Herald   m   1895
MoHi: Sep 1895. "Devoted to Reform."

ATLANTA (Macon County)

Argus   w   1892-1895
Burned out 1895.

Express   w   1908+
MoHi: 1919-Mar 30, 1933. Film, Oct 10, 1913-1918.

News   w   1896-1907
MoHi: Film, 1903--May 31, 1907.

AUD (Osage County)

News Visitor   w   1895-1898?
In Rowell 1896-1899, Ayer 1896.

AUGUSTA (St. Charles County)

Record   w   1883-1884
In Rowell 1884-1885.

AULLVILLE (Lafayette County)

Herald   w   1872
In Rowell 1873.

AULLVILLE (continued)

Times   w   1873?
In Rowell 1874 and county history.

AURORA (Lawrence County)

Advertiser   w,d   1886?+
MoHi: D, Nov 1948-50. Film 1951+ W, Mar 20),
1908-1944; 1945-Oct 28, 1948. Earlier attempt
at daily ceased in 1895. Began daily again
1948.
KHi: W, Sep 7, 1922; D, Oct 23, 1924.

Advertiser-Herald   w   1889-1903
MoHi: Jan 8-Aug 6, 1903. Became Christian Herald
Aug 6, 1903.

Argus   d   1891-1911   w   1886-1899?
MoHi: Jly 1903-Jun 1904; Mar 13, 1903.

Christian Herald   w   1903-1904
MoHi: Aug 11-Dec 29, 1903.

Cresset   w   1881-1883?
Mentioned by Hammond.

Daily Light   d   1914-1918?
In Ayer 1918-1919.

Herald   d,w   1888-1895
Evening Herald   1888-1894. Weekly called
Lawrence County Herald. See Republican.
In Ayer 1891, 1894.

Free Press   w   1933+
First in Ayer 1948.

Gazette   w   1888-1894?
In Rowell 1889-1892, Ayer 1895.

Menace   w   1911-1919?
MoHi: Nov 11, 1911-Dec 6, 1919. Anti-Catholic.
MoSHi: Jun 28, Jly 19, 1913; Jan 22, 1916; Apr
20, Nov 16, 1919; Jan 11, 1919.
CoD: Jan 4, 1913; Apr 15, 1916.
DLC: Film, Jun 3-Dec 1911; 1912-1915.
KHi: Oct 28, 1911-Oct 24, 1914 inc; Apr 26, Nov
22, 1913; Dec 6, 1919.
MnHi: Jan 15, Feb 12, Apr 22, 1916.
NcD: Nov 1, 1913; Apr 10, 1915; Jun 29, Aug 10-
31, Sep-Dec 1918; Jan 4, 11, 25, Feb 1, 8, Jun
28, Aug 9-23, Sep-Dec 6, 1919.
PHi: Jun 29, Oct 26, Nov 2, 23, 1912.
T: Jan 23, 1915.
WHi: Sep 23, Oct 28, 1911: Oct 10, 1914-Dec 6, 1914.

Mining News   w   1891
In Ayer 1891.

Monitor   w   1911?-1941
WHi: Jan 7, 1928-1937.
In Ayer 1941-1942 with 1911 founding date.

AURORA (continued)

Nationalist w 1888-1892?
In Rowell 1893 with 1888 founding date.

News d 1888?-1913?
Associated with weekly Argus 1897, Southwest Republican 1907. Nameplate for Daily News, May 31, 1898, is Vol II, No. 216.

New Menace w 1921-1929?
MoHi: Nov 19, 1921-Oct 20, 1928 inc. Also published at Branson.
MoSHi: Dec 21, 1928; Feb 16, 23, Mar 2-16, Apr 27, May 4, 1929.
KHi: Jun 21-Aug 2, 1924; Oct 16, 1926.

Register w 1882
Mentioned in county histories.

Republican w 1888-?
In Apr 1895 Missouri Republican reported Herald had changed name to Republican.

Southwest Miner w 1901-1904
In Rowell 1902-1903, Ayer 1902-1905.

Times w 1886-1890, 1896
MoHi: Oct 24, 1890. Apparently another Times later, since Missouri Editor, Sep 1896, notes "The Aurora Times has suspended. Cause - out of paper and no money to buy paper with."

Torch sm 1920-1922?
NcD: Jun 15, Jly 1, 15, Aug 1, Sep 15, Oct 15, Nov 1, 15, 1920; Jan 1, Feb 1, 15, Mar 15, Apr 15, May 1, 15, Jun 15, Jly 1, 15, Aug 1, 15, Sep 15, 1921; Jan 1, 15, May 1, 1922.
NN: Apr 1, 1922.
WHi: Apr 15, 1921.

World d 1914-1916
MoHi: Jly 6, 1914.

AURORA SPRINGS (Lawrence County)

Autogram w 1883-1884
In Rowell 1884-1885, Ayer 1883. In 1885 Became Tuscumbia Miller County Autogram.

Democrat w 1888-1889?
MoHi: Mar 30, 1888. Film, Apr 6, 1888-Aug 29, 1889.

Eldon Register w 1881
In Rowell 1882.

Messenger w 1886-1887?
In Ayer 1886-1887, Rowell 1887.

AUXVASSE (Callaway County)

Optic w 1899
In Ayer 1900.

AUXVASSE (continued)

Review w 1888-1962
MoHi: 1903-1944; Oct 30, 1890; Mar 1, 8, 1939. Film, Jan 11, 1889-Mar 25, 1891; May 7, 1891-1902; 1945-1962.
MoSHi: Nov 16, 1911; Jun 12, Jly 31, Aug 7, 21, Sep 4, 1913. Suspended Sep 26, 1962.

AVA (Douglas County)

Douglas County Advance w 1905?-1909
In Ayer 1910 with 1905 founding date.

Douglas County Advocate and the Ozark Breeze w 1905-1909
MoHi: Feb 25, 1909.

Douglas County Capital w 1930-1938
In Ayer 1931-1938.

Douglas County Democrat w 1887-1904?, 1901-1907?, 1916-1918?
Apparently three under this title.

Douglas County Herald w 1887+
MoHi: Feb 20, 1899-Feb 1900; Feb 28, 1901-Dec 1913; 1916-1944; Feb 22, 1906. Film, Mar 10, 1887-Feb 21, 1901; 1914-1915; 1945+

Douglas County Journal w 1916-1920
MoHi: Feb 20, 1919-Sep 9, 1920. Formerly Douglas County Democrat.

Douglas County Leader w 1877?
In Pettengill 1877, no founding date.

Douglas County Public Record w 1885-1886?
In Rowell-Ayer 1886.

Douglas County Record w 1910-1916
See Enterprise.

Douglas County Republican w 1885, 1903-1904?
Apparently two under this title.

Enterprise w 1910-1915
MoHi: Oct 1913-Oct 1915. Became Douglas County Record Nov 4, 1915.

Farm Record w 1890-1902?
Supported Farmers' and Laborers' Union.

Ozark Breeze w 1905-1909
See Douglas County Advocate.

Times w 1879-1880
In Rowell 1880-1881, Ayer 1880.

AVALON (Livingston County)
Aurora w 1880-1906?
Last in Rowell 1907, Ayer 1906.

AVONDALE (Clay County)
Sentinel w 1926-1930?
In Ayer 1928-1930.

BAGNELL (Miller County)

Dam News   w   1929
    Start noted in Editor & Publisher Aug 10, 1929.

BAKER (St. Clair County)

Banner of Truth   m   1882-1884
    Anti-Masonic, anti-secret society.

BAKERSFIELD (Ozark County)

Blade   w   1913-1914
    In Ayer 1915.

Boomerange   w   1898-1902
    MoHi: Film, Feb 8,15,22,1901; Jly 27,1901-Jly
    5,1902.

Breeze   w   1903
    In Rowell-Ayer 1904.

Informer   w   1894-1898
    Last in Rowell 1899.

News   w   1905-1914?,1915-1925,1928-1945?
    MoHi: Apr 15,1905-1906; 1909-1910.
    At least three different News.

Observer   w   1915?
    In Ayer 1915 with 1905 founding date.

Republican   w   1879?-1899?,1903-1904?
    Ayer 1900 lists one, founded 1879. Ayer 1905 lists
    second.

Republican-Informer   w   1901
    In Rowell-Ayer 1901.

Tidings of the Times   w   1885-1886
    In Rowell 1887.

BALLWIN (St. Louis County)

Community Press   w   1935-1951?
    Last in Ayer 1951.

BARING (Knox County)

Messenger   w   1905-1912,1915-1917?
    Apparently two under this title.

Record   w   1889-1890
    In Rowell 1890-1891, Ayer 1889-1890.

Review   w   1916
    In Ayer 1917.

BARNARD (Nodaway County)

Advertiser   w   1888-1889
    In Rowell 1889-1890, Ayer 1888-1889.

BARNARD (continued)

Bulletin   w   1889-1941
    Discontinued 1941.

Chronicle   w   1883?-1885?
    In Rowell-Ayer 1886.

Gazette   w   1883-1887
    Followed by Regulator.

Herald   w   1890-?
    In Ayer 1890-1891, Rowell 1891.

Regulator   w   1887-1888?
    Apparently succeeded Gazette in 1887.

Rustler   w   1891-1899?
    Last in Ayer 1900.

Times   w   1877-1881
    Issued in Maryville Jan 7,1881.

BARNETT (Morgan County)

Enterprise   w   1905
    In Rowell-Ayer 1906.

BELGRADE (Washington County)

Messenger   w   1898-1900
    In Ayer 1900 as District Messenger.

BELL CITY (Stoddard County)

News   w   1919?
    MoCat: 1919.

BELLE (Maries County)

Banner   w   1904+
    MoHi: Sep 12,1929-1944. Film, 1945+
    Publisher lists 1904 founding.

Maries County Times   w   1896-1901
    MoHi: Under Times, Mar 22,1906-Sep 2,1909.
    Film, Jan 2,1903-Dec 24,1903. Merged with
    Republican-Star to form Star-Times Aug 21,1903.
    On Dec 24,1903 changed to Times.

Republican-Star   w   1902-1903
    MoHi: Film, Jan 2-Aug 14,1903. See Times.

Review   w   1904-1908
    MoHi: Dec 27,1907; Jan 3,1908; Apr 5,1906-1907.

Star-Times   w   1903
    MoHi: Film, Aug 21-Dec 18,1903. Formed by merg-
    er Aug 21,1903. Became Times Dec 24,1903.

Times   w   1896-1916
    MoHi: Mar 22,1906-Sep 2,1909. Film, Jan 2-
    Dec 24,1903.

BELLEVIEW (Iron County)

Ozark Banner   w   1905-1908?
   In Rowell 1907-1908, Ayer 1907-1910.

People's Banner   w   1905
   MoSHi: Apr 29,1905. Apparently name used by
   Ozark Banner for 1905.

BELLFLOWER (Montgomery County)

News   w   1903-1940
   MoHi: Jly 26,1906-Jun 1918.

Montgomery County Times   w   1915-1916
   In Ayer 1917.

Telegram   w   1903-1906
   MoHi: Film, 1904-Jly 6,1906. Changed to News
   Jly 26,1906.

BELMONT (Mississippi County)

Recruit   w   1898-1900?
   In Ayer 1899, Rowell 1899-1901.

BELTON (Cass County)

Cass County Leader   w   1880-1895
   MoSHi: Jly 31,1886.

Cass County Review   w   1896
   In Ayer 1897.

Herald   w   1891-1923
   MoHi: Aug 16,1901-1903; 1905-1906; 1913-1916.
   Film, 1904; 1919,1922. Became Star-Herald
   May 17,1923.
   KHi: Mar 3,1921.

Mirror   w   1880-1882
   Became Cass County Leader 1882.

Progress   w   1875-1876
   ICHi: Jan 8,1876. In Rowell 1876.

Reporter   w   1874-1875
   In Rowell 1875.

Shopper   w   1958+
   Free distribution paper.

Star   w   1916-1923
   In Ayer 1919-1923.

Star-Herald   w   1891+
   MoHi: 1923-1928; Mar 7,21,28,Apr 4,18,May 9,
   16,Jun 6,13,Jly 4,11,25,Aug 1,8,Sep 26,Oct
   3,10,31,1929; Mar 13,1930. See Herald.
   KHi: Dec 27,1923.

BENTON (Scott County)

Enterprise   w   1894-1895
   In Rowell 1895, Dauchy 1896.

BENTON (continued)

Express   w   1880-1895
   Record established 1879, bought Express 1884,
   became Express-Record.

Express-Record   w   1884
   See Record.

Free Press   w   1884-1886
   In Rowell 1886-1887, Dauchy 1885.

Record   w   1879-1908
   MoHi: Oct 31,1890; Nov 25,1898-1899; 1903-
   1908.

Scott County Kicker   w   1902-1917
   Listed as socialist paper.

Scott County Democrat   w   1908+
   MoHi: 1909-1944. Film, 1945+

Scott County Newsboy   w   1888-1902
   Listed Ayer 1902 as Newsboy.

BERKELEY (St. Louis County)

Public News   w   1949+
   In Ayer 1961.

BERNIE (Stoddard County)

Banner   w   1929?-1949
   Bakersfield News, Banner combined 1946.

Independent   w   1899
   In Ayer 1900.

News   w   1913-1915
   MoHi: Film, Oct 17,1913-Jly 30,1915. Merged
   with Star to form Star-News Oct 8,1915.

Newsboy   w   1923-1935
   MoHi: Feb 22,1923-Nov 21,1929. Moved to Poplar
   Bluff 1935, became Butler County Leader.

Progress   w   1920-1922
   In Ayer 1921-1923.

Star   w   1906-1915
   MoHi: Aug 2-23,Sep 20,Oct 4-25,Nov 1-29,Dec
   20,1912; Jan 3,10,24,1913. See News.

Star-News   w   1915-1920?
   MoHi: Mar 30,1917. Film,Oct 8,Nov 19,1915;
   Jan 28,1916-Dec 26,1919.

Times   w   1900-1901?
   In Ayer 1901.

BETHANY (Harrison County)

Broadax   w   1877-1890
   Name changed to Democrat 1890?

BETHANY (continued)

Clipper   w   1905-1929
   MoHi: Oct 7,1905-Jan 30,1929. Merged with
   Republican Feb 6,1929. See Blythedale
   Clipper.

Democrat   w   1877-1920?
   MoHi: Jly 24,1901-Oct 1920. Also called Harrison
   County Democrat.

Farmers' Rustler   w   1894-1895?
   People's Party paper in Dauchy 1896.

Harrison County Herald   w   1859-1876
   Union List says known as Star 1859-1865?, North
      Missouri Tribune 1865-1871?, Tribune 1872-1874.
   ICHi: Jly 20,1876.
   MWA: Jan 25,1866.

Harrison County Press   w   1868-1870
   Became Watchman 1870, moved to Grant City as
   Worth County Times.

Harrison County Times and Gilman City Guide   w
1931-1956
   MoHi: Sep 1931-1944. Film, 1945-Nov 24,1949;
      Feb 9,1950-Dec 1954; 1955-Jan 5,1956.
      Suspended Jan 5,1956.

Harrison County Tribune   w   1897-1898
   In Rowell 1897-1898, Ayer 1898-1899.

North Missouri Tribune   w   1865-1871
   See Harrison County Herald.

Owl   w   1901-1904?
   MoHi: Film, Jly 8-Dec 30,1903.

Republican   w   1873-1929
   MoHi: Jly 1901-1902; 1904-1905; 1908-1921;
      1924-Jan 30,1929; May 6,1888; Dec 12,1887;
      Sep 3,1908; Dec 19,1889. Film, 1903;
      1906-1907; 1922-1923. Merged with Clipper
      Feb 6,1929.
   KHi: Jun 1,1927.
   ICHi: Jly 6,13,1876.

Republican-Clipper   w   1873+
   MoHi: Feb 6,1929-1943. Film 1944+
      See Clipper and Republican.

Star   w   1859-1861
   MoHi: Jan 5,1860. Renamed Weekly Union 1861.
   MoKc: Aug 4,1859-Jun 6,1860, inc.

Tribune   w   1872-1874
   See Harrison County Herald.

Watchman   w   1870-1873
   See Harrison County Press.

Weekly Union   w   1861-1863
   See next listing.

BETHANY (continued)

Weekly Union of States   w   1863-1865
   Formerly Star, later Weekly Union. In 1865 became
   North Missouri Tribune.

BETHEL (Shelby County)

Missouri Sun   w   1896-1903?
   In Rowell 1900 as Missourian.

News   w   1896-1898
   In Rowell 1897-1899, Ayer 1897-1898.

BEVIER (Macon County)

Appeal   w   1889-1925
   MoHi: Jly 26,1901-Sep 1921; Oct 31,1890; Feb
      10,1905. Moved to Clarence, became the
      Shelby County Independent.

Macon County Citizen   w   1893-1896
   In Rowell 1894-1896, Ayer 1894-1897.

Macon County Journal and Bevier Press-Appeal   w
1889-?
   MWA: Apr 5,1932.
   Union List says 1889-1923 as Appeal; 1924-32?
      Press-Appeal Ayer 1934-35 lists paper as
      established 1922. Final listing Ayer 1935.

Post   w   1888-1890
   MoHi: Photostat Aug 21,1889.

Press-Appeal   w   1924-1932?
   See Macon County Journal. Name probably used
   for dates shown.

Western Sun-Burst   w   1881-1882?
   In Rowell 1882.

BIGELOW (Holt County)

Enterprise   w   1902-1904
   MoHi: Jan 1-Jly 1,15,1904.

BILLINGS (Christian County)

Advertiser   w   1885-1886?
   In Rowell 1886-1887, Ayer 1886.

Banner   w   1904
   In Rowell 1905.

Bee   w   1891-1899?
   In Rowell 1892-1903, Ayer 1892-1900.

Journal   w   1903
   In Ayer 1904.

News Record   w   1881-1882?
   In Rowell 1882.

Post   w   1891-1902
   In Ayer 1903.

BILLINGS (continued)

Record   w   1881-1882
   Name also used for News Record, as listed in
   Ayer 1882.

Reformer   w   1875-1876
   In Rowell 1876.
   ICHi: Mar 8, 1876.

Southwest Missourian   w   1878?
   In Pettengill 1878.

Times   w   1882-1953
   MoHi: Dec 1898-Nov 1899; Jun 1900-1920;
      1925-1944. Film, 1945-1953. Suspended Oct
      29, 1953, merged with Ozark Christian County
      Republican.
   MoSHi: Dec 4, 1919.
   KHi: Jan 10, 1924.

BIRCH TREE   (Shannon County)

Eagle   w   1906-1907
   In Rowell 1907-1908, Ayer 1907.

Planer   w   1893
   In Rowell 1894.

Record   w   1893-1907
   MoHi: Dec 1, 1898-Jun 1905.

Shannon County Herald   w   1907-1948
   MoHi: 1914-1918; Jun 1919-1922.
   KHi: Mar 27, 1924.

Shannon County Times   w   1889
   In Ayer 1889 with 1889 founding date.

BIRMINGHAM   (Clay County)

Locomotive   w   1888-1889?
   In Ayer-Rowell 1889.

BISMARCK   (St. Francois County)

Banner   w   1904
   WHi: Aug 20, 1904.

Blade   w   1891
   In Ayer 1891 with 1891 founding date.

Gazette   w   1901+
   MoHi: 1908-1919; May 1932-1944. Film, May 4,
      1906-Dec 27, 1907; 1945+

Herald   w   1890
   In Ayer 1890.

Sun   w   1902-1905?
   In Rowell 1902-1906, Ayer 1903.

Telegram   w   1885-1888?
   In Rowell 1886-1888, Ayer 1887.

BLACKBURN   (Saline County)

Bulletin   w   1883
   In Rowell 1884.

Globe   w   1883-1887
   In Rowell 1885-1888, Ayer 1887.

New Record   w   1920-1922?
   In Ayer 1921-1923.

Record   w   1889-1914
   MoHi: Jly 26, 1901-Sep 1914; Feb 10, 1905.
   MoSHi: Sep 26, 1913.

Reporter   w   1883
   In Dauchy 1884

BLACK OAK   (Caldwell County)

Comet   w   1881
   Listed in Rowell 1882.

BLACKWATER   (Cooper County)

Advance   w   1889
   In Rowell 1889 with 1889 founding date.

Echo   w   1893
   In Rowell 1893 with 1893 founding date.

News   w   1898-1923, 1938-?
   MoHi: Jly 26, 1901-May 1917. Two different
      News in Blackwater.

Times   w   1895-1897
   In Rowell-Ayer 1896. Death reported in Country
      Editor, Feb 1897.

Wave   w   1890
   In Ayer 1890 with 1890 founding date.

BLACKWELL   (St. Francois County)

Herald   w   1913-1915?
   In Ayer 1915-1916.

BLAIRSTOWN   (Henry County)

Banner   w   1891-1892?
   MoHi: Nov 19, 1891.

Courier   w   1904
   In Rowell 1905.

Herald   w   1902-1917?
   Last listed in Ayer 1918.

Record   w   1914-1924, 1925-1950?
   Two different Records appeared.

Times   w   1893-1902?
   In Rowell 1901-1903, Ayer 1895-1900.

BLAND (Gasconade County)

Courier w 1904+
    MoHi: May 6, 1904-1912; 1923-1924. Film,
      Jan 3, 1913-Dec 22, 1922.
    KHi: Feb 22, 1924.

BLOOMFIELD (Stoddard County)

Argus w 1866-1873?, 1896
    Two under this title. In Rowell 1869-1871 with
    1866 founding date. Missouri Editor, Mar 1896,
    tells of Argus start.

Cosmos w 1896-1900
    In Rowell 1897-1901, Ayer 1897-1900.

Courier w 1900-1905?
    In Rowell 1906, Ayer 1901-1909.

Enterprise w 1896-1900
    Populist. In Rowell 1898-1901, Ayer 1900.

Enterprise-Messenger w 1879-1880?
    See Dexter City reference.

Herald w 1858-1861 w 1833?
    Apparently two since DLC has copy of Herald,
    Oct 3, 1833.

Southeast Reporter w 1871-1874
    MoHi: Film, Jan 17-Jly 30, 1874. In Rowell
    1873-1875.

Stars and Stripes w 1861-?
    NN: Nov 9, 1861, photostat.
    DLC: Nov 9, 1861, first issue.
    Published temporarily in Herald plant.

Stoddard County Guard w 1896-1901?
    Populist paper in Rowell 1902.

Stoddard County Messenger w 1874-1877
    MoHi: Jan 1-29, 1876.
    ICHi: Jun 17, Jly 8, 1876.
    To Dexter, consolidated with Enterprise.

Stoddard County Republican w 1910-1912? w 1896
    Another under this title in 1896, apparently failed
    to last long enough for inclusion in a directory.

Stoddard Tribune w 1913-1935?
    MoHi: 1917-Jun 1922; 1923-Dec 18, 1934.

Vindicator w 1878+
    MoHi: May 1902-1903; 1908-1918; 1921-1944;
    Sep 1, Oct 6, Nov 3, 17, 24, Dec 1, 29, 1888;
    Jan 5, 19, 26, Feb 2, 1889; Mar 19, Jan 8, 1909;
    Jly 28, 1905; May 1, 1908. Film, Sep 25, 1880-
    Dec 10, 1881; 1882-1887; Jan 28, 1888-1891;
    1894; Nov 22, 1895-Dec 11, 1896; 1897-Nov
    24, 1899; Feb 23, 1900-May 1902; 1904-1907;
    1919-1920; 1945+

BLOOMINGTON (Macon County)

Central Register w 1854-1856
    Formerly Republican, later Messenger, according to
    Organ.

Gazette w 1848-1853
    MoHi: Jan 22, Feb 5, Jun 4, 1851 photostat. One
    source says became Journal 1853.
Herald w 1856
    In Newspaper Record 1856.

Journal 1853-1854
    MoSHi: Jly 2, 1853
    NcD: Jly 9, 1853.

Macon Legion w 1859-1861
    Mentioned by Organ.

Messenger w 1856-1859
    Formerly Central Register, later Macon Legion.

Republican w 1851-1854
    See Central Register.

BLUE SPRINGS (Jackson County)

Herald w 1887-1890, 1923-1951
    MoHi: Nov 23, 1923-1934; 1941-1944. Film, 1935-
    1938; 1939-1940; 1945-Oct 26, 1951. Merged
    with Buckner Record and Blue Springs Jackson
    County Democrat to become Blue Springs Herald
    Democrat Nov 2, 1951.
    KHi: Jun 24, 1927.

Herald-Democrat w 1951-1952?
    MoHi: Film, Nov 2, 1951-Jan 4, 1952.

Jackson County Democrat w 1911+
    MoHi: Film, 1950-Oct 26, 1951; Jan 11-Apr 11,
    1952. Published at Buckner Apr 18, 1952, prior
    to 1950 at Fairmont.

Leader w 1956+
    MoHi: Aug 1958+. First in Ayer 1958.

News w 1891-1900?
    Last listed Rowell-Ayer 1901.

Sentinel w 1959?
    In Ayer 1959 with founding date 1866.

Sni-a-Bar Voice w 1901-1923
    MoHi: 1906-Dec 21, 1923; Sep 15, 1905. Film,
    1903-1905. Merged with Herald Dec 28, 1923.

BLYTHEDALE (Harrison County)

Clipper w 1877-1882
    Established as Eagleville Clipper, moved to
    Bethany 1882, according to Hammond. Not in
    Ayer until 1907.

Gazette w 1898-1905
    In Rowell 1898-1906, Ayer 1900-1905.

BLYTHEDALE (continued)

Review w 1895-1897?
In Ayer 1896-1898.

BOGARD (Carroll County)

Blade w 1894-1895
In Rowell-Ayer 1895.

Chronicle w 1893
In Ayer 1893-1894

Dispatch w 1900-1936
MWA: Jun 27,1924.
Equipment sold to Carrollton Dispatch 1936.

Independent w 1884-1888
In Rowell 1885-1888.

Journal w 1897
Listed in Ayer 1898.

BOIS D'ARC (Greene County)

Buzz Saw w 1898
Start noted in Country Editor, Mar 1898.

Enterprise w 1902-1913?
Last listed in Ayer 1914.

Flag w 1905
In Rowell-Ayer 1906.

Greene County Sentinel w 1898
In Ayer 1899.

Progress w 1913
In Ayer 1914.

BOLCKOW (Andrew County)

Andrew County Enterprise w 1904-1905
In Ayer 1905-1906, Rowell 1905-1906.

Blade w 1889-1898?
Last in Ayer 1898.

Enterprise w 1900
In Rowell-Ayer 1901.

Herald w 1880-1890?, 1906-1942
MoHi: Feb 1933-Oct 1942.
Two under this title. Last suspended Oct 1942.

Independent w 1877-1879
In Rowell-Ayer 1880.

Lantern w 1899-1900?
In Rowell 1900-1903, Ayer 1900.

BOLIVAR (Polk County)

Courier w 1856-1861
IHi: May 31,1856-May 18,1861,inc.

BOLIVAR (continued)

Dispatch w 1867-1869?
In Rowell 1869.

Free Press w 1868+
MoHi: Nov 14,1901-1907; 1910-1944; Jun 24,
1869; Oct 23,1890; Jly 9,1908; Jun 25,1914.
Film, Jan 4,1868-May 20, 1875; May 1879-May
19,1881; May 24,1883-1901; 1908-1909; 1945+
ICHi: Jan 13,1873; Jly 6,1876.

Herald w 1871+
MoHi: Mar 30,1899-Dec 1944; Oct 30,1890;
Sep 17,1903; Feb 9, Jun 1,8, Jly 20,27, Aug
3,Sep 14,Oct 19,Nov 16,Dec 7,14,28,1905;
Jan 4,11,25, 1906; Aug 8,15,22,29,1907; Jun
4,1908; Nov 20,1913; Jun 25, Jly 2,1914. Film,
Apr 5,1894-Mar 23,1899; 1945+
MoSHi: Apr 1,Dec 9,1886; May 26, Jun 2,23,1887;
Jly 3,1890.
MoSp: Jly 6,1876.
IHi: Apr 30,1891; Feb 13,1913.
ICHi: Oct 26,1876.

Pilot w 1859?
IHi: Jun 18, Sep 17,Oct 1,1859.

Polk County Farmer w 1891-1894
In Rowell 1892-1893, Ayer 1893-1894.

Polk County Leader w 1884-1887
Consolidated with Humansville Star 1887.

Polk County News w 1914
MoHi: Jly 1,1914.

Polk County Register w 1889-1890
Farmers' Alliance, in Rowell 1891.

Polk County Review w 1874-1875
Moved to Humansville 1875, later to Springfield.

Sentinel w 1865-1867?
MoHi: Aug 25,Sep 15,Nov 10,Dec 1,1865; Jly
27-Aug 31,1866.
IHi: Jan 26,1866.

Union w 1866-1867
Moved to Carthage 1867, merged with Banner.

BONNE TERRE (St. Francois County)

Bulletin w 1931-1952
MoHi: Nov 22,1935-1937; 1939-1944. Film,
1938; 1945-1952. Merged with Star News-
Register May 1,1952.

Critic w 1887-1888
In Rowell 1888-1889, Ayer 1887-1889.

Democrat w 1890-1893
In Rowell 1891-1893, Ayer 1890-1894.

ONNE TERRE (continued)

Democrat-Register w 1890-1905
    MoHi: Nov 25,1898-Nov 30,1900; Jly 13,1901-
    Jan 20,1905. Became Register Jan 27,1905.

Merit sw 1889
    Listed in Rowell 1890.

News w 1912-1918
    MoHi: 1917-Nov 28,1918. See Register.

News-Register w 1912-1919
    MoHi: Dec 12,1918-Sep 11,1919. Merged with
    Star as Star and News-Register Sep 17,1919.

People's Friend w 1880
    In Ayer 1881.

Post w 1939-1940
    Free paper ceased, MPN, May 1940, noted.

Register w 1885+
    MoHi: Jan 27,1905-1908; 1913-1916; Jun 12,19,
    Jly 10,1885; Aug 13,1886; Jan 21,Mar 4,11,
    Apr 22,Jun 17,24,Oct 7,14,Nov 25-Dec 23,
    1887; Mar 2-16,May 18,25,Jun 1,15,Jly 6,13,
    Aug 24,Oct 5-Dec 28,1888; Jly 12,19,1889;
    Jan 1-May 7,1909. Film, 1917-1928. May 1952+
    MoSHi: Sep 24,1953. Formerly Democrat-Register.
    Merged with News Dec 5,1918.

Reporter w 1883-1884
    In Rowell 1884-1885.

Star w 1896-1919
    MoHi: Nov 25,1898-Nov 24,1899; 1912-Sep 12,1919.
    See News-Register.

Star-News-Register w 1919-1952
    MoHi: Dec 5,1919-Dec 29,1922; Apr 21,1939-1944.
    Film, 1945-Apr 1952. Merged with Bulletin to
    become Register May 1,1952. Star and the News-
    Register bound Sep 19-Nov 28,1919.

St. Francois County Banner w 1878-1879
    MoHi: Film, May 31,1878-Aug 8,1879.

BOONVILLE (Cooper County)

Advance w 1902-1904
    MoHi: Apr 10,May 8,22,29,Jun 19,26,Jly 3,10,
    24,Aug 14,21,Sep 11,18,Oct 2,Nov 1,6,Dec
    25,1902; 1903; Jan 14,22,Feb 11,18,Mar 17,
    24,Apr 7,1904. Film, 1903.

Advertiser w,sw 1840+ d 1875-1877
    MoHi: d, Oct 25,1875-Oct 24,1877. w, May 2-
    Dec 26,1868; Oct 1873-1883; 1891; 1894; 1906;
    Dec 30,1920-1944; May 2-Dec 1868; Oct 1873-
    1883; Aug 29,1868; Jan 2-Feb 6,Feb 20-May 1,
    1869; Mar 19,1870; May 23,30,Jun 6,13,20,27,
    Jly 11,18,25,Aug 1,8,15,22,Sep 5,12,1873;

BOONVILLE (continued)

Advertiser (continued)
    Dec 8,1876; Apr 11,1884; Jly 14,1899; Nov 30
    1900; Jly 22,1938; Jly 26,1940; Jly 25,1941;
    Jly 31,1942; Jly 29,1949; Jly 28,1950; Jly 27,
    1951; Jan 16,30,Feb 27,Mar 6,Apr 24,1869;
    Film, 1884-1890; 1892-1893; 1895-1905; 1907-
    Dec 24,1920; 1945+
    MoSHi: w, Oct 25,1872; Jun 27,1924; Rural Life
    Editions, 1929,1930,1934. w, Mar 3,1911-Jly
    4,1924; d, Feb 22,1876; Jun 14,1878; Christ-
    mas 1885; Jan 8,29,Feb 5,12,Apr 30, Christ-
    mas 1886; Christmas 1889; Nov 13,1891; Feb
    17,1893; Film, May 16,1879; Jan 4,Oct 18,1901.
    CSmH: Jly 26,1940.
    ICHi: May 26,Aug 25,1876.

Argus w 1840
    Campaign paper, mentioned by Organ.

Call d 1908-1910?
    MoHi: Nov 12,14,23,1908; Jan 21,Apr 5,1909.
    Film, Apr 7,1909-Mar 8,1910.

Central Missouri Advertiser
    MoSHi: Sep 13,1862; Jun 6,1863; Apr 22, Jly 8,
    Sep 2,23,1865; Nov 2,1866; Jan 25,Mar 7,
    21,1868. Name used briefly by Advertiser.

Central Missourier w 1868-1907?
    MoHi: Oct 1874-1907,Sep 1,1881; Oct 30,1890.
    Boonville HS Library; 1883-1896.
    ICHi: Jly 20,1876. German.

Central Missourian d 1919-1928
    MoHi: Dec 1926-Aug 4,1928; Formerly Daily
    Republican. In 1928 sold to Advertiser,
    merged.

Central Missouri Republican w 1884-1927
    MoHi: 1919-Jun 1926. Film, Jly 29,1884-1918.
    Merged with Daily News 1927.
    KHi: Dec 13,1923.
    MoSHi: Oct 25,1888; 1904-1908 inc; 1911-1917,
    1919, scattered issues.

Commercial Bulletin w 1846-1854
    MoSHi: Under Bulletin, Sep 18-Dec 30,1847; Jan
    6-Feb 17,Mar 2,Apr 27,1848. Under Com-
    mercial Bulletin, Apr 11,18,May 30,Jun 6-
    Aug 13,27-Dec 31,1846; Jan 7-Feb 18,Mar 4-
    Jun 24,Aug 5-Sep 9,1847.

Coon Hunter w 1844
    MWA: Apr-May 3,24,Jun 7-14,1844. Campaign
    paper, published by Democratic Union.

Cooper County Democrat w 1890-1893
    MoHi: Dec 20,27,1889. Film, 1890-Jly 1,1893.
    MoSHi: Oct 23,30,1891. Became Missouri
    Democrat Jly 7,1893.

BOONVILLE (continued)

Cooper County Record   w   1876+
    MoHi: Sep 1937-1944. Film, 1945+

Cooper County Republican   w,d   1929-1942
    MoHi: Feb 24-May 1,1933. Changed to Daily
    Republican-Sun May 8,1933; MoHi: May 8,
    1933-Jan 1934.

Democrat   w   1848-1854
    MoSHi: Dec 22,1848; Jan 12,26, Feb 2-23,1849;
    Mar 8,1840. Followed Commercial Bulletin.

Democratic Union   w   1844-1849
    Mentioned by Organ

Eagle   w   1865-1878   d   1869?
    MoHi: w,1871-Jly 25,1879; Feb 3, Jun 16,1871.
    Film,May 2,1868-1870. D,Sep 29,30,Oct 1,
    1869.
    MoSHi: Dec 30,1865; Feb 8,1868; Jly 16,1870.
    ICHi: Aug 11,1876.
    MWA: Oct 21,1865; Feb 3,1866; Oct 20,1871.
    Moved to Sedalia Aug 2,1878.

Echo   w   1898-1899?
    MoHi: Aug 20,27,Oct 29,Dec 31,1898; Mar 18,1899.

Enterprise   d   ?
    MoHi: May 17,22,1905.

Erzahler (Der)   w   1875-1907?
    MoHi: May 1875-1907. Supplement to Central
    Missourier.

Friday Morning Independent   w   1898-1899
    MoHi: Jly 8-22,Aug 5,Dec 30,1898; Jan 6,1899.
    Film, Jly 8,1898-Oct 20,1899.

Gazette   d   1909-1910
    MoHi: Jun 17-Jly 7,Sep 9,20,21,1909. Founded
    as Cooper County Democrat.

Herald   w   1833-1899
    MoHi: Aug 8,1834.
    MoSHi: Mar 28,1834.
    ICHi: Nov 29,1833. Renamed Western Emigrant
    1838, later Observer.

Independent   w   1898-1899
    See Friday Morning Independent.

Inquirer   w   1856
    In Newspaper Record 1856.

Item   sw   1891
    In Rowell 1892.

Message   w   1916-1918
    MoSHi: 1916-1918, scattered issues.

Mid-Week Star   w   1906
    In Ayer-Rowell 1907.

BOONVILLE   (continued)

Missouri Advertiser   w   1873-1875
    Name used briefly for Advertiser.

Missouri Democrat   w   1890-1909   d   1909
    MoHi: w, Jly 1-Dec 29,1893. Film, Jly 7,1893-
    Jly 1,1898; Jun 23,1899-Nov 22,1901; Jan
    31,1902-Dec 7,1908 inc. D,Apr 8-Jun 17,
    1909; Oct 16,1896; May 23,1902; Jly 10,1903
    Apr 7,1909; Apr 6,1908. Under Boonville
    Missouri Democrat, Nov 9,1894-Jly 10,1896.
    MoSHi: May 17,1895.

Missouri Farmer   w   1873-1874
    In Rowell 1875.

Missouri Register   w   1839-1853
    MoHi: May 1840-Jun 1841; Aug 1843-Feb 1845;
    Jly 1845.
    MWA: Aug 8,1839; Jly 19,1845.

Missourian   w,m   1913-1951?
    MoHi: Oct 8-29,Nov 5-Dec 3,1937; 1940-Apr
    3,1942.
    MoSHi: Aug 1948. Changed to monthly Apr 1942.
    See Pilot Grove, Marshall data on Record.

Monitor   w   1862-1864
    MoHi: Feb 13-Aug 6,1864.
    MoSHi: Jun 4,1864.

News   d   1919+   w   1880-1884
    MoHi: Aug 6,1928-1950. Film, 1951+. Earlier
    News, w, film, Feb 12,Sep 24,Dec 2,1881;
    Aug 19,30,Oct 11,1882; Mar 2-Apr 6,1883.
    NHi: Jan 4,1884.

Observer   w,tw   1840-1862?
    MoHi: Mar 13,1844-Dec 23,1845; Jan-Jly 1,Dec
    1846; Jan 1847-Jan 12,1848; Mar 21,1850-
    May 27,1851; Mar 1854-1856. Mar 10,1852
    photostat. Later named Advertiser.
    MoSHi: Aug 13,Dec 17,1840; Apr 17,1844; Feb
    3,1855; Dec 11,1858; Feb 26,Mar 5,19,26,
    Apr 2-30,May 28,Jun 11,Jly 9-30,Aug 13,Oct
    15,22,Nov 5-19,Dec 3,1859; Aug 11-25,Sep
    22,Oct 13,Nov 3-17,Dec 8,1860; Jan 12,19,
    Feb 2-23,Apr 13,20,1861.
    MWA: tw, 1850-Mar 8,1851.

Patriot   w   1856-1861
    MoSHi: American Patriot, Jun 18,1861. Patriot,
    Feb 25, May 26,1860; Aug 19,1861 extra.
    See Advertiser.

Republican   w   1919-1929   d   1929-1933
    MoHi: Jan 27,31,Feb 9,Apr 21,Jun 17,29,Aug
    27,30-31,Sep 12,25,28,Oct 7,14-16,18-20
    Nov 2,4,8,10-11,18,Dec 7,17,1920; Apr 7,
    8,11,1921; Jan 2,Feb 3,1922; Feb 24-May 1,
    1933. D, May 8,1933-Jan 1934 as Republican-
    Sun, name taken May 8,1933.

BOONVILLE (continued)

Republican-Sun   w   1929-1933   d   1933-1934
   MoHi: d, May 8, 1933-Jan 1934. Merged with
   Daily News 1934.

Star   sw   1886-1894
   MoHi: Film, Apr 18-Sep 5, 1906; Nov 25, 1886-
   Jun 7, 1893; Mar 3, 1889; Dec 31, 1892; Mar 11,
   15, Apr 19, Mar 24, 27, 1894; Oct 25, Nov 1, 1888;
   May 30, 1906.
   MoSHi: Nov 1, 1888.

Success   w   1902
   MoHi: May 3, 1902.

Saturday Morning Wasp   w   1904?
   MoHi: Feb 27, Mar 12, 26, 1904.

Saturday Museum   w   1843-1844
   Mentioned by Organ.

Topic   w, tw   1877-1890?
   MoHi: Sep 9-Dec 26, 1884; 1885-Dec 13, 1889;
   Jan 1, Oct 8, 15, 1886; May 8, 1885.
   MoSHi: Oct 6, 1882; Oct 23, Dec 4, 11, 1885;
   Jan 1, 15, Feb 19, 1886.

Wachter am Missouri (Der)   w   1868-1874
   In Rowell 1870-1874.

Western Emigrant   w   1838-1840
   MoHi: Jan 1839-Mar 19, 1840.
   MoSHi: Mar 26, 1840.
   MWA: Oct 31, 1839.

BOSWORTH (Carroll County)

Advertiser   w   1888-1890
   Listed in Ayer 1890.

Clipper   w   1888-1889
   In Rowell-Ayer 1889.

Sentinel   w   1891-1950
   MoHi: Mar 12, 1942-1944. Film, Apr 17, 1891-
   Apr 7, 1893; 1945-Jan 13, 1950. Merged with
   Pilot Grove Star Jan 20, 1950.
   KHi: Mar 22, Nov 29, 1923.

Star   w   1900
   In Rowell-Ayer 1901.

Star-Sentinel   w   1891-1905
   Listed under Sentinel other dates.

BOURBON (Crawford County)

Breeze   w   1897
   Start noted in Country Editor, Nov 1897.

Herald   1954-1961
   MoHi: Film, May 3, 1956-1961.

BOURBON (continued)

Standard   w   1906-1952?
   Last in Ayer 1953.

BOWLING GREEN (Pike County)

Democratic Banner   w   1833-1846
   MoHi: Mar 15, 1845. Film, Feb 1, 1845-Apr 11,
   1846. Moved to Louisiana Apr 18, 1845.

Free Press   w   1845
   Mentioned by Organ.

Herald   w   1924
   Mentioned in E & P, Jly 12, 1924.

Jeffersonian   w   1924-1927
   MoHi: Jly 9, 1924-1925. Film, 1926-Nov 2, 1927.

Journal   w   1844-1848
   MoHi: Under Missouri Journal copies for Sep 14,
   1844; Oct 14, 28, Nov 4, Dec 16, 23, 1846; Jan
   13, 20, 1847. Became the Seventy-Six in 1848,
   ceased 1849.

Missouri Journal
   See Journal.

News   w   1898
   Mentioned in Country Editor, Jun 1898.

Olive Branch   w   1841-1861
   Mentioned by Organ, Hammond.

Pike County Democrat   w   1884-1885
   In Rowell 1885-1886.

Pike County Express   w   1875-1879
   In Rowell 1877-1880, Ayer 1880.

Pike County Press   w   1923
   In Ayer 1924.

Pike County Post   w   1871-1918
   MoHi: Oct 30, 1890; Dec 17, 1913. Film, Feb 11,
   1914-Oct 11, 1918. Formerly the Post-Observer.

Post-Observer   w   1871-1885
   MoHi: Aug 9, 1878-Jly 29, 1880. Changed to Pike
   County Post 1885.

Radical   w   1841-1845
   MoHi: Aug 10, 1844. Film, Nov 13, 1841-Jan 25,
   1845. DLC has Vol. 1, No. 51, dated Oct 22,
   1842.

Record   w   1856
   Listed in Newspaper Record 1856.

BOWLING GREEN (continued)

Salt River Journal   w   1833-1841
   MoHi: Feb 26, 1835; Nov 29-Dec·6, 13, 27, 1837;
      Feb 27, Sep 1, 1838; Jan 5, 26, 1839; Sep 18,
      1841. Film, Nov 23, Dec 14, 1839; Feb 1, 1840-
      Oct 30, 1841.
   DLC: Dec 4, 1833.
   ·ICHi: Apr 23, 30, 1834; Feb 20, 1841.
      Became Radical 1841, Democratic Banner 1845,
      then to Louisiana 1846.

Seventy-Six   w   1848-1849
   See Journal.

Southern Pike Progress   w   1961
   Sister publication of Times to serve Clarksville.

Times   w   1874+
   MoHi: 1903-1907; 1914-1944; Sep 13-Oct 4, 18,
      1894. Film, Oct 7, 1880-1902; 1945+
   Publisher says started in Curryville 1874 as
   Pike County Express.

BRADLEYVILLE   (Taney County)

Missouri Tidings   w   1890. 1893
   In Rowell 1893-1894, Ayer 1894.

Taney County Sentinel   w   1890, 1899?
   In Rowell 1895, Ayer 1899-1900.

BRANSON   (Taney County)

Beacon   w   1957+
   In Ayer 1963.

Echo   w   1905-1909
   MoHi: Film, Nov 17, 1905-Nov 5, 1909.

Sentinel   w   1910-1915?
   MoHi: Nov 14, 1913-Oct 9, 1914.
   KHi: May 3, 1912.

Taney County Democrat   w   1910-1911
   MoHi: Feb 10-Nov 17, 1910. In Ayer 1911-1912.

White River Leader   w   1913+
   MoHi: May 9, 1913-Jun 1919; 1925-1926; 1932-
      1935; 1937-1944. Film, Jan 6, 1927-1931;
      1936; 1945+

BRASHEAR   (Adair County)

Bugle   w   1896
   Start noted in Missouri Editor, Mar 1896.

Citizen   w   1886
   In Rowell-Ayer 1887.

Gazette   w   1889-1890
   In Ayer 1891.

BRASHEAR   (continued)

News   w   1885-1939?
   MoHi: 1919-Jly 1926; 1932-Mar 1937. Film, Oct
      31, 1902-Jan 1906; May 1912-1918.

BRAYMER   (Caldwell County)

Bee   w   1887+
   MoHi: Dec 2, 1898-Nov 1916. Film, Sep 1958+
   Hamilton Public Library, several years, un-
   catalogued.

Comet   w   1891-1914
   MoHi: Jan-Jun, 1898; Nov 1908-1909. Film,
      1910-1912.

BRECKENRIDGE   (Caldwell County)

Bulletin   w   1875+
   MoHi: Jly 27, 1901-1902; 1905-1925; 1928-1944;
      Dec 31, 1897; Jan 21, 28, Feb 4, 18, 25, Mar 11,
      18, 25, Apr 1, 8, 15, 22, 29, May 6, 20, Jun 3, 17,
      24, 1898; May 31, 1908. Film, Dec 10, 1875-
      Mar 2, 1877; Oct 30, 1879-Oct 7, 1886; Oct 11
      1888-Oct 16, 1890; Aug 9, 1895-Nov 24, 1899;
      Jan 2, 1903-Dec 23, 1904; 1926-1927; 1945+
   ICHi: Jun 23, Jly 7, 1876.

Globe   w   1894-1895
   Moved to O'Fallon, Ill., 1895.

Herald   w   1901-1902?
   In Rowell 1902-1905, Ayer 1902-1903.

Journal   w   1870
   In Rowell 1871.

Missouri Advocate   m   1881-1883?
   In Ayer 1881 as monthly. Hammond says ended
   1883-1884.

News   w   1911
   In Ayer 1912.

Mooresville News   w   1916-1917
   In Ayer 1918.

Republican   w   1876
   In Rowell-Pettengill 1877.

BRENTWOOD   (St. Louis County)

Scope   w   1950
   Mostly free distribution.

BRIMSON   (Grundy County)

Banner   w   1902-1905?
   In Ayer 1904-1906, Rowell 1904-1906.

Booster   w   1904-1906?
   In Ayer-Rowell 1905. Name in Rowell 1907.

BRINKTOWN (Maries County)

Home Adviser w 1903-1905
In Rowell 1904-1906, minister as editor.

BRONAUGH (Vernon County)

Business Bringer w 1896-1898
In Rowell 1897-1899, Ayer 1897.

Journal w 1904-1950?
Last listed in Ayer 1951.

Sentinel w 1900
In Ayer 1901.

BROOKFIELD (Linn County)

Advertiser w 1880
In Ayer 1880, founding date of 1880.

Argus w,d,sw,tw 1882-1952?
MoHi: Nov 4,1914-1924; 1926-1944. Film, 1925;
1945-Sep 1949. D, Nov 4,1914-Jan 19,1943.
TW, Jan 20,Aug 9,1943; sw, Aug 10,1943-
Sep 1949; w, 1904-Oct 1914; Jly 21,1888;
Sep 19,1903.
CoD: w, Aug 20,1887.
KHi: d, Aug 26,1921; Sep 7,Dec 8,1923.

Argus-Farmer w 1953
Subscription list sold to News-Bulletin, according
to MPN, Sep 1953.

Blade and Messenger w 1946-1950?
MoHi: Film, Jan 1,1946-Aug 5,1948.
Formerly Laclede Blade and Meadville Messenger.
Moved to Brookfield, first issue there Jan 1,1946.

Budget w 1895-1904?
MoHi: Film, Feb 1,1895-1898; 1901-May 1904.
Became Linn County Budget 1905.

Chronicle w 1876-1886?
ICHi: Aug 2,1876. In Ayer 1887.

Democrat w 1870-1871.
In Rowell 1871-1872.

Eagle d 1898
Death noted in Country Editor, Oct 1898.

Freeman's Journal d 1877
Mentioned in county history.

Gazette w 1867-1927
MoHi: Apr 23,1867-Apr 17,1874; 1875-1879; 1919-
1926. Film, 1880-Dec 21,1918.
MoSHi: Jan 14,1876; Jan 4,1919.
ICHi: Aug 24,1876.
Consolidated with Budget, became Linn County
Budget-Gazette Jan 26,1927.

BROOKFIELD (continued)

Linn County Budget w,d,sw,tw 1895-1944
MoHi: w, Jan-Dec 10,1920; Oct 15,1926-
Jan 26,1927. Film, Mar 4,1905-1919. D,
Dec 14,1920-Oct 14,1926.
KHi: d, Dec 18,1923.

Linn County Budget-Gazette d,w,sw,tw 1895-1944
MoHi: Film, Jan 1,1946-Jly 1948. Formerly
Linneus Linn County News, moved to Brookfield
1946. Merged with Daily News Aug 2,1948.
Became Daily News 1948. MoHi has d, Aug 2,
1948; film, Jan 2-22,1951, as News and Linn
County News.

Missouri State Press w 1898
Called "The anti-ring paper of Missouri."

Missouri State Times w 1898
In Rowell 1898, founding date 1898.

Missouri State Union w 1893-1898
See Union.

Montfort's Weekly w 1895-1896
In Rowell 1896-1897.

New Era w 1874
Also called Linn County New Era.

News
See Linn County News.

News-Bulletin d 1881+
MoHi: film, 1951+
MoSHi: Jly 17,1959.
Micro-Photo: film, 1957+
Formed by merger News, Linneus Bulletin Feb
23,1951.

Star w 1905
In Ayer-Rowell 1906.

Sunday Argus w 1882?
In Dauchy 1885, founding date 1882.

Times w 1890
In Rowell 1890, founding date 1890.

Union w 1890-1893
Became Missouri State Union 1893, ended 1898.

Union State Press w 1899
Death noted in Country Editor, Mar 1899.

BROWN BRANCH (Taney County)

Mountaineer w 1890-1891
In Rowell 1892.

BROWNING (Linn County)

Herald w 1883-1885
In Rowell-Ayer 1886.

Leader w 1893-1896
Later became Leader-Record.

Leader-Record w 1886+
MoHi: 1911-1944. Film, Mar 3, 1905-1908; 1909-
1910; 1945+ Mar 3, 1905-Sep 20, 1906.
KHi: Jan 10, 1924; Jan 13, 1927.

Monitor w 1877-1878
In Rowell 1879.

News w 1923-1924
In Ayer 1924-1925.

Record w 1886-1896
See Leader-Record.

Reporter w 1881-1882
In Rowell 1882-1883, Ayer 1882.

BROWNINGTON (Henry County)

Argus w 1887-1889
MoHi: Oct 4, 18, 25, Nov 22, 29, Dec 6, 1888; Jan
3, 10, 1889.

Boomer w 1885-1886
In Rowell, Ayer 1886-1887.

Index w 1907-1908?
In Rowell 1908, Ayer 1909-1910.

News w 1889-1891?
MoHi: Oct 23, 1890.

Progress w 1895-1896
In Rowell 1896-1897.

BROWNSVILLE (Saline County)

Banner w 1871-1874
In Rowell 1872-1875.

Democrat w 1877?
Mentioned by Hammond.

Herald w 1874-1886
MoHi: 1881-Sep 12, 1884. Film, Aug 20, 1874-
Sep 3, 1880.
ICHi: Jun 30, 1876.
See Jefferson City Tribune, Apr 14, 1887, on
change in name of town.

Saline County Messenger w 1876
ICHi: May 12, Jly 1, 1876.

BRUNSWICK (Chariton County)

Brunswicker w 1847+
MoHi: May 23, 1930-1944; Oct 15, 1870; Dec 23,
1881; May 21, 1887; Sep 7, 1889; Jly 11, 1896;
Jly 10, 1903 Film, Jan 7, Sep 9, Oct 28, 1854-
Mar 28, 1857; Jly 26, 1901-1903; 1945+
MoSHi: Mar 17, 1866; Nov 30, Dec 7, 1872; Jan 4-
Apr 12, 26, May 3-17, Jly 26, Aug 16, 23, Nov 15-
29, Dec 6, 13, 1873; Nov 3, 1875; Jan 5, 1883-
Dec 26, 1884; Jan 2, 1885-Sep 4, 1886; 1890-
1895; Mar 28, 1896-May 28, 1898; Jan 15, 1906-
Dec 27, 1907; 1908-Nov 3, 1911; 1912-1916;
Oct 14, 1947-Sep 19, 1953.
MWA: Feb 3, 1866.
NHi: Oct 14, 1848; Feb 1, 1873.
DLC: Jun 12, Sep-Dec 1869.
KHi: Jly 7, 1916; Jun 15, 1923.
ICHi: Aug 12, 1876.
WHi: Film, Jan 7-Sep 9, 1854; Oct 28, 1854-Mar
28, 1857.

Central City w 1856?
Name used briefly for paper that united with
Brunswicker.

Central City and Brunswicker w 1859?-1864?
MoHi: Jun 29, 1861.
MoSHi: Apr 6, Jun 15, 29, Jly 20, Aug 10, Sep 7,
14, 1859; Apr 13, 20, May 4, 11, Jun 1, 1861;
Jly 24, Aug 28, Sep 4-18, Oct 2, 16-30, Nov 6,
1862; Jan 29, Feb 12, 26, Mar 5-26, Jly 2, 9,
1863; May 7, 1864.

Central City Brunswicker w 1864?
MoHi: Jan 30, 1864. Name used briefly.

Chariton County Republican w 1894-1902?
MoSHi: Sep 14, 1894-Jly 5, 1901.

Chariton County News w 1893-1900?
MoSHi: Mar 18, 1893-1895; Jly 4, 1896-Feb 6, 1897.

Gazette w 1861
In American Newspaper Directory 1861.

News w 1875-1893
ICHi: Jly 22, 1876.
Listed as Chariton County News in 1894.

Press w 1858-1860
Mentioned by Organ.

Reporter w 1847
Published briefly before being renamed Brunswicker.

Republican w 1894-1902? 1875?
MoSHi: Jun 25, Jly 2-30, Aug 6, 20, 1875. Name used
at times for Chariton County Republican.

BUCKLIN (Linn County)

Advertiser w 1880-?
In Rowell-Ayer 1881.

BUCKLIN (continued)

Booster   w   1919-1920
    In Ayer 1920-1921.

Herald   w   1886-1947
    MoHi: 1899-1900; 1906-1944; Sep 22,1888; Apr
    24,1891; May 19,1899; Jan 19,1906; Film,
    1901-1905; 1945-Mar 13,1947. Merged with
    Marceline News 1947.

News and Bucklin Herald   1947-1958?
    Published in Marceline. See Herald.

BRUSHY KNOB (Douglas County)

World's Cresset   1904-1914?
    MoHi: Nov 10,1910-Dec 1914. 1910 issues bound
    as Norwood World's Cresset. Also in Trask,
    Pomona and Fowler. In 1916 became Mountain
    Grove World's Cresset. Moved to Fremont 1918,
    later to Leachville, Ark. Religious publication.

BUCKNER   (Jackson County)

Democrat   w   1894-1896?
    In Ayer 1895-1897.

Fort Osage News   w   1961+
    Listed in Ayer 1963.

Jackson County Democrat   w   1911+
    MoHi: Film, Apr 18-Dec 25,1952; 1953+
    Formerly Blue Springs Jackson County Democrat;
    moved to Buckner Apr 18,1952. In Ayer 1963.

Record   w   1907-1951
    MoHi: Film, May 31-Oct 1951. Merged with Blue
    Springs Herald and Jackson County Democrat in
    1951.
    KHi: Mar 15,1923; Oct 15,1925.

Star   w   1897-1902
    Listed as Silver Democrat Ayer 1903.

Tribune   w   1897-1907?
    NN: Jun 30,1903. In Rowell 1903-1908, Ayer
    1904-1906.

BUFFALO (Dallas County)

Dallas County Courier   w   1875-1876
    ICHi: Courier, Jly 7,1876. In Rowell 1876-1877.
    At times as Courier.

Dallas County Democrat   w   1887-1888
    In Rowell-Ayer 1888-1889.

Dallas County Record   w   1894-1921
    See Record. Longer title in 1890's.

Dallas County Republican   w   1927+
    First listed in Ayer 1928.

BUFFALO (continued)

Herald   w   1855-1857
    Later to Marshfield, as Sentinel.

People's Paper   w   1892-1894
    In Rowell 1893-1894, Ayer 1894 as Populist paper.

Record   w   1894-1921
    MoHi: 1920-Mar 1921; Apr 2,1908. Film, Apr 13,
    1899-Jan 27,1900; Dec 26,1901-Nov 13,1902;
    1909-Oct 6,1910; Jan 8,1914-1919. Also
    called Dallas County Record.

Reflex   w   1869+
    MoHi: 1921-1944; Sep 11,1869; Mar 19,1880;
    Nov 29,1888. Film, Aug 21,1869-Aug 22,1873;
    Feb 8,1878-Feb 27,1880; May 27,1881-1920;
    1945+ (Except 1897)
    MoSp: Jly 6,1876.
    ICHi: Jun 1, Jly 6,1876.

Register   w   1879-1884
    MoHi: Film, Apr 17,1879-Mar 18,1880; 1883.

Union   w   1859-1861?
    In American Newspaper Directory 1861.

BUNCETON (Cooper County)

Eagle   w   1888-1943
    MoHi: Jly 26,1907-Oct 29,1943; Oct 4,1901;
    May 9,1902. Film, Nov 4,1892-Jly 19,1907.

Enterprise   w   1887
    MoHi: Jly 1, Sep 2,1887.

News   w   1893-1895
    MoHi: Mar 1895.

Telegram   w   1888-1889
    In Rowell 1889-1890, Ayer 1888-1889.

Times   w   1895
    In Rowell 1896.

Tribune   w,sw   1895-1911
    MoHi: Aug 9,1901-Dec 23,1910; Feb 7, Apr 24,
    May 22,29, Jun 19,26, Jly 31, Aug 21, Sep 11,
    Oct 2,9,16,23,30, Nov 6,13, Dec 25,1896;
    Jan 8,22,29, Feb 5-Mar 12, Apr 16, Sep 3, Dec 3,
    1897; Jan 14,1898; Jun 14,1901; Nov 2,1909;
    Jan 3-Jun 30,1911. Film, Jly 6,1895-Jly 11,1902.
    MoSHi: Mar 6,1896.

BUNKER (Reynolds County)

Tri-County Leader   w   1914-1915
    In Ayer 1915-1916.

BURLINGTON JUNCTION (Nodaway County)

Democratic Freeman   w   1883
    In Rowell 1884.

BURLINGTON (continued)

Ledger   w   1890-1898
   MoHi: Oct 23, 1890.

Post   w   1879+
   MoHi: Jly 27, 1901-Mar 2, 1944; Nov 1, 1890;
      Dec 7, 1901; Jan 14, 1905; Jly 11, 1918. In Ayer
      1963 as founded 1884.

Post-News   w   1879+
   Union of Post, Skidmore News 1954.

World   w   1903-1906?
   In Rowell 1904-1908, Ayer 1904-1906.

BURROWS (Bates County)

Border Chief   w   1890-1891
   In Ayer 1892.

BUTLER   (Bates County)

Bates County Advocate   w   1878-1881?
   MoHi: Film, May 29, 1878-Nov 23, 1881.

Bates County Democrat   w   1869+
   MoHi: 1908-1909; 1911-1944; Aug 9, 1902;
      May 16, 1907; Apr 16, 1908; Mar 4, 1909;
      May 29, 1913; May 28, 1914; May 25, 1916.
      Film, Sep 3, 1903-Feb 11, 1904; 1945+.

Bates County News-Press   w   1957
   In Ayer 1958. Published by Democrat, formerly
   Times-Press.

Bates County Record   w   1866-1918
   MoHi: 1913-Apr 1918; Jun 19, 1869; Oct 4, 1873.
      Film, Jly 4, 1868-Jun 22, 1872; Jun 28, 1873-
      Jun 1886; 1888-Dec 28, 1912.
   ICHi: Jly 7, 1876.

Bates County Republican   w   1882-1886, 1899-1900
   Two papers under this title.

Bates County Standard   w   1858-1860
   MoHi: Feb 8, 15, Apr 5, 1859. Became Western
      Times 1860, ended 1861.

Bates County Times   w   1878-1881
   See Times. Changed to Weekly Times, started 1881.

Democrat   d   1889-1959
   KHi: Feb 8, 1923. Final edition, Jan 16, 1959.

Free Press   w   1888-1901
   MoHi: Film, Jan 3, 1896-Jly 26, 1901.
   NcD: May 29, Aug 14, 1896; Dec 23, 1898.

Independent   w   1880
   In Ayer 1880, founding date of 1880.

Local News   w   1889
   MoHi: Film, Mar 22-Nov 23, 1889. Became Weekly
      Union, 1890, with Free Press 1895?

BUTLER (continued)

Mining Review   ?   1909-1911?
   MoHi: May 1, 1909; May 1, 1911.

Republican Press   w   1888-1950
   MoHi: Jly 26, 1901-1944. Film, 1945-Aug 1950.
      Formerly Free Press. Became Republican Press
      Jly 1901. Merged with Weekly Times Sep 1,
      1950, became Times-Press.

Thomas Cat   w   1885
   Sunday comic. A free paper, began by J. Davis
   Orear in Butler and Rich Hill, Jun 20, 1885.

Times   w, d   1878-1950
   MoHi: Nov 7, 1901-1944; Oct 29, Nov 12, 1890;
      Jun 3, 1915; Mar 25, 1916; Jly 16, 1903; May
      18, 1905; May 17, 1906; Apr 23, 1908. Film,
      Dec 7, 1881-Oct 31, 1901; 1945-Aug 1950.
   MoSHi: Jun 9, 23, 1921; Jly 5, 1928; Oct 4, 1929;
      Feb 21, 1935; Aug 17, Dec 14, 21, 28, 1939;
      Jan 4, Feb 29, Sep 5, Dec 26, 1940; 1941; Oct
      1-Dec 24, 1942; Jan 7, Feb 4, 18, Mar 18, Apr 1-
      Dec 30, 1943.
   KHi: w, Oct 27, 1927.
   LU: Jun 7, 1907.

Times-Press   w   1950-1957
   MoHi: Film, Sep 7, 1950-Jun 27, 1957. Merged
      with Bates County Democrat 1957.

Weekly Union   w   1888-1895
   MoHi: Film, Mar 16, 1893-Dec 27, 1895.
   NcD: Jun 7, 1895. See Local News.

Western Times   w   1860-1861
   See Bates County Standard.

BUTTERFIELD (Barry County)

Barry County Times   w   1893
   In Rowell 1894.

CABOOL (Texas County)

Democrat   w   1899-1900?
   In Rowell-Ayer 1900.

Enterprise   w   1906-1917, 1928+
   MoHi: Apr 20, 1906-Sep 4, 1908; Jan 29, 1914-
      1916. Film, Jan 4-11, 1917. Became Enterprise-
      Press Jan 18, 1917. Renamed Enterprise 1928.
      Ayer 1963 lists 1889 founding date.

Enterprise-Press   w   1906-1928
   MoHi: 1919-Apr 1921. Film, Jan 25, 1917-Dec
      19, 1918. See Enterprise.
   MoSHi: Jan 18, 1917.
   KHi: Sep 11, 1924.

Record   w   1884-1898
   Subscription list sold to Ozark Mountain News.

CABOOL (Texas County)

Ozark Mountain News   w   1890-1904?
  Last listed in Rowell 1905.

Press   w   1913-1916
  Combined with Enterprise 1916.

Texas County Sentinel   w   1890-1894
  In Rowell 1894, Ayer 1894-1895.

Times   w   1903-1911?
  In Rowell 1904-1908, Ayer 1904-1912.

CAINSVILLE (Harrison County)

Booster   w   1914-1915
  MoHi: Film, Dec 11, 1914-Oct 8, 1915.

Expositor   w   1894
  Reform paper listed by Ashcraft.

Independent   w   1913-1914
  MoHi: Film, Sep 25, 1913-Jly 23, 1914.

News   w   1886+
  MoHi: Jly 25, 1901-Sep 23, 1943; Oct 30, 1890;
  1963+

Sentinel   w   1885-1886
  Mentioned by Hammond.

Signal   w   1883-1884?
  In Rowell 1884-1885.

CALHOUN (Henry County)

Call   w   1896
  In Ayer 1897.

Clarion   w   1902-1918
  MoHi: Jan 2, 1904-Dec 31, 1908; Jan 1913-Dec
  1915; Jan 3-Oct 10, 1918. Film, Mar 15, 1902-
  Dec 26, 1903; Jan 2-Sep 5, 1909; Nov 6, 1909-
  Oct 22, 1910; Mar 11, 1911-1912; 1916-Dec 20,
  1917.
  NN: Jly 4, 1903.

Courier   w   1891-1900
  Farmers' Alliance, People's Party paper.

Free Press   w   1901
  In Ayer 1902.

Gleaner   w   1887-1890
  Rowell 1888 says started 1887. MHR, Jan 1960,
  says 1889, continued for year.

Journal   w   1889-1890
  In Rowell 1891.

Star   w   1919-1951
  Subscription list to Windsor Review.

CALIFORNIA (Moniteau County)

Central Missouri Push   w   1899-1900
  In Rowell 1900-1901, Ayer 1900.

Central Missouri Star   w   1900
  Negro paper in Rowell-Ayer 1901.

Central Missourian   w   1865-1871
  MoHi: Film, Jly 15, 1865-Dec 19, 1868. Name
  apparently used for Democrat during these years.

Democrat   w   1858+
  MoHi: 1901-Sep 1903; 1911-1944. Film, 1872;
  Feb 6, 1873-1910; 1945+ Formerly Moniteau
  County Democrat, also Weekly California News.

Die Deutsche Zeitung   w   1888-1889
  In Ayer 1889.

Dispatch   w   1896-1908
  MoHi: 1899-1900; 1903; Jan 1, 8, 15, 22, 29, Feb
  5, 12, Jly 22, 1904. Also, Sep 22, 1897 Daily
  Fair Dispatch; Aug 2, 1903, Sunday Morning
  Dispatch. Film, Jly 16, 1896-1898; Jan 18,
  1907-May 29, 1908.
  NN: May 15, 22, 1903.

Greenback Derrick   w   1882-1884
  MoHi: Mar 25, 1882-Feb 2, 1883. Succeeded by
  Newspaper.

Herald   w   1889-1893
  MoHi: Film, May 23, 1889-Sep 20, 1893. See
  Moniteau County Herald, name after Sep 27, 1893.

Loyal Journal   w   1867-1869
  MoHi: Sep 4, 1867-Nov 11, 1869, Jun 19, 1869; Nov
  21, 1868. Formerly Loyal Missourian. Became
  Moniteau Journal Nov 18, 1869.

Loyal Missourian   w   1866-1867
  MoHi: Jun 28, 1866-Aug 29, 1867. Became Loyal
  Journal Sep 4, 1867.

Moniteau County Democrat   w   1858-1872
  MoHi: Film, Jan 22, 1870-Dec 9, 1871. Became
  Democrat Jan 4, 1872.

Moniteau County Herald   w   1889+
  MoHi: 1911-1944; Aug-Dec 1901; May 2, Aug 8,
  Oct 17, 1902. Film, Sep 1893-1910; 1945+
  See Herald.
  KHi: May 27, 1926.

Moniteau Journal   w   1866-1875
  MoHi: Nov 18, 1869; Oct 30, 1873; Dec 5, 1874-
  Dec 9, 1875. See Loyal Journal, Loyal Missourian.
  MoSHi: Oct 5, 1871.

Moniteau Monitor   w   1880-1882
  MoHi: Mar 24, 1880-Mar 15, 1882.

CALIFORNIA (continued)

News   w   1858-1869
   MoHi: Film, Nov 6,1858-Nov 16; 1861; Jan 18,
   1862-May 1865. Changed name to Moniteau
   County Democrat 1869, Democrat 1872.
   Irregular career during Civil War.

Newspaper   w   1884-1896
   MoHi: May 8,1884-1885; Apr 8,1886-1887; 1888-
   Jly 9,1896. See Greenback Derrick.

Phifer's Paper   w   1884-1885

Pioneer   w   1861
   In American Newspaper Directory 1861.

Republican   sw   1888
   MoHi: Sep 1,13,26,29,Oct 3,6,31,Nov 24,
   Dec 1,1888.

CALLAO (Macon County)

Courier   w   1890-1891
   In Rowell-Ayer 1892.

Gath   w   1883
   In Rowell 1884.

Herald   w   1898-1906
   Last in Rowell 1908, Ayer 1906.

Journal   w   1895-1899, 1908-1942
   Two papers by this name.

News   w   1889-1891?
   In Rowell 1890-1891, Ayer 1891.

World   w   1894
   Start noted in Missouri Editor, Jun 1894.

CAMDEN (Ray County)

Bee   w   1895-1905, 1914-1918
   Two papers by this name.

Journal   w   1922-1945?
   Last listed in Ayer 1945.

CAMDEN POINT (Platte County)

Dictagraph   w   1912-1916
   In Ayer 1914-1917.

Home Bee   w   1903-1910?
   Last listed in Ayer 1911.

Platte County News   w   1917-1918
   MoHi: Film, Dec 7,1917-Nov 1,1918.

Star-Press   w   1895-1902
   In Rowell 1900-1903, Ayer 1901.

CAMDENTON (Camden County)

Central Missouri Leader   w   1903+
   MoHi: Film, Jun 1,1948+ Founded at Macks Creek
   moved to Camdenton 1935.

Reveille   w   1879+
   MoHi: Apr 24,1931-1944. Film, 1945+ Published
   in Linn Creek to Apr 1931.

CAMERON (Clinton County)

Cameron   w   1876?
   ICHi: Jly 7,14,1876.

Chronotype   w   1867
   Became Observer 1868.

Clinton County Register   w   1866?-1878
   In Rowell-Pettengill 1878.

Democrat   w   1874,1900
   Two papers, both short lived.

District Herald   w   1882
   In Ayer 1883.

Free Lance   w   1899-1900
   In Rowell 1900-1901, Ayer 1900.

Globe   d   1895
   See Little Globe.

Hammer   w   1896
   MoHi: Aug 14,1896. Also dated at Turney.

Herald   w   1882?
   May be District Herald. Rowell lists Herald in 188

Little Globe   d   1895
   Missouri Editor notes start of Little Globe in Feb
   1895, end of Globe Jly 1895. Apparently same pap

Missouri Sun   w   1902-1914
   See Sun.

News   d   1905-1920
   MoHi: Oct 1,1913-Sep 15,1920. Merged with
   Observer to become News-Observer Sep 1920.

News-Observer   w,d   1905+
   MoHi: Sep 16,1920-1922; 1924-1950. Film, Jan 2
   1923-Dec 31,1923; 1951+ Formed by merger 192

Observer   d   1892-1920   w   1868-1920
   MoHi: d, Aug 8,1901-Sep 15,1920. Film, Mar 8,
   1892-Aug 1893; Mar 8,1894-Sep 8,1897 inc;
   Mar 8,1898-Sep 8,1899; Sep 8,1900-Jly 24,
   1901. W, film, Jly 23,1875-Jly 12,1878; Aug
   22,1878-Mar 27,1890 inc; 1891-1895; 1897-
   Aug 31,1899; 1907; 1909. See News.

Press   w   1922-1941?
   End of 19th year noted in MPN, Aug 1941.

CAMERON (continued)

Progress w 1923-1957?
    MoHi: Aug 18, 1932-Jun 15, 1933. Kidder Weekly
        Institute combined with Progress in 1946.

Republican w 1898-1900
    MoHi: Mar 16, 1900.

Sun w 1886+
    MoHi: Aug 15, 1902-Sep 16, 1920; Jly 10, 1896.
        Merged with Weekly Observer Sep 1920 to be-
        come Sun and Weekly Observer. Called Cameron
        Sun 1887-Sep 19, 1902; Cameron Missouri Sun
        Sep 19, 1902-Apr 9, 1914; Cameron Sun Apr 16,
        1914-Sep 16, 1920; Cameron Sun and Weekly
        Observer Sep 23, 1920-1950.

Sun and Observer w, d 1868+
    MoHi: Sep 23, 1920-1921; 1926-1944. Film, 1922-
        1925, 1945+ See Sun. Ayer 1863 lists this title
        for daily, Sun for weekly.

Vindicator w 1876-1892, d 1881-1892
    MoHi: d, Jun 10, 1881-Sep 21, 1888; Apr 18, 1882.
        W, Sep 7, 14, 21, 28, Oct 5, 12, 19, Nov 30, Dec
        7, 14, 1888; Jan 4, 11, Feb 1, Mar 1, 15, 1889.
        Film, Jun 8, 1876-Jun 5, 1879.
    MoSHi: Oct 24, 1884.

CAMPBELL (Dunklin County)

Citizen w 1900+
    MoHi: Oct 16, 1903-Nov 1904; 1908-1944; Mar 2,
        Jun 7, Jly 5, 1917; Oct 25, 1918. Film, 1945+
        Listed at times as Dunklin County Citizen.

Independent w 1896-1898
    In Rowell 1897-1899, Ayer 1898-1899.

Times w 1898
    In Ayer 1899.

CANTON (Lewis County)

Cantonian w 1916-1919
    In Ayer 1917-1920.

Common Sense w 1899-1900
    In Rowell 1900, Ayer 1901.

Express w 1843
    Hammond says first paper in county.

Lewis County Gazette w 1869
    In Rowell 1870.

Lewis County Journal w 1879+
    MoHi: Sep 19, 1929-1944. Film, 1945+ See Monti-
        cello and Canton Record. Some references to
        Lewis County Journal-News and Lewistown News.

Mississippi Sawyer w 1920-1922
    Under News in Union List as name used for 1920-1922.

CANTON (continued)

Missouri Plebeian w 1848-1849
    MoHi: Jun 16, 1848-Apr 27, 1849. Changed to
        Northeast Reporter Jun 7, 1849.

News w 1880-1928
    MoHi: Jly 25, 1901-Nov 26, 1908; Feb 14, 1913-Sep
        5, 1918; Mar 22, 1889; Oct 24, 1890. Merged
        with Press, became Press-News Nov 16, 1928.

Northeast Reporter w 1849-1861
    MoHi: Jun 14, 1849-May 20, 1850; Jun 24, 1852-
        Oct 2, 1856. Photostat Jun 7, 1849. See Missouri
        Plebeian.
    MoSHi: Jun 30, 1853.

Press w 1862-1928
    MoHi: Jly 16, 1862-1919; 1924-Nov 16, 1928; Feb
        28, Sep 19, 1879; Aug 22, 1884; Apr 3, 1885;
        Oct 31, 1890. Film, 1920-1923. See News.
    ICHi: Sep 1, 1876.

Press-News w 1928+
    MoHi: Nov 22, 1928-1944. Film, 1945+ Press and
        News merged in 1928.

Press-News and Record w 1861+
    See above. Final consolidation 1940.

Record w 1929-1941
    Consolidated with Press-News 1941.

Register w 1861
    In American Newspaper Directory 1861.

Reporter w 1856-1861
    Listed in directories 1856, 1861.

CAPE GIRARDEAU (Cape Girardeau County)

Advocate and Jeffersonian 1854
    Earlier in Jackson, according to Organ.

Der Anzeiger w 1884-1885
    Listed in Rowell-Ayer 1885.

Argus w 1863-1869
    In Rowell 1869-1870. One source says combined
    with Missouri Democracy.

Camp Fremont Register w 1861
    WHi: Sep 25, 1861. Vol 1, No 1.

Cape County Herald w 1898-1913
    MoHi: Mar 3, 10, 17, 31, Apr 21, May 12, 19, Jun 2,
        30, Jly 21, Aug 4-Oct 6, 20, Nov 3, 1911; May
        24, 1912.

Cape Daily Tribune d 1914-1918
    MoSHi: Feb 20, 1916.

-23-

Cape Tribune   w   1902-1919   d   1914-1918
   MoHi: Film, w, Feb 6,1914-Jun 20,1919. D, film,
   Mar 13,1914-Oct 16,1918. Followed by
   Morning Sun.

Cape Talk   sw   1886
   ·In Rowell 1887.

Censor   w   1842?-1846
   Mentioned by Hammond.

Courier   w   1880-1884
   In Rowell 1881-1885, Ayer 1881-1883.

Democrat   w   1875-1909   d   1889-1909
   MoHi: Film, Jan 1891-Dec 1900; Jan 1902-May
   29,1909.
   Cape Girardeau Library: d, 1893-1909. W, film,
   1891-1909. Apparently an earlier Democrat,
   1854, which later became Expositor.

Democracy   w   1866
   Mentioned by Hammond.

Eagle   w   1847-1862
   MoHi: Oct 29, Nov 12, 26, Dec 3,10,31,1857;
   Jan 14, 21, Mar 4, 11, Oct 14, 21, 1858; May
   26, Jun 9, 16, 1859; Apr 26, Aug 30, Nov 22,
   29, Dec 6, 20, 27, 1860; Jan 10, 17, Feb 21,
   Mar 7-21, Jun 25, 1861. Film, May 10-24,
   Jly 16-26, 1862.
   Cape Girardeau Library: May 10-Aug 16, 1862.
   MWA: Dec 16, 1853.
   MHi: Jly 26, 1862.
   WHi: May 10-24, Jun 21-Aug 16, 1862. Also
   known as Western Eagle. Some issues published
   by Union troops.

Era   d   1892-1894   w   1865?-1894
   Also known as New Democratic Era.

Expositor   w   1854-1856
   Mentioned by Organ. Exposition in 1851?

Farmer   w   1831
   Said to be first in community.

Gazette   w   1895
   Formerly published in DeSoto.

Girardean   sw   1936-1938
   In Ayer 1939-1940.

Girardean Press   w   1938-1939
   Formerly Girardean.

Herald   w   1919-1924?
   MoCaT: 1919-Jan 1924 (Union List)

Marble City News   w   1865-1874?
   See News.

Mississippi Valley Globe   w   1872
   In Rowell 1872-1873.

Missouri Cultivator   w   1888-1891
   In Rowell 1889-1892, Ayer 1888-1889.

Missouri Democracy   w   1868-1869?
   In Rowell 1869-1870.

New Democratic Era   w   1888-1894
   Apparently weekly edition of Era.

News   w   1865-1888, 1929-1953   d   1910
   ICHi: w, Feb 2, Jly 5, 1876.
   Weekly halted 30 months during World War II.
   D in Ayer 1910-1911.

Patriot   w   1836-1842
   Later South Missourian, ended 1846.

Progress   w,sw   1901-1909
   MoHi: 1906-1909; Sep 19, 1903. Film, Apr 26,
   1902-1905. SW, Sep 3, 1902-Jun 27, 1903.

Republican   w,d   1901-1918
   MoHi: w, Jan 2, 1910-Mar 7, 1918; May 15, 1908.
   Film, Feb 7-Dec 4, 1908; 1909. D, Dec 1, 1903-
   Sep 9, 1904. Film, Oct 3, 1904; Mar 8, 1918.
   MoSHi: 1908-1913, scattered editions, w. Became
   Southeast Missourian Mar 8, 1918.

Review   w   1892-1896
   In Rowell 1893-1894, Ayer 1894-1897.

Southeast Bulletin   w   1929+
   MoHi: Film, 1955+ First in Ayer 1954.

Southeast Champion   w   1872
   In Rowell 1873.

Southeast Democrat   w   1857-1858
   MoHi: May 5, 1858.

Southeast Gazette   w   1890-1900
   NcD: Jun 11, 1896. In Rowell 1897-1901, Ayer
   1896-1900.

Southeast Missourian   w,d   1901+
   MoHi: w, Mar 8, 1918-1920; Sep 11, 1925. D,
   Jan 25, 1923-1950. Film, d, Mar 1918-Mar
   20, 1923; 1951+
   MoSHi: Oct 2, 1954; Feb 1, 1958; Jan 28, 1950.
   Cape Girardeau County Library: 1919+ Formerly
   Republican.

Southeast Radical   w   1865-1866
   MWA: Mar 9, 1866.

Southern Advocate and State Journal   w   1835-1845?
   Mentioned by Organ.

Southern Standard   w   1849?
   MoSHi: Sep 5, 1849.

South Missourian   w   1842-1846
   See Patriot.

CAPE GIRARDEAU (continued)

Sun   d   1919-1922
MoHi: Aug 27,1919-Aug 1922. Formerly Daily
Tribune to Aug 26,1919.

Times   w   1918?
MoHi: Oct 25-Dec 19,1918.

Wall's Argus   w   1885
Called "Republican Organ 14th District."

Western Eagle   w   1847-1861
MoHi: Film, Mar 31,1848-Mar 23,1849; May 11,
1849-Mar 21,1851. See Eagle.
MoSHi: Apr 11,1851; Sep 15,1855; Mar 15,1860.
WHi: May 11,1849-Mar 21,1851.

Western Press   w   1873-1875   d   1874
MoHi: Sep 10,1875.
ICHi: May 19,1876. Rowell lists d 1874, Sunday
1873.

Westliche Press   w   1871-1876
In Rowell 1872-1876.

(Die) Zeitung   1879-1880?
ICHi: May 27,1876. In Rowell 1880.

CARDWELL (Dunklin County)

Outlook   w   1913-1923?
MoHi: Sep 5,1919.

Sentinel   w   1897-1899
In Ayer 1899-1900.

Times   w   1923-1937
Subscription list to Dunklin Democrat 1937.

CARIO (Randolph County)

Dispatch   w   1895
Start noted in Missouri Editor, Aug 1895.

CARL JUNCTION (Jasper County)

Democrat   w   1899-1900
In Rowell 1900-1901, Ayer 1901.

Graphic   d   1907
MoHi: Film, Jan 1-Apr 20,1907.

Jasper County World   w   1900-1907
MoHi: Film, Oct 26,1906-Dec 27,1907.

Plaindealer   w   1900-1915
MoHi: 1908-May 20,1915. Became Times May
20,1915.

Socialist News   w   1906-1907
MoHi: Film, Oct 2,1906-Apr 16,1907.

CARL JUNCTION (continued)

Standard   w   1890+
MoHi: Dec 16,1898-Dec 28,1906; Jan 20,1911-
1912; 1917-1944. Film, 1913-1916; 1945+
KHi: Aug 25,1922.
T: Aug 21,1891.

Sunbeam   w   1881-1882
In Ayer 1883.

Times   w   1900-1917?
MoHi: May 20-Dec 30,1915; Jan 4-Feb 1,1917.
Film, 1916. See Plaindealer.

CARROLLTON (Carroll County)

Carroll Record   w   1868+
MoHi: Jun 21,Oct 4,1888. Film, Aug 17,1878-
Jly 26,1888. Also Oct 31,1880 copy of Carroll
County Record. See Wakanda Record.

Cottage Visitor   w   1856?
Destroyed by fire, re-established as Democrat before Civil War. Suppressed at start of War.

Democrat   w   1860-1861, 1875+   d   1882+
MoHi: W, 1911; 1914-1944. Film, Nov 12,1875-
Nov 10,1876; 1877-1889; Jan 1893-1910; Jan
5,1912-Dec 26,1913; 1945+ Daily, Jly 1,1928-
Jun 30,1929; 1930-1950; Nov 13,1910; Oct 18,
1932; Mar 18,1897. Film, 1883-1889; 1893-
Jun 30,1928; Jly 1-Dec 1929; 1951+ American
Newspaper Directory lists Democrat in 1861; see
Cottage Visitor.
MoSHi: Oct 31,1919.
MWA: w, Oct 13,1933.
NHi: Oct 13,1933.
Micro-Photo: Film, 1958+
KHi: d, Jun 13,1922; Jan 5,Dec 8,1923.
ICHi: w, Aug 25,1876.

Journal   w,sw   1865-1889?
MoHi: Nov 16,1877-Nov 14,1879. Film, Dec 2,
1881-Dec 22,1882.
MWA: Oct 13,1865.
ICHi: w, Jly 21,1876.
Rowell lists semi-weekly in 1888, daily 1889.

Missouri Protest   w   1883-1887
In Rowell-Ayer 1887.

Record   w   1868+   d   1894,1899
Apparently two dailies. See Wakanda Record.

Republican-Record   w   1868+
MoHi: Jan 7,1904-1944. Film, 1945+
Represents consolidation of Wakanda Record,
Carroll Record, and Republican 1894.

Republican   w   1891-1894
In Rowell 1892-1895, Ayer 1891-1895.

CARROLLTON (continued)

Wakanda Record   w   1868-1878
MoHi: Nov 6,1869. Film, Jan 19,1872-Jan 19,
1878. Suspended Jan 19,1878. Began new series
as Carroll Record Aug 17,1878.
ICHi: Aug 25,1876.

CARTERVILLE (Jasper County)

Advertiser   w   1883
In Ayer 1883, Rowell 1884.

Evening Record   d   1900-1920
Last listed in Ayer 1921.

Free Press   w   1890
MoHi: Nov 1,1890.

Globe   w   1882
In Rowell 1883.

Journal   w,d   1893-1899?
Irregular publishing as daily. In Rowell 1894-
1900, Ayer 1894-1900. One says d established
1892, other 1893, w 1891 and 1892. Nameplate
for Jun 10,1898 is Vol VII, No 23.

Miners' Weekly Drift   w   1889
In Rowell 1890.

Mining Review   w   1884-1889
In Rowell 1885-1889, Ayer 1887-1889.

Morning Rocket   d   1900-1901
In Ayer 1902; Evening Rocket in Rowell 1901.

News   d   1921   w   1922-1929
In Ayer 1922-1930.

Record   d   1900?-1920
In Ayer 1919-1921, with 1900 starting.

Republican   w   1891-1892
In Rowell 1892-1893, Ayer 1892.

Southwestern Miner   w   1892-1893
In Rowell 1893-1894, Ayer 1894.

CARTHAGE (Jasper County)

Advance   w   1873-1877?
ICHi: Jun 29,1876. In Rowell 1874-1878.

Banner   w   1866-1892   d   1876-1892
MoHi: (Banner) Jan 16,30, Feb 6,13,20, Mar 6,
13,20,27, Apr 3,10,17, May 1,9,20, Jly 17,
24,31, Aug 6, Sep 4, Oct 2,9,23, Nov 6,20,
Dec 25,1873; (Carthage Banner) Feb 12, Apr 9,
Aug 6, Oct 15,22, Dec 3,1874; Jan 28, Mar 11,
25, Apr 8,15,22, Jun 10, Nov 25, Dec 9,1875;
Apr 6, Sep 7,14, Oct 12,19, Nov 2,9,16,1876;
May 17,1877; Feb 5, Jly 18,1879; Dec 13,1888.
(Weekly Banner) Jun 18,1868; Feb 4, Mar 4, Aug

CARTHAGE (continued)

Banner (continued)
19,26, Sep 23,30,1869; Jun 16,1870; Jan 5,
19,26, Feb 9, Apr 20, Jun 22, Oct 12,19, Nov
16,30, Dec 7,21,1871; Feb 8,15, May 9, Jly
4, Aug 15,29, Sep 26, Oct 3,10,31,1872; Jan
16,30, Feb 6,13,20, Mar 6,13,20,27, Apr 3,10,
17, May 1,29, Jun 26, Jly 24,27,31, Aug 6, Sep 4,
Oct 2,9,23, Nov 6,20, Dec 25,1873. Film,
(Weekly Banner) Dec 22,1866-1869; Mar 10,
1870-Dec 23,1875; Feb 1-Nov 8,1877; 1878-
Jly 3,1879; Jan 1-Dec 23,1880; 1882-1887.
See Boliver Union.
ICHi: w, Aug 31,1876.

Democrat   d   1884-1942
MoHi: 1912-1913; 1915-Jan 12,1917; Mar 24,
1937-1942; Aug 4,1905; Jly 25,1914. Film,
Jan 12-Sep 30,1909; Jan 1-Jun 28,1910;
Aug 20-Dec 31,1910; 1914.
KHi: Jun 10, Nov 8,1924; Feb 3,1925.

Dollar Transcript   w   1883
In Ayer 1883, founding date of 1883.

Jasper County Democrat   w   1884-1942
MoHi: 1920-1941; Jan 5,1906; Jly 24,1914.
Film, Aug 30,1884-Aug 21,1885; Dec 8,1898-
1919; Jan 2-Aug 21,1942; Sep 4, Dec 17,1942.
Weekly edition of Democrat.

Jasper County Gazette   sw   1884
In Dauchy 1884.

Jasper County News   w   1901-1904
MoHi: Jan 5,1904. Film, Oct 1,1901-1903.

Labor's Tribune   w   1889-1900?
See People's Voice. At times backed Populists.

Missouri Opinion   w   1892
In Ayer 1892, founding date 1892.

Patriot   w   1870-1887?   d   1876-1887?
MoHi: D, Feb 29,1879. Film, Jun 27, Jly 1,2,7,
Aug 11,1876; Aug 13,1887-May 27,1878.
ICHi: w, Jly 6,1876. D, Jly 7,1876.

People's Voice   w   1888-1890
Basically labor, published by Populists.

People's Press   w   1872-1881
MoHi: Film, Apr 25-Dec 1872; 1873-1878; May
1879-Jly 7,1881. Became Carthage Press
Jly 14,1881.
ICHi: Apr 27,1876.

Pioneer   w   1857-?
Became Star of the West, later Southwestern Star.

CARTHAGE (continued)

Press   w   1872+   d   1885+
    MoHi: W, Jan 7,1904-Sep 5,1921; Aug 23,30,
    Sep 6,20,Dec 20,1888; Jly 13,20,1905; Jly
    23,1914. Film, Jly 14,1881-1882; 1885; Jly
    14,1887-1901; Jly 25,1901-1903. See
    People's Press. D, Sep 1921-Jun 1926; Oct
    1926-1950; Jly 23,24,25,1914. Film, Jly-
    Sep 28,1886; 1890; Mar 14-Sep 28,1891;
    Jan-Jun 1892; Feb-Dec 1895; 1898-Mar 16,
    1899; 1900-1921; Jly 1,1926-Sep 30,1926;
    1951+
    MWA: Aug 17,1876.
    T: d, Mar 13,1943.

Record   1869?
    In Rowell 1869, no other data.

Record Reporter   1908?
    MoHi: Mar 16,1908.

Republican   w   1878-1879?
    MoHi: Jun 19-Dec 18,1884; Sep 11,Oct 2,23,
    30,1879. Possibly another Republican appeared
    shortly after this.

Silver Review   w   1896-1900
    In Rowell 1897-1901, Ayer 1897-1901.

Southwestern   w   1879
    In Rowell 1880,founding date 1879.

Southwest News   w   1859?
    Mentioned in Union List.

Southwestern Star   w   1859?-1861
    See Pioneer. Date of name change uncertain.
    Press taken by Confederates in 1861.

Star of the West   w   1858?-1859?
    See Pioneer.

Transcript   d   1883
    In Rowell 1884, Ayer 1883.

Western Critic   w   1893-1896
    End noted in Missouri Editor, May 1896.

CARUTHERSVILLE (Pemiscot County)

Democrat   w   1868-1921   sw   1900-1921
    MoHi: Film, Feb 19-Oct 21,1892; 1895; Feb 21,
    1896-Apr 22,1897; May 6,1897-Jan 19,1900.
    Became Twice-a-Week Democrat Jan 26,1900.
    Oct 1908-1919; 1921. Film, Jan 26,1900-1906;
    1908; 1920. Became Democrat-Argus Dec 6,1921.

Democrat-Argus   w,sw   1868+
    MoHi: Dec 6,1921-1925; 1931-1944. Film, 1926-
    1930; 1945+ Became w Jun 12,1942.

Journal   w   1963+
    See Republican.

CARUTHERSVILLE (continued)

Pemiscot Argus   w   1898-1921
    MoHi: 1919-Nov 24,1921. Film, Jly 19-Nov 1,
    1907; Sep 24-Dec 1908; Mar 1909-1918.
    Formerly published in Hayti. Merged with
    Twice-a-Week Democrat to become Democrat-
    Argus Dec 6,1921.

Pemiscot Press   w,sw   1894-1908
    MoHi: sw, Jan 3,1902-Dec 12,1906; Sep 25-
    Dec 25,1908. Listed as sw in Rowell 1907.

Republican   w   1910-1963
    MoHi: 1917-1921; 1925-1944. Film, 1945-1963.
    Renamed Journal.

Southeast Scimitar   bw   1901
    MoHi: Film, May 23-Dec 26,1901.

Times   w   1900-1901?
    In Ayer 1902.

Twice-a-Week Democrat   tw   1900-1921
    See Democrat.

CASSVILLE (Barry County)

Advocate   w   1874
    In Rowell 1875 as Barry County Advocate.

Barry County Banner   w   1868-1871
    Merged with Cassville True Democrat 1871,
    according to MHR, Jly 1956.

Barry County Gazette   w   1913
    In Ayer 1914-1915.

Barry County Reformer   w   1893-1896
    People's Party paper, brief career.

Democrat   w   1871+
    MoHi: Nov 18,1899; Dec 28,1901; Aug 30-
    Dec 6,1902; 1903-May 1906; 1911-1916;
    1920-1944; Nov 14,1903. Film, Jun 6,1906-
    1909; Jan 19,1917-1919; 1945+
    KHi: Oct 4,1924.
    ICHi: Jan 22,1876.

Register   w   1857-1858
    Formerly Lawrence County Register.

Republican   w   1872+
    MoHi: Aug 3,1899-1944; Oct 30,1890; May 11,
    1893; Jly 9,1896. Film, Mar 20,1890-Jly
    27,1899; 1945+ See Corsicana Valley Press.

True Democrat   w   1871
    See Barry County Banner.

Valley Press   w   1872?-1878
    MoHi: Oct 18,1878.

CEDAR CITY (Callaway County)

Chronicle   w   1894-1903
    MoHi: Nov 2, 1899-May 21, 1903. Merged with
    Reporter to form Chronicle-Reporter Jly 2, 1903.

Chronicle-Reporter   w   1894-1914?
    MoHi: Jly 2, 1903-Dec 23, 1906.

Clarion   w   1872-1879?
    Mentioned by Hammond.

Gazette   w   1874-1875
    In Rowell 1875-1876.

Herald   w   1904-1905
    In Rowell 1905-1906.

Reporter   w   1899-1903
    In Rowell 1901-1903, Ayer 1900-1903.

Vindicator   w   1873
    Also known as Callaway Vindicator. In Rowell 1874.

CENTER (Ralls County)

Censor   w   1898
    In Rowell 1898-1899.

Courier   w   1890-1902
    In Rowell 1894-1903, Ayer 1894-1898.

Herald   w   1904+
    MoHi: 1919-1944. Film, 1945+

Intelligencer   w   1898-1902
    MoHi: Under Ralls County Intelligencer, film,
    Oct 25, 1901-Jly 11, 1902.

CENTERTOWN (Cole County)

Central Missouri Leader   w   1902-1917?
    Last listed in Ayer 1918.

CENTERVIEW (Johnson County)

Banner   w   1907-1911?
    In Rowell 1908, Ayer 1908-1912.

Centreview Mugwump   w   1886
    Started Sep 25, 1886. Printed in Warrensburg.

Record   w   1898-1906
    MoHi: Jan 26, Feb 2, 9, 23, Mar 2-23, 1906.

CENTERVILLE (Reynolds County)

Echo   w   1877-1878
    ICHi: Jly 8, 1876.
        Became Reynolds County Outlook 1878?

Missouri and Kansas Miner   w   1898

CENTERVILLE (continued)

Reformer   w   1891-1911
    MoHi: Film, Mar 3, 1904-Dec 26, 1907.

Reynolds County Courier   w   1923-1952
    MoHi: Nov 18, 1926-1937; 1941-1944. Film,
    1938-1940; 1945-1952. Merged with Ellington
    Press Jan 3, 1952. Published in Ellington as
    Courier-Press.
    KHi: Jly 5, 1928.

Reynolds County Outlook   w   1877-1925
    Originally Echo. In Rowell 1879-1908, Ayer
    1880-1926.

CENTRALIA (Boone County)

Courier   w   1891-1931
    MoHi: 1919-1926; 1929-Sep 1933; 1934. Film,
    Jan 29, 1915-1918; Jan 13, 1927-1928.
    Suspended Mar 5, 1931.

Christian Worker   w
    MoHi: Film, Oct 1, 1894-Jun 1895

Fireside Guard   w   1868+
    MoHi: Mar 27, 1903-1926; 1929-1944. Film,
    Mar 18, 1871-Dec 27, 1873; Mar 21, 1874-May
    29, 1875; Jan 13, 1877-1901; 1927-1928; 1945+
    KHi: Aug 11, 1922.

Home Circle   1868-1870
    MoHi: Dec 15, 1868. Also known as Southern
    Home Circle. Later became Sturgeon Independent.
    Material also used for Fireside Guard. Name
    used also for Southern Home Circle.

Home Circle and Literary Gem   w   1868
    MoHi: Jan 25, 1869. See Home Circle.

Methodist Flash   w
    MoHi: Film, Nov 1-Dec 6, 1894; Jan 6, 1895.

Picket   w   1889
    In Ayer 1889, founding date 1889.

Southern Home Circle   w   1868-1870
    MoHi: Film, Feb 1869-Feb 1870.

CENTROPOLIS (Jackson County)

Jackson County Advocate   w   1887-1890?
    Listed Rowell 1889 as Jackson County Advocate and
    Blue Valley Pioneer.

Sheffield Times   w   1888-1889?
    In Rowell 1890.

CHAFFEE (Scott County)

Leader   w   1954-1960
    Combined with Signal 1960.

CHAFFEE (continued)

Review   w   1905-1911?
   In Rowell 1907, Ayer 1907-1912.

Signal   w   1910+
   MoHi: Film, Jan 5, 1917-Dec 19, 1919.

CHAMOIS (Osage County)

Battle Flag   w   1879
   Hammond says temperance paper.

Headlight   w   1898
   In Rowell 1898, Ayer 1899.

Liberalist   w   1879-1888
   MoHi: Apr 19, 1883. Became Osage County
   Enterprise Mar 1, 1888.

News of Osage County   w   1916-1958
   Merged with Linn Osage County Republican Dec
   4, 1958.

Osage County Enterprise   w   1888-1918?
   MoHi: Oct 23, 30, 1890; Jly 9, 1896.

Osage County Herold   w   1892-1898?
   German paper issued by Osage County Enterprise.
   Herold spelling used by Rowell.

Osage County Leader   w   1872-1879?
   Also known as Osage Leader. In Rowell 1873-1879,
   at times as Osage Leader.

Osage County Ledger   w
   ICHi: Jan 28, Jly 7, 1876.

CHARLESTON (Mississippi County)

Bee   w   1907?
   MoHi: Oct 1, Nov 1, 1907.

Call   w, d   1895-1896?
   In Ayer 1897.

Chronicle   w   1899
   In Ayer 1900.

Courier   w   1902-1915
   MoHi: 1903-Mar 31, 1911; Oct 27, 1911-Dec 24,
   1914; Jly 18, 22, Aug 1, Sep 12, 19, 1862; Aug
   21, 1908; Jan-Apr 1915. Merged with Enterprise
   to form Enterprise-Courier Apr 22, 1915.
   ICHi: Aug 31, 1876.

Courier-Gazette   w   1877-1880?
   Result of merger of Courier and Gazette in 1877.
   Later moved to Malden. Some sources give found-
   ing as 1857.

CHARLESTON (continued)

Democrat   w   1929-1955
   MoHi: Feb 17, 1933-1944. Film, 1945-1954.
   Charleston Library; 1933-Oct 11, 1945; 1945-46;
   Oct 24, 1946-Oct 16, 1947; 1949-1950.
   Merged with Enterprise-Courier Nov 24, 1955.

Enterprise   w   1875-1915   d   1891-1915
   MoHi: W, May 15, 1902-1909; 1913-Apr 16, 1915.
   Film, Jly 29, 1879-Apr 12, 1889; 1892-1897;
   Jun 1901-May 9, 1902; 1910-1912. D, Dec 20,
   1898-Apr 24, 1899; Nov 19, 1898. Film, Oct
   1891-1897; Jun 1900-Jly 13, 1901. Merged
   with Courier Apr 22, 1915.

Enterprise-Courier   w   1875+
   MoHi: Apr 22, 1915-1944. Film, 1945+
   Charleston Library: Sep 28, 1939-Sep 19, 1940;
   Sep 25, 1941+

Gazette   w   1875-1877
   ICHi: Sep 23, 1876. In Rowell 1876-1878.

Independent   w   1862
   KHi: Mar 10, 1862.

Index   d   1919-1923
   KHi: Jan 31, 1923. In Ayer 1920-1924.

Journal   w   1855-1861
   Mentioned by Organ.

New Idea   d   1915-1918?
   In Ayer 1917-1919.

News   tw, d   1896-1897
   Rowell 1897 lists d, Ayer 1898 tw.

Republican   w   1906-1917
   MoHi: Oct 6, 1906-Aug 13, 1914; Mar 15-Apr 19,
   1917. Film, Jan 4-Apr 19, 1917.

Sentinel   w   1879-1880
   In Rowell 1880-1881, Ayer 1881.

Star   w   1901-1905?
   MoHi: Feb 12, 1904

Times   w   1921-1928
   MoHi: 1925-Sep 7, 1928. Bought by Enterprise-
   Courier, Sep 1928.

Volunteer   w   1862?
   First copy appeared Jan 27, 1862.

CHILHOWEE (Johnson County)

Blade   w   1915-1921
   MoHi: Jan 22, 1915-Dec 16, 1921.

Journal   w   1942?
   MPN, Sep 1942, said News had resumed under name
   of Journal. No other listing.

CHILHOWEE (continued)

News   w   1896-1941?
    MoHi: Nov 18, 1898-Nov 24, 1899; Jly 26, 1901-
    Oct 1, 1914.

CHILLICOTHE (Livingston County)

Christian Pioneer   w,m   1854-1870
    MoHi: Film, Apr 8, 1869-Nov 3, 1870. Conflict in
    data. Some say descended from Western Pioneer
    of Trenton, started in 1851. First a religious
    monthly; w after Apr 8, 1869.
    NcD: Aug 12, 19, 26, Sep 2, 1869; Jan 10, Feb 3,
    Mar 10-24, 1870.

Constitution   w,sw   1860-1928   d   1887-1928
    MoHi: W, Jan 5, 1911-Dec 1924; 1927-Mar 1, 1928;
    Apr 25, 1863; Nov 12, 1864; Jan 12, 1865; Apr
    18, 1919; Feb 9, 11, 1916. Film, Oct 10, 1872-
    Oct 22, 1874; Dec 12, 1898-1910; Jan 1, 1925-
    Dec 30, 1926. Semi-weekly, film, Dec 12, 1889-
    Apr 25, 1892. D, Feb 9, 11, 1916; Apr 18, 1919.
    Film, Dec 2, 1889-Jun 30, 1890; May 29, 1890-
    Mar 31, 1892; 1902-Jun 1903; Apr-Jun 1904;
    Apr 1905-Sep 1915; Jly 1916-Mar 16, 1928.
    Merged with Tribune to become Constitution-
    Tribune Mar 1928.
    MoSHi: W, Jan 9, 1861; Apr 6, 1865.
    WHi: W, Jun 20, Sep 5, Oct 17-24, Nov 26, Dec
    10, 24, 1863; Jan 14, 1864.
    Micro-Photo: Film, d, 1889-1928. W, 1901-1921;
    1925+
    KHi: Jly 1, 1916; Dec 30, 1924; Feb 13, 21, 1925.
    IChi: W, Aug 31, 1876.

Constitution-Tribune   d,w   1928+ (1843)
    MoHi: W, Mar 1, 1928-1944. Film, 1945+
    D, Mar 1, 1928-1950. Film, 1951+ See Con-
    stitution. History traced to Grand River Chronicle,
    1843, founding date now used.
    MWA: Apr 12, 1866.
    Micro-Photo: Film, d, 1928+

Crisis   w   1877-1911?
    MoHi: Aug 30, 1877-Aug 6, 1885; Sep 17, 1903.

Democrat   d   1892-1905
    MoHi: Sep 8, 1903-Oct 10, 1905; Jly 2, 1881;
    May 22, 1903. Formerly Mail & Star.

First Kansas   w   1861-1862
    KHi: Film, Oct 16, 1861; Jan 18, 1862. Military
    publication.

Gazette   w   1899
    Start noted in Country Editor, Mar 1899.

Grand River Chronicle   w   1843-?
    MoHi: Jly 31, 1846. Later Spectator, Tribune.

CHILLICOTHE (continued)

Intellectual Elevator   w   1890-1895?
    MoHi: Oct 18, 1890. Missouri Editor, Jly 1895,
    says paper just started. However, Oct 18, 1890
    issue is Vol 1, No 1, to be published every 10
    weeks. By 1895 is bm.

Journal   w   1870-1872?
    MoHi: Apr 28, 1870.

Living Issue   w   1883
    In Ayer 1883, temperance organ.

Mail & Star   w,sw,d   1892-1899
    MoHi: Film, Dec 1, 1898-Nov 30, 1899. Rowell
    1893 lists Evening Mail; sw; 1899 w. Mail
    and Star and Times consolidated 1898.

Missouri World   w   1888-1908
    MoHi: Mar 20, 1895; Jun 21, 1899. Film, Jly 24,
    1901-Nov 11, 1908.
    MnHi: Feb 24-Mar 2, Apr 13, 1892; Dec 27, 1893;
    May 20, Sep 23-Oct 7, 28-Nov 4, 25, 1896; Jan
    6-13, May 5, 1897; Jan 30, 1907; Apr 8, Nov 11,
    1908.
    WHi: Apr 8, 1908.
    NcA: Jly 17, 1895.
    NcD: Aug 23, 1893; Mar 4, Aug 12, 1896.

National Beacon   w   1882
    In Ayer 1883, Greenback paper.

News   w,sw,tw,d   1881?-1936?
    MoHi: News, w, Oct 12, 1928-Jan 2, 1936. Sold
    to Constitution-Tribune 1936.
    Ayer 1881 lists d, est. 1881. Apparently ended
    before 1886, becoming w 1883. Missouri Editor,
    Dec 1896, says Daily News is a new venture.
    Another News started 1928.

News and Chula Chronicle   sw   1923-1931?
    In Ayer 1930-1932.

News-Chronicle   w,sw   1928-?
    Apparently name for News 1932-1936.

North Missouri Press   w   1935-1936
    Sold to Constitution-Tribune 1936.

Republican   w   1884-1899
    Dauchy 1884 lists Republican. Country Editor,
    May 1889, tells of Republican as a new venture.

Spectator   w   1866-1869?
    MoHi: Mar 8, 1866-Mar 7, 1867. One source
    indicates Spector spelling for brief time.

Standard Dollar Daily Democrat   w,d   1882
    In Rowell 1882 as w. Hammond uses longer title.

Star   d   1885-1891
    MoHi: Sep 21, 1888.

CHILLICOTHE (continued)

Times   d,w   1896-1898
  Hale City Times to Chillicothe 1896.

Tribune   w   1866-1928   d   1881-1928
  MoHi: d, Sep 15,1910-Dec 31,1913; Jan 2,1916-
  Mar 1,1917; Jan 1927-Feb 29,1928; Apr 28,1891;
  Jun 23,30, Jly 7,14,28, Aug 4,25, Sep 1,8,15,
  1891; Feb 9,1893. Film, Feb 1-Nov 19,1886;
  1914-1915; Nov 22,1924-1926. W, film, Jan 9-
  Dec 26,1919. Merged with Constitution Mar 1,
  1928.
  Micro-Photo; Film, 1927 inc.

Visitor   w   1880?
  Mentioned by Hammond.

CHULA (Livingston County)

Bazoo   w   1897-1898
  In Rowell 1897-1898, Ayer 1898.

Chronicle   w   1923-1928
  United with News to form News and Chula
  Chronicle.

Graphic   w   1895-1896
  In Rowell-Ayer 1896-1897.

News   w   1911-1923
  In Ayer 1913-1924.

News of Chula   w   1899-1911
  MoHi: Mar 30,1906-Dec 22,1910; Jan 12,1911.
  Apparently became News 1911.

CLARENCE (Shelby County)

Courier   w   1881+
  MoHi: 1903-Mar 16,1928. Film, Jly 31,1901-
  1902; Jan 16,1946+. Sold to Shelby County
  Independent Mar 16,1928; called Independent-
  Courier Mar 20,1928-Jan 9,1946. Courier
  since Jan 16,1946.
  KHi: Jun 2,1926.

Farmer's Favorite   w   1889-1911
  MoHi: Film, May 19-Dec 22,1899; Jan 4-11,
  Jly 26,Nov 1,1901. Formerly Republican.

Independent-Courier   w   1928-1946
  MoHi: Mar 20,1928-1944. Film, 1945-Jan 9,
  1946. See Courier.

Liberal Republican   w   1872
  In Rowell 1873.

Republican   w   1889-1911
  MoHi: Film, Dec 2,1898-May 12,1899.
  Changed to Farmer's Favorite May 19,1899.

Sentinel   w   1915
  In Ayer 1916.

CLARENCE (continued)

Shelby County Independent   w   1925-1928
  MoHi: May 5,1925-Mar 16,1928. See Courier.

Tribune   w   1875-1878?
  Printed at Macon Independent office, later
  Macon Democrat.

CLARK (Randolph County)

Chronicle   w   1902-1938
  MoHi: 1904-1922. Film, 1923-Nov 13,1924.

Herald   w   1894
  Start noted in Missouri Editor, Mar 1894.

Zephyr   w   1897-1898
  In Rowell 1898-1899.

CLARKSBURG (Moniteau County)

Crescent   w   1888-1899
  MoHi: Oct 9,1890. In Rowell 1891-1901, Ayer
  1891-1900.

Harbinger   w   1886-1888
  In Rowell 1888-1889, Ayer 1887,1889.

Messenger   w   1885-1886
  MoHi: Jan 29,1886.

Moniteau County News   w   1908
  In Ayer 1909.

Our Home   w   1888-1899
  In Ayer 1896-1900, Rowell 1889-1899.

Review   w   1899-1906?
  In Rowell 1900-1907, Ayer 1900-1905.

Visitor   w   1898

CLARKSDALE (DeKalb County)

Banner   w   1896-1897
  In Ayer 1897-1898.

Herald   w   1888
  In Rowell 1889.

Journal   w   1902-1928   w   1897-1900, 1939-?
  MoHi: Feb 19,1904-1908; 1914-Aug 13,1925.
  Merged with Stewartsville Record 1928. Ayer
  1899-1901 lists Journal. MPN, Dec 1939,
  says Journal started.

New Era   w   1892-1893
  In Rowell 1893-1894.

CLARKSVILLE (Pike County)

Banner   w   1898-1909
  MoHi: Sep 18,1903. Film, Mar 22,1901-Dec 4,

CLARKSVILLE (continued)

Banner (continued)
1907; Jan 6-Jun 3, 1909. Formerly Calumet
Banner. Merged with Sentinel, Jly 7, 1909,
as Banner-Sentinel.

Banner-Sentinel w 1909-1928
MoHi: 1914-1919; Mar 8, 1923-1927; Dec 10,
1913. Film, Jly 7, 1909-1910; 1912-1913;
1920-Jan 11, 1922; Dec 13, 1922-Mar 1, 1923.
Merged with Piker Nov 1, 1917. Renamed
Sentinel Jan 5, 1928.

Calumet Banner w 1898-1901
MoHi: Film, Sep 1898-Oct 12, 1900; Jan-Mar
15, 1901. Became Banner Mar 22, 1901.
MoSHi: Mar 3, 1899.

Graphic w 1894-1896
For brief time issued twice-a-week.

Monitor w 1862-1867
Formerly Hannibal Monitor. Later Sentinel.
Conflicting data.

Piker w 1903-1917
MoHi: May 24, 1906-Jan 9, 1908; Dec 22, 1910-
Nov 1, 1917; Feb 5, 1914. Film, Jan 16, 1908-
Dec 15, 1910. Merged with Banner-Sentinel
Nov 1, 1917.

Pike Union w 1860-1865
Mentioned by Organ. Succeeded by Monitor,
Sentinel. ICN lists copy of Union, Oct 12, 1860.

Sentinel w 1866-1950
MoHi: 1934-1936; 1938-1944; Jun 10, 1869.
Film, Jly 4, 1867-Sep 30, 1869; 1888-Sep
1, 1899; Jan 5, 1928-Aug 1932; Aug 17-Dec
1933; 1937; 1945-Sep 21, 1950. Merged with
Banner 1909. Renamed Sentinel 1928. Suspended
Sep 21, 1950.
Clarksville Library: Many papers to 1880's not
classified.
ICHi: Feb 25, Jly 7, 1876.

CLARKTON (Dunklin County)

Advertiser w 1873-1874
Also known as Southeast Advertiser. May have
moved to Kennett.

Dunklin County Advocate w 1877-1879
To Malden as Clipper, later Kennett.

Gazette w 1913-1917
Listed in Ayer 1917-1918.

News w 1940+
MoHi: Film, Feb 6, 1947-Oct 6, 1949. Published
for time in Gideon.

CLAYTON (St. Louis County)

Argus w 1877-1921
MoHi: Nov 25, 1879-1920; Sep 7, 1888. Merged
with St. Louis County Sentinel Jan 7, 1921.

Claytonian w 1939-1960
First in Ayer 1953. Under Claytonian-Tribune
Ayer 1960.

Claytonian-Tribune w, bm 1939+
Listed as fortnightly in Ayer 1963.

Democrat w 1879-1887?
MoHi: Film, Mar 13-Sep 18, 1879.
MoSHi: Aug 28, 1879.

People's Advocate w 1896-1898
In Rowell 1897-1899, Ayer 1896-1897.

St. Louis County Advocate w 1896-1903
MoHi: Jly 10, 1903. Film, Aug 7-Nov 13, 1903.
Apparently same as People's Advocate. Merged
with St. Louis County Watchman to become
Watchman-Advocate Nov 20, 1903.

St. Louis County Leader w 1923-1954
MoHi: 1923-1944. Film, 1945-1954.
MoSHi: Feb 3-17, Mar 3-Jun 23, Jly 21, Aug 4-
Dec 29, 1933; 1934-1935 inc.

St. Louis County Sentinel w 1921-1924
MoHi: 1921-Jan 31, 1924. Formerly Argus.
Became Sentinel-Democrat Feb 7, 1924.

St. Louis County Wachter w 1878-1910
MoHi: Jan 16-Dec 25, 1903. German.

St. Louis Countian d 1902+
MoHi: Film, 1962. Court, business paper.

St. Louis County Watchman w 1881-1903
MoHi: Jly 26, 1901-Nov 13, 1903; Jly 13, 1882;
Oct 24, 1890; Jly 10, 1903. Film, Sep 29, 1881-
Aug 28, 1903; Sep 4-Nov 13, 1903.
MoSHi: Jly 1, 1887 & Jly 9, 1887 fragment.
Merged with St. Louis County Advocate to
Watchman-Advocate Nov 20, 1903.

Sentinel-Democrat w 1919-1926
MoHi: Feb 7-Dec 25, 1923. Film, 1925-Apr 1,
1926.

Star-Republican w 1878-1882
MoHi: Oct 21, 1881.

Watchman-Advocate w 1881-1961 d 1961+
MoHi: w, Jly 26, 1907-1924; 1926-1944; Apr
10, 1908. Film, Nov 20, 1903-Aug 11, 1905;
1925; 1924+ Became d 1961. MoHi: d, Jly
5, 1961+
MoSHi: w, 1911-1917 inc; Scattered copies
for 1919, 1924, 1931-1940, 1949. 1950; 1952-
1958-with few exceptions; Jan 1959.

CLAYTON (continued)

West-Town Advertiser   w   1955
In Ayer 1956.

CLEARMONT (Nodaway County)

Ledger   w   1911-1912
Under News for these years.

News   w   1888+
KHi: Jan 13, 1927.

Owl   w   1888
In Rowell 1889.

CLEVER (Christian County)

Clarion   w   1910?
In Ayer 1917, founding date 1910.

News   w   1917-1922
In Ayer 1919-1923.

CLIFTON HILL (Randolph County)

Banner   w   1896-1900?
In Rowell 1897-1901, Ayer 1897-1898.

News   w   1904?
Listed by Williams 1904.

Rustler   w   1899+
First in Rowell-Ayer 1901.

CLIMAX SPRINGS (Camden County)

Advocate   w   1889-1890
MoHi: Nov 19, 1890.

CLINTON (Henry County)

Advocate   w   1866-1889?   d   1882-1889
MoHi: w, Jun 3, 1869; Jan-Mar 1875; Mar-Apr
1881; 1883; 1885-1887; 1889-Mar 1891.
Daily, Sep 1883-Jan 1884; 1885-Aug 1887;
Apr 30-Dec 1888; Jan-Sep 1889.
ICHi: Jly 6, Aug 3, 1876.

Bee   d   1883
Listed in Rowell-Dauchy 1884.

Commonwealth   w   1894
Mentioned in Missouri Editor, Oct 1894.

Democrat   d   1886+
MoHi: Nov 19, 1891; Oct 3, 6-10, 15-17, 20, 21,
23, 24, 26-31, 1896; Aug 3, 1908; May 9, 1914;
Jan 26, 1954; Mar-Dec 1911. Film, Oct 18,
1893-1903; Feb 7-Dec 1905; May 21, 1959+.
See Henry County Democrat.

Enterprise   w   1872
Mentioned by Hammond.

CLINTON (continued)

Eye   w, sw   1885+
MoHi: 1919-1944. Film, Nov 14, 1885-Nov 3,
1900; 1945+
KHi: May 30, 1919. Became sw Nov 16, 1954.

Farmers and Laborers Journal   w   1880
In Rowell-Ayer 1881, Greenback paper.

Farmers and Laborers Plain Dealer   w   1890?
MoHi: Oct 25, 1890.

Hash   d   1882
Listed in Ayer 1883.

Henry County Democrat   w   1868?+
MoHi: Jly 1875-Jly 1883; 1911-1929; 1934-1944;
Jun 24, 1869; Dec 27, 1888; May 30, Jly 4, 18,
Oct 24, 1889; Oct 30, 1890; Jly 6, 1916. Film,
Oct 1893-Dec 1894; Feb-Dec 1895; 1898-1910;
1930-1933; 1945+ Weekly, Democrat.
MoSHi: Dec 16-30, 1920; Jan 6, 13, 1921.
ICHi: Feb 3, 1876.

Henry County Republican   w   1865-1917   d   1896-1917?
MoHi: w, Jly 30, 1903. Film, Apr 1891-1895; Feb
1898-Jan 1900; Feb 1901-Sep 1902; 1903-1907;
1909-1917. D, 1911; Jan-Apr 1913; Nov-Dec
1913; Mar 27-Apr 1916. Film, Mar 30-Apr 6,
1892; Aug 15-Oct 1896; Apr 1904-Mar 13, 1906;
Sep-Dec 1910. Copy, Evening Republican, Aug
3, 1908. Conflicting data on daily: sources say
1892, 1896, 1904 for starting. Also, evidence of
new weekly 1924-1925. Name became Progressive
Republican Oct 1, 1914, used until Mar 25, 1915,
when renamed Henry County Republican.

Independent   w   1867-1868?
Listed in Rowell 1869.

Journal   w   1858-1861?
KHi: Jly 4, 1861. Mentioned by Organ, in Rowell
1869.

Messenger   w   1881-1883
In Rowell 1882-1884, Ayer 1883.

News   w   1873
Mentioned by Hammond.

Progressive Missourian   w   1914-1915
See Henry County Republican.

Pen and Sword Daily   d   1885
MoHi: Oct 29, 1885, Vol I, No 1.

Record   d   1919
Listed in Ayer 1920.

Republican   d   1896, 1904-1917?
See Henry County Republican.

Sentinel   w   1881-1882?
In Ayer 1881, county history.

CLINTON (continued)

  Southwest Outlook w 1873
    Mentioned by Hammond.

  Tribune d 1913-1916 sw 1895-1916
    MoHi: D, Jun 27, 1914.

CLYDE (Nodaway County)

  Leader w 1891-1893
    In Rowell, Ayer 1892-1894.

  Times w 1893-1914
    MoHi: 1904-1914; Aug 28, 1903.

COFFEYBURG (Daviess County)
(Under Coffey in some directories)

  American w 1923-1924
    Listed in Ayer 1924-1925

  Enterprise w 1904-1913?
    MoHi: Mar 23, 1905.

  Headlight w 1902-1903
    In Rowell 1904-1905, Ayer 1904.

  Life w 1897-1898
    In Rowell 1897-1899, Ayer 1898-1899.

  Mail & Star w 1896
    Listed in Ayer 1897.

  Record w 1916
    Listed in Ayer 1917.

  Sun w 1899-1901
    MoHi: Aug 29, 1901. Film, May 25, 1899-
    Nov 7, 1901.

COLE CAMP (Benton County)

  Courier w 1893+
    MoHi: Jan 4, 1905-Dec 30, 1937. Film, Jly 25,
    1901-1904. Merged with Warsaw Times and
    Benton County Enterprise to form Warsaw
    Benton County Guide Jan 1, 1938. As Courier
    in Ayer 1963. Resumed in 1956.

  Journal w 1914-1916
    Listed in Ayer 1916-1917.

COLLEGE MOUND (Macon County)

  North Missouri Miner w 1888, 1891-1892
    Apparently two; second one labor.

  Observer w 1917
    Listed in Ayer 1918.

COLLINS (St. Clair County)

  Advance w 1897-1907
    In Rowell 1897-1908, Ayer 1898, 1906.

COLLINS (continued)

  Clipper w 1888
    Listed in Ayer 1889.

  Comet w 1916-1920
    Listed in Ayer 1918-1921.

  Enterprise w 1895
    Listed in Ayer 1896.

  Kollins Kicker w 1892
    In Ayer 1892, founding date 1892.

  Headlight w 1888
    In Ayer 1888, founding date 1888.

COLUMBIA (Boone County)

  Advance d 1894

  Boone County Citizen w 1908

  Boone County Journal w 1869-1871
    MoHi: Feb 5, 1869-Dec 22, 1870.
    DLC: Jly 7, 1870. Became Herald Jan 5, 1871.

  Boone County Sentinel w 1877-1887
    MoHi: May 19, 1877.

  Boone County Standard w 1861?
    MoHi: Jun 21, 1861.

  Chronicle w 1895-1896
    Irregular publication.

  Columbian w 1877, 1899-1900
    Listed in Rowell 1888 with 1877 founding; Ayer
    1901 with 1899 founding. Issue Jly 1, 1887
    listed as Vol 1, No 1, under Columbian series,
    Vol XI, No 21 under Sentinel series.

  Commercial w 1900?-1904?
    In Rowell 1901-1905, Ayer 1901.

  Dollar Missouri Journal w 1852-1855
    MoHi: Jun 1-22, Jly 6, 27, Aug 3, 1854; Jan 4-
    Dec 13, 1855.
    DLC: 1855.
    KHi: Film, Jan 4-Dec 13, 1855. Formerly Missouri
    Sentinel, later Missouri State Journal.

  Fair Bulletin d 1870
    MoHi: Sep 3, 1870.

  Globe w 1847-1848
    MoSHi: Dec 1847; Jan 7-Feb 11, Mar 3-24, 1848.

  Golden Age w 1875-1876?
    Listed in Rowell 1876 as temperance paper.

  Herald w 1869-1913 d 1906-1913
    MoHi: d, Mar 17, 1906; Mar 18, 1892. Film, Feb
    12-Dec 31, 1906. W, Jan 1872; May 30-Nov 7, 18

Herald (continued)
  KHi: Jun 4, 1885.
    Weekly became Missouri Herald late 1872; under
    this title MoHi has Jan 5, 1871-May 15, 1873;
    Apr 11, 1878-1907; 1909; Sep 18, 1873; Oct 1,
    1874; Mar 15, Apr 5, Aug 23, 1877; Oct 31,
    1890; Jun 5, 1896; Jly 16, 1897; Apr 5, 12,
    Jun 7, Sep 13, Oct 11, 18, 25, 1901; Aug 26,
    1908; May 31, 1909. Film, 1908; 1910-Aug
    29, 1913. See Herald-Statesman, Missouri
    Herald.

Herald-Statesman   w   1913-1938
  MoHi: 1922-1934; 1936-Jun 30, 1938. Film,
    Sep 12, 1913-1921; Jan 31-Dec 26, 1935.
    Missouri Statesman and Missouri Herald
    merged Sep 12, 1913, suspended Jun 30, 1938.
  MWA: Jly 1, 1823; Mar 6, 27, May 8, 22, Jun 12,
    Jly 10, Aug 21, Sep 11, 1824; Jan 13, 1826;
    Dec 16, 1853; Mar 15, 1861, as Missouri
    Statesman.

Hornet   d   1899

Missouri Herald   w   1868-1911?   d   1906-1909?
  MoHi: Aug 11-14, 16-21, Sep 24, 1897 "issued
    at Moses U. Payne Camp Meeting." Copies
    of daily for Mar 18, 1892; Apr 28, 29, May 2,
    4, 5, 1898; Mar 17, 1906.
  MoSHi: Dec 17, 1897; Jly 1, Dec 16, 1898; Dec
    15, 1899; Dec 23, 1904; Jan 6, 1905.
  DLC: w, Jly 31, 1879.
  ICHi: w, Sep 14, 1876.

Missouri Farm Bureau News   w   1921-1922?
  MoHi: Nov 4, 1921-Mar 24, 1922.

Missouri Intelligencer   w   1819-1835
  MoHi: Film, May 4, 1830-Dec 12, 1835. Founded
    in Franklin, moved to Fayette 1826, to Columbia
    May 4, 1830. Became Patriot Dec 12, 1835.
  DLC: Dec 4, 1830; Oct 6, 1832.
  ICHi: Mar 19, 1831.

Missouri Journal-News   w   1923-1924?
  Listed in Ayer 1925.

Missouri Sentinel   w   1852-1853
  MoHi: Mar 4-Dec 30, 1852; Jan 27-Dec 8, 1853;
    Jun 3, 1852; Jan 13, 20, Jly 14, 1853. Became
    Dollar Missouri Journal Dec 1853.
  AzTP: Film, Mar 4, 1852-Dec 8, 1853.
  DLC: Mar 4-Dec 1852; Jan-Dec 8, 1853.
  KHi: Film, Mar 4, 1852-Dec 8, 1853.

Missouri State Journal   w   1852-1856
  MoHi: Jan 17-Oct 2, 1856. Formerly Missouri
    Sentinel, Dollar Missouri Journal; later
    Union Democrat.
  DLC: Jan 17-Oct 2, 1856.
  KHi: Film, Jan 17-Oct 2, 1856.

Missouri Statesman   w   1819-1913   d   1879
  MoHi: w, 1861-Aug 28, 1889; Jly 2, 1891-1899;
    1901-1910; Dec 30, 1853; Jan 6, 1843; Mar
    10, 1854; Mar 12, 1869; Mar 9, 1877; Jun 2,
    1885; May 28, 1886; Oct 29, 1890; Jun 10,
    1891; Apr 27, 1893; 1843-1860; Jan 29, 1890-
    Jun 24, 1891; 1900; 1911-Sep 4, 1913. See
    Herald-Statesman. D, Aug 6-Dec 13, 1879.
  MoSHi: Jan 27, 1843; Jun 23, 1865; Mar 1, 1867;
    Dec 25, 1868.
  DLC: w, Jan 20, 1843; May 17, 1844; Apr-Dec
    1849; 1851; Oct 29, 1852; Dec 30, 1859; Mar
    16, 1860; Aug 30, 1861; Jly 10, 1863; Aug 30,
    1867; May 23, 1879; Jly 19, 1880.
  ICHi: w, Sep 1, 1876.
  KHi: w, film, Jan 1854-Dec 1855.
    History traced to Missouri Intelligencer for
    1819 date.

Missourian   d   1908+
  MoHi: 1940+ Film, Sep 14, 1908-1939; 1951+.
    Several titles used: University Missourian Sep
    14, 1908; Daily Missourian Aug 2, 1916;
    Evening Missourian Sep 17, 1917; Columbia
    Missourian Jun 1, 1923.
  MoSHi: May 6, 1918. Supplements Nov-Dec 1914.
    Under University Missourian, Sep 14, 1908-Jun
    2, 1909; May 2, 1913; Nov 15-30, Dec 1914;
    Jan 1-18, exc. 12, 1915; Jan 17, 1951.
  MoU: 1908+

Missourian Magazine   w   1924-1931
  MoHi: Nov 1, 1924-May 1925; Oct 1925-Jun
    1926; Oct 1926-May 1927; Oct 1927-May
    1928; Sep 1928-May 1929; Sep 1929-May
    1930; 1931.

Patriot   w   1835-1842
  MoHi: Nov 11, 1837; Apr 3, 17, 24, May 15, Jly 3,
    1841; Jan 8, 1842. Film, Dec 12, 1835; Mar
    6, 1841-Dec 23, 1842.
  DLC: Mar 6, 1841.
    See Missouri Intelligencer. Became Missouri
    Statesman 1843.

Professional World   w   1901-1920
  MoHi: Apr 23, 1909. Film, Nov 1, 1901-1903.

Red Rover   w   1834
  Mentioned by Organ.

Sentinel   w   1907-1908
  MoHi: Mar 27, May 8, 1908. Film, Nov 15, 1907-
    May 8, 1908.

Standard   w   1862-?
  Mentioned by Organ.

State Argus   w   1852-1860?
  MoSHi: Sep 17, 1857.
    Early known as Missouri Sentinel.

COLUMBIA (continued)

Statesman   w   1843-1913
MoHi: Jan 3-17, Mar 13, 20, Jun 12, 1908. See
Missouri Statesman.

That Same Old Coon   w   1844
Whig campaign paper.

Times   d 1911-1919   w 1911-1915?
MoHi: d, Jun 8, 1911-1912; 1915-1919. Film,
1913-1914. W, film, Mar 5, 1914-Jan 3, 1915.

Tribune   d 1894   d 1901+
MoHi: 1901-1917; Sep 1918-1919; 1921-1950.
Film, Sep 3, 1901-1906; 1908-1933; 1951+.
Early Tribune, Dec 10-13, 15, 19, 20-22, 26,
27, 1894.
MoSHi: Apr 8, Jun 1, 22, 1915.
KHi: Sep 1, 1923.
MoU: 1936-1953.

Union Democrat   w   1856-1857
MoHi: Apr 30, 1857.
DLC: Oct 16-Dec 25, 1856; Apr 16, 1857. Formerly
Dollar Missouri Journal.

COMMERCE (Scott County)

Agricultural Wheel   w   1888
Listed in Rowell-Ayer 1889.

Dispatch   w   1865-1880?
ICHi: Jan 29, Jly 8, 1876. In Rowell 1881.

Record   w   1891-1892
Apparently edition of Benton Record.

Scott County Republican   w   1892-1893
Listed in Ayer 1892-1894.

Transcript   w   1878?
Listed in Rowell 1879.

CONCEPTION JUNCTION (Nodaway County)

Courier   w   1907-1941
In Ayer 1941 as Maryville New Tribune and
Conception.

Morning Star   d   1938?
MoSHi: Feb 21, 1938.

CONCORD (Callaway County)

Observer   w   1883
Mentioned by Hammond.

CONCORDIA (Lafayette County)

Concordian   w   1893+
MoHi: Dec 1, 1898-1900; 1914-Apr 1919; 1939-
1944. Film, 1945+

CONCORDIA (continued)

Missouri Thalbote   w   1870-1892
In Rowell 1882-1892 with 1871, 1872 founding dates
In Ayer 1881-1891 with 1870 founding date. Germa

Watchman   w   1870-1873
Mentioned by Hammond.

CONWAY (Laclede County)

Advance   w   1883-1887
In Rowell 1884-1887, Ayer 1887.

Chief   w   1890-1893
In Rowell 1891-1894, Ayer 1892-1894.

Chronicle   w   1937-1951?
MoHi: Jun 3, 1937-1944. Film, 1945-1948. Formerly Weekly Record to Jun 3, 1937.

Record   w   1891-1937
MoHi: 1920-Apr 1937. Film, Feb 11, 1915-
Dec 19, 1918.

Water Wagon   w   1916?
MoHi: Jly-Oct 1916. Prohibition paper.

CORDER (Lafayette County)

Bee   w   1903
In Ayer 1903, no founding date.

Dispatch   w   1894-1902?
In Rowell 1895-1903, Ayer 1896-1900.

Gazette   w   1892-1896?
Last in Rowell-Ayer 1897.

Journal   w   1909-1961
MoHi: 1920-1944. Film, Jan 8, 1914-Dec 18,
1919; 1945-1961.
KHi: Feb 27, 1925.

Press   w   1905
Listed in Ayer 1906.

CORNING (Holt County)

Chronicle   w   1896-1898
In Rowell 1897-1899, Ayer 1897-1898.

Eagle   w   1882
Moved to Fairfax, became Independent.

Herald   w   1879-1880
Greenback paper in Rowell-Ayer 1880.

Mirror   w   1904-1925
Sold to Craig Leader 1925.

CORRIDON (Reynolds County)

Headlight   w   1911-1912
Listed in Ayer 1912-1913.

CORSICANA (Barry County)

Valley Press w 1872-1876
    To Cassville 1876, became Republican.

COSBY (Andrew County)

Tribune w 1897-1898
    In Rowell 1897-1899, Ayer 1898.

COWGILL (Caldwell County)

Caldwell County Democrat w 1897-1898
    MoHi: Jan 13,20,27,Feb 24,Mar 10-May 5,19-
    Jun 23,1898.

Chief w 1887-1942
    MoHi: 1917-Jan 16,1936; Oct 24,1890; Jan 26
    1906. Film, May 6,1887-Nov 13,1891; Apr
    21,1899-Apr 19,1907.
    KHi: Apr 20,1923.
    Braymer Bee took over subscription list Jly 14,
    1942.

Democrat w 1892?
    Listed in Rowell 1893.

Enquirer w 1891
    Listed in Ayer-Rowell 1892.

News w 1921-1926
    MoHi: Sep 9,1921-Feb 1926.

Record w 1906
    Listed in Rowell-Ayer 1907.

CRAIG (Holt County)

Courier w 1896-1897
    See Democrat-Courier.

Democrat w 1872
    Hammond says a three-month paper.

Democrat-Courier w 1896-1899
    In Rowell-Ayer 1898-1900.

Enterprise w 1877-1879
    Listed in Rowell 1878-1879.

Gazette w 1879-1881
    In Rowell 1880-1881, Ayer 1880.

Leader w 1886-1953
    MoHi: 1921-1932; Nov 14,1890; Jan 5-Mar 9,
    30,Apr 9,13, Jun 22-Jly 20,Aug 3-17,1906.
    Film, Oct 9,1903-1905; Oct 22,1948-1955.
    KHi: Aug 12,1921. Moved to Mound City as
    Holt County Democrat and Craig Leader Jan
    13,1933. Moved back, renamed Craig Leader
    Oct 8,1948.

Meteor w 1882-1886
    Succeeded by Leader.

CRAIG (continued)

Mirror w 1904?-1909
    Corning Mirror printed Craig edition.

People's Call w 1891
    People's Party paper in Rowell 1892.

Tribune w 1933-1943
    Formerly Fairfax Tribune.

CRANE (Stone County)

Chronicle w 1904+
    MoHi: Apr 26,1906-1910; 1913-1914. Film,
    1911-1912; 1945+
    MoSHi: Jan 14, Jly 29,1915.

Stone County Republican w 1907-1909
    Listed in Ayer 1908-1910.

CREIGHTON (Cass County)

Banner w 1927+
    Suspended 1942; reactivated 1948.

Champion w 1892-1898?
    In Rowell 1894-1899, Ayer 1895-1897.

Clipper w 1886
    Listed in Rowell-Ayer 1887.

Ledger w 1889-1890
    MoHi: Oct 25,1890.

Missouri Free Press w 1887-1888
    In Rowell 1888-1889, Ayer 1887-1888.

News w 1899-1927
    KHi: Jun 14,Dec 6,1923. Plant moved to Pleasant
    Hill 1927.

Times w 1891-1893
    In Ayer 1892-1894, Rowell 1893-1894.

CROCKER (Pulaski County)

Banner w 1898
    In Rowell 1898, Ayer 1899.

Impetus w 1905
    MoHi: Film, Aug 4-Sep 22,1905. Formerly Iberia
    Impetus. Became News Sep 29,1905.

News w 1905-1953
    MoHi: Sep 13-27,Oct 11,18,1907. Film, Sep 29-
    Dec 1905; Jan-Aug 1907; 1949-1953. Later
    became Dixon Pulaski County Pilot-News.
    Ended Feb 26,1953.

Pulaski Republican w 1886
    Listed in Rowell 1887.

Winner w 1898
    Start noted in Country Editor, May 1898.

CROSS TIMBERS (Hickory County)

Advocate w 1889-1890
Listed in Ayer 1891.

Record w 1893
Listed in Ayer 1894.

CRYSTAL CITY (Jefferson County)

Jefferson County Press sw 1936-1950
MoHi: Jun 8,1936-1944. Film, 1945-Oct 5,1950.
Formerly Press. Four-times-weekly Dec 1937.
In 1938 w. Merged with Herculaneum Times
Oct 5,1950 to become Jefferson County Press-
Times.

Jefferson County Press-Times w 1916+
MoHi: Film, Oct 5,1950+ See Jefferson County
Press.

Press w 1916-1936
MoHi: Jan 9,1919-Jun 8,1936. Consolidated with
Festus Press Jun 8,1936 to become Jefferson
County Press.

Tri-City Leader w 1939?
Reference to move from Crystal City to Festus. No
listing under Crystal City.

CUBA (Crawford County)

Crawford Champion w 1884-1888?
Formerly Maries County Democrat before moving
to Cuba where it became Democrat 1884, Champion
1885, according to Hammond.

Crawford County Telephone w 1894-1898
MoHi: Film, 1896-1898. Became Telephone Jan
6,1899.

Democrat 1884
See Crawford Champion.

Mirror w 1872-1875.
Ayer 1959 listed Mirror, published in Steelville,
circulated in Cuba.

News w 1933-1948
Consolidated with Review 1948.

News and Review 1948-1955?
Listed in Ayer 1949-1955.

Register w 1877?
In Rowell 1877 under Cuba City.

Review w 1894-1948
MoHi: 1903-1919; Feb 9,1905. Known as Telephone
1894-1903.
KHi: Dec 3,1925.

Shield w 1876-1877
In Rowell 1877-1878, temperance paper.

CUBA (continued)

Telephone w 1894-1903
MoHi: Jan-Oct 1903. Film, 1899-1902. See
Crawford County Telephone.

Times w 1954+
First listed in Ayer 1957.

CUNNINGHAM (Chariton County)

Chariton County Enterprise w 1883-1884
In Dauchy 1884, Rowell 1885.

Utilitarian w 1886-1887?
In Rowell 1886-1887, Ayer 1886.

CURRYVILLE (Pike County)

Courier w 1882-1886?
Later became Bowling Green Times.

Pike County Express w 1874-1876
ICHi: May 24, Jly 5,1876. Moved to Bowling
Green 1876.

DADEVILLE (Dade County)

Courier w 1902
Listed in Ayer 1903.

Miner w 1900
In Rowell 1901-1903, Ayer 1901.

Rustic w 1896-1898, 1915-1920?
In Rowell 1897-1899, Ayer 1897-1898, 1917-1921.

Rustler w 1896?
Noted in Missouri Editor, Feb 1896. May be error,
referring to Rustic.

DALLAS (Jackson County)

Commonwealth w 1902-1903
In Rowell 1904, Ayer 1903-1904.

DALTON (Chariton County)

News w 1900
Listed in Rowell-Ayer 1901.

DANVILLE (Montgomery County)

Chronicle w 1859-1861
Formerly Montgomery City Journal, later Danville
Herald.

Herald w 1861?
Suspended at start of Civil War.

Ray w 1871-1875
Moved to Montgomery City 1875.

Star w 1867-1868?
MoSHi: Jun 27,1867.

DARLINGTON (Gentry County)

Gentry County Republican w 1884-1886
    In Rowell 1885-1887, Ayer 1887.

Record w 1891-1907
    MoHi: Film, Feb 5-Jun 26,1907.

DAWN (Livingston County)

Clipper w 1882-1899?
    Last listed in Ayer 1900.

Dawn & Clipper w 1900
    Listed in Ayer 1901.

Enterprise w 1896?
    Listed in Ayer 1897.

Reporter w 1923-1929
    Listed in Ayer 1925-1930.

Star w 1884
    Listed in Dauchy 1884.

DEARBORN (Platte County)

Democrat w 1890+
    MoHi: Jly 26,1901-1904; 1906-Jun 1922; Sep
    12,1941-1944. Film, Jly 1,1898-Dec 28,
    1900; 1945+

News w 1891
    In Ayer 1891, founding date 1891.

Star-Press w 1903
    In Ayer 1903 without founding date.

DEEPWATER (Henry County)

American Citizen w 1907-1908?
    Listed in Ayer 1909.

Chronicle w 1893
    Listed in Ayer 1894.

Citizen w 1890-1892?
    In Rowell-Ayer 1891-1892.

Democrat w 1885-1890?
    Last listed in Ayer 1890.

World w 1890-1942
    MoHi: Jly 24,1901-Oct 1902; 1903; 1914-Jly
    1918; Jly 8,1896.

DEKALB (Buchanan County)

Criterion w 1896
    Start noted in Missouri Editor, Jun 1896.

Herald w 1929-1931
    Listed in Ayer 1931-1932.

DEKALB (continued)

News w 1892-1893?
    Listed in Ayer 1894.

Record w 1892-1894,1896?
    Apparently two short-lived papers.

Tribune w 1897-1925
    MoHi: 1903-1909; 1911-Nov 1922; Mar-Aug 1923.
    Film, 1910.

DENISON (Barton County)

Advance Guard w 1885
    Listed in Rowell 1886.

Banner w 1886
    In Ayer 1886. founding date 1886.

DENT COURT HOUSE (Dent County)

Salem Monitor w 1869?
    In Rowell 1869, incomplete data.

DENVER (Worth County)

Bee w 1914
    Listed in Ayer 1915.

Herald w 1903-1909?
    Last listed in Ayer 1910.

Leader w 1917-1918
    Listed in Ayer 1919.

New Era w 1881-1886?
    In Rowell 1882-1887, Ayer 1881,1883,1887.

Tribune w 1897-1900?
    In Rowell 1897-1903, Ayer 1898-1900.

DESLOGE (St. Francois County)

Search Light w 1898-1899?
    Listed in Ayer 1900.

Sun w 1908-1925
    MoHi: Jan 6-Jun 23,1925. Film, 1917-1919.
    Merged with Flat River Lead Belt News Jun
    30,1925.

DESOTO (Jefferson County)

Facts w 1889-1900? d 1893
    MoHi: Film, Jun 6,1895-1896; Dec 8,1898-1899.
    MoSHi: Sep 1,1892.

Herald w 1888
    In Ayer 1888. Organ says Farmington Herald moved
    in 1872 to DeSoto, published there briefly.

Independent DeSoto Press w 1869
    WHi: Sep 1,1869.

DESOTO (continued)

Jefferson County Herald   w   1859-1861
    MoSHi: Confederate issue, May 21, 1861.

Jefferson Republic   w   1889+
    MoHi: Film, Jun 23, 1949+. Formerly Jefferson
    County Republican to Jun 22, 1949.

Jefferson County Republican   w   1906-1949
    MoHi: Sep 1906-1944. Film, 1945-Jun 15, 1949.
    KHi: Apr 1, 1926.

Jefferson Watchman   w   1882-1887?
    MoHi: Jly 26, Aug 2, Oct 25, 1888. Film, Nov 30,
    1883-Dec 5, 1884.

Messenger   w   1878-1881,   d   1880
    Greenback paper, in Rowell 1879-1881, Ayer
    1880-1881.

News   w   1882-1889
    MoHi: Jan 31, 1889.

Phoenix   w   1875
    Listed in Rowell 1876.

Press   w   1891+
    MoHi: 1906-Oct 1908; 1914-1917. Film, 1896-
    1905; Apr 5, 1955+.

Republican   w   1889-1906.
    MoHi: Sep 27, 1901-Aug 31, 1906. Became
    Jefferson County Republican Sep 1906.

South Eastern   w   1876-1877
    Listed in Rowell 1877-1878.

Southeast Gazette   w   1890-1894
    In Rowell 1891-1895, Ayer 1891, 1894-1895.

Times   w   1915-1918
    MoHi: Film, May 28, 1915-Apr 12, 1918.

Tribune   w   1873-1874, 1882-1890, 1934-1940
    In Rowell 1874-1875, 1890; MPN, Sep 1934,
    Feb 1940.

U.S. American Volunteer   1861?
    Listed under Jefferson County Herald as name
    carried on opposite side.

DEWITT (Carroll County)

Carroll Farmer's Herald   w   1889-1918
    MoHi: Jly 26, 1901-1914; 1919-1934 as Herald.
    Film, 1915-1918.

Herald   w   1889-1944?
    Irregular publication.

Missouri Valley Yeoman   w   1870
    Hammond says started Feb 14, 1870.

DEWITT (continued)

News   w   1880
    Mentioned by Hammond.

Optic   w   1883-1888
    In Rowell 1885-1888, Ayer 1887.

Times   w   1881-1882?
    In Ayer 1881, Rowell 1882.

DEXTER (Stoddard County)

Enterprise   w   1875-1879
    ICHi: Jly 12, Aug 2, 1876. See Bloomfield.

Enterprise-Messenger   w   1875-1893?
    MoHi: Oct 23, 1890.
    NcD: May 8, 1890.

Messenger   w   1875+
    MoHi: Jan 23, 1941-1944. Film, 1917-1919; 1945
    Dexter Public Library: 1931-1957. Industrial
    Edition 1888-1889. Bloomfield Messenger moved
    to Dexter 1877, consolidated with Enterprise.
    Later renamed Messenger.

New Southeast   m   1889
    MoHi: Jly 1889. Immigration paper.

Roll Call   w   1883
    In Ayer 1883, Rowell 1884.

Statesman   w   1910+
    MoHi: Mar 30, 1910-1913; Jan 3, 1919-1944.
    Film, 1914-1918; 1945+

Stoddard County Democrat   w   1891-1904
    MoHi: Film, Nov 24, 1898-1899.

Stoddard County Republican   w   1896
    Listed in Ayer 1897.

DIAMOND (Newton County)

News   w   1910, 1930+
    First in Ayer 1912; then Ayer 1935+. Full title
    is Newton County News.
    MoHi: Film, 1951+.
    MnHi: Mar 6, 20, Apr 3, 17, May 1, 1937.

DIXON (Pulaski County)

Echo   w   1889-1905
    MoHi: Film, 1902; Jan 5, 1904-Oct 13, 1905.

Echo-Enterprise   w   1891?-1896
    In Ayer, Rowell 1897 under this title.

Enterprise   w   1914
    Listed in Ayer 1915.

Headlight   w   1881
    Listed in Rowell 1882.

DIXON (continued)

News   w   1882-1884?
    To Waynesville as Pulaski County News.

Pilot   w   1911-1953
    MoHi: 1919-1944. Film, 1914-1918; 1945-1953.
    Merged with Crocker News Mar 5, 1953, as
    Pulaski County Pilot-News.

Progress   w   1905-1913?
    In Rowell 1907, Ayer 1907-1914.

Pulaski County Pilot-News   w   1911+
    MoHi: Film, Mar 5, 1953+. See Pilot.

DOE RUN (St. Francois County)

Ledger   w   1889
    In Ayer 1889, founding date 1889.

Miner   w   1890
    In Ayer 1890, founding date 1890.

DONIPHAN (Ripley County)

Bee   w   1887, 1938
    Later edition mimeographed by 11-year-old boy.

Current River News   w   1878-1883
    Merged with Prospect as Prospect-News 1883.

Enterprise   w   1881?-1901
    Listed only in Ayer 1902.

Echo   w   1894
    Start noted in Missouri Editor, Sep 1894.

Exponent   w   1903-1904?
    In Ayer 1905, Rowell 1905-1906.

Headlight   w   1895-1898
    In Rowell 1897-1899, Ayer 1898.

Hustler   w   1898-1904?
    MoHi: May 22, 1903.

New Light   w   1895
    Listed in Rowell-Ayer 1896.

News   w   1875?-1883
    Apparently refers to Current River News.

Prospect   w   1874-1883
    MoHi: Aug 11, 1876.
    ICHi: Jun 30, 1876.

Prospect-News   w   1874+
    MoHi: 1901-1944; Jan 23, 1891. Film, Nov 24,
    1898-Dec 27, 1900; 1945+.
    Doniphan Public Library: Mostly complete, some
    missing in 1930's.

DONIPHAN (continued)

Republican   w   1905-1938
    MoHi: 1920-Feb 10, 1938. Film, Dec 9, 1915-
    1919. Sold to Prospect-News 1938.

Ripley County Democrat   w   1898-1920
    MoHi: Nov 17, 1905-Sep 1918.

Ripley County Echo   w   1894-1895?
    Apparently another name for Echo.

Ripley County Republican   w   1898
    Listed in Rowell-Ayer 1899.

Southeast Enterprise   w   1890
    In Ayer 1890, founding date 1890.

Star of Doniphan   w   1884
    Listed in Rowell 1885.

DOVER (Lafayette County)

Democrat   w   1896-1898
    Listed in Rowell 1897-1899.

Gazette   w   1896
    In Missouri Editor, Apr 1896, new paper.

Tribune   w   1900-1902?
    In Rowell 1901-1903, Ayer 1901.

DOWNING (Schuyler County)

Courant   w   1891
    Listed in Ayer 1892.

News   w   1892+
    MoHi: Mar 17, 1934-1942.

Record   w   1889-1890
    In Ayer 1889-1890, Rowell 1891.

Schuyler County Democrat   w   1891-1894
    In Rowell 1893-1894, Ayer 1894-1895.

DREXEL (Cass County)

Star   w   1892?+
    MoHi: Nov 1898-Oct 1904; 1914-1944. Film,
    Aug 25, 1892-Oct 3, 1902; 1945+. Some
    sources list 1891 founding.

Times   w   1891
    Listed in Rowell 1892.

DURHAM (Lewis County)

Mississippi Sawyer   w   1897
    Start noted in Country Editor, Sep 1897.

EAGLEVILLE (Harrison County)

Clipper   w   1877-1880
    Moved to Blythedale, later Bethany.

EAGLEVILLE (continued)

Enterprise w 1881-1884
    In Rowell 1884-1885, Ayer 1881-1883.

Gazette w 1897-1898
    In Rowell 1897-1899, Ayer 1898.

Harrison County Eagle w 1874-1875
    To Bethany, merged with Republican.

Journal w 1885
    Listed in Rowell 1886.

Monitor w 1891-1896
    Listed in Rowell, Ayer, 1892-1897.

News w 1876
    Mentioned by Hammond.

Sentinel w 1897-1898
    In Rowell 1898-1899, Ayer 1899.

EAST LYNNE (Cass County)

Bee w 1885-1886
    Listed in Rowell-Ayer 1886.

Echo w 1884
    Listed in Rowell-Dauchy 1885.

Enterprise w 1884
    Listed in Dauchy 1884.

Index w 1898
    Start noted in Country Editor, Jan 1898.

Star w 1897
    Start noted in Country Editor, Feb 1897.

State of Affairs w 1900.
    Listed in Ayer 1901

EAST PRAIRIE (Mississippi County)

Eagle w 1905+
    MoHi: Jun 1, 1905-1944. Film, 1945+
    Called Prairie Eagle to Dec 14, 1906.

Hibbard Banner w 1900
    Listed in Ayer 1900-1901.

Hibbard Call w 1895
    Start noted in Missouri Editor, Feb 1895.

Hibbard Herald w 1892-1893?
    In Rowell 1893, Ayer 1894.

Prairie Journal w 1908-1909
    Listed in Ayer 1910.

EASTON (Buchanan County)

Banner, Times and Observer w 1870-1877?
    ICHi: Apr 29, 1876. Rowell 1871 lists Banner.

EASTON (continued)

Buchanan County Journal w 1870-1879?
    In Rowell 1879, with founding date 1870.

Tribune w 1900
    Listed in Ayer 1901.

EDGERTON (Platte County)

County Press w 1888-1891?
    Published by Platte County Republican. Listed in
    Ayer 1892.

Courier w 1884-1885
    Listed in Rowell 1884-1886.

Gospel Herald w 1902-1903
    MoHi: Jan 7-Oct 7, 1903.

Journal w 1895-1942
    MoHi: 1898-1900; Sep-Dec 1903; 1914-Sep 1942;
    Mar 24, 1898; Jly 12, 1912.

Platte County Republican w 1888-1891
    In Rowell 1891-1892, Ayer 1891.

Rustler w 1888-1893?
    In Rowell 1893-1894, Ayer 1894.

EDINA (Know County)

Democrat w 1906-1926?, 1857-1858
    MoHi: 1913-Jly 1915. Film, Oct 6, 1905-1912.
    Formerly Knox County Democrat. Became
    Democrat 1906. Renamed full title Jly 16,
    1915. Earlier Democrat followed Eagle.

Eagle w 1857
    Renamed Democrat at end of year.

Emancipator w 1896
    Start noted in Missouri Editor, Mar 1896.

Globe w 1883
    Listed in Ayer 1883, Rowell 1884.

Herald w 1860-1861
    MoHi: Jun 12, 1861. Formerly Knox County Argus.

Independent w 1892
    Ashcraft mentions as reform paper.

Knox County Argus w 1859-1860
    See Herald.

Knox County Democrat w 1870-1925
    MoHi: Jly 16, 1915-Sep 3, 1925; May 8, 23, 1878;
    Feb 13, 20, 1879; Sep 4, 27, 1883; Jly 31, Aug
    21, 28, Sep 3, Oct 9, 1884; May 4, 11, 1893;
    Apr 18, May 9, Aug 1-15, Dec 12, 26, 1895; Jan
    10, 1901. Film, Mar 4, 1871-Sep 1872; 1874-
    Mar 1886; Dec 2, 1886-Jun 1893; Dec 1893-
    Aug 17, 1905. Merged with Sentinel Sep 10, 1925
    MoSHi: Sep 25, 1884.

EDINA (continued)

Knox County Gazette   w   1865-1866
    Later became Missouri Watchman.

Knox County Independent   w   1882-1894?
    MoHi: Oct 25, 1888; Oct 30, 1890.

Knox County Populist   w   1896
    Start noted in Missouri Editor, Feb 1896.

Knox County Register   w   1898-1906?
    MoHi: Jly 25, 1901-1905.

Knox County Republican   w   1883-1897?
    In Rowell 1896-1897, Ayer 1896.

Missouri Watchman   w   1866-1869?
    See Knox County Gazette; later published in St.
    Louis as Western Watchman.

National   w   1879-1880
    MoHi: Film, Nov 6, 1879-May 12, 1880.

Pell Mell Greenbacker   w   1881-?
    MoHi: Film, Mar 21, Apr 7, Jun 16, 1881.

Rebel and Copperhead Ventilator   w   1861
    A few issues published in Herald plant.

Sentinel   w   1868+
    MoHi: 1874-1883; Jly 20, 1905-Sep 3, 1925; Oct
    28, 1880; Aug 31, 1888; Oct 16, 1890. Film,
    Jun 17, 1869-Apr 22, 1875; Jun 21, 1883-Sep
    21, 1905. See Knox County Democrat.
    ICHi: Jun 15, 1876.

Sentinel and Knox County Democrat   w   1868+
    MoHi: Sep 10, 1925-1944. Film, 1945+. Fuller
    name for Sentinel but Ayer 1963 uses only Sentinel.

EDINBURG (Grundy County)

Light and Truth   w   1895
    Start noted in Missouri Editor, May 1895.

ELDON (Miller County)

Advertiser   w   1894+
    MoHi: 1906; 1911-1944. Film, Jly 5, 1894-Mar 8,
    1900; Jun 12, 1902-1904; May 4-Dec 28, 1905;
    1907-1910; 1945+
    MoSHi: Jly 3, 1913.

Bagnell Dam News   w   1930-1931
    Became Lake of the Ozark News Sep 4, 1931.

Eagle   w   1903-1904?
    MoHi: Sep 11, 1903. Film, Sep 11-Dec 25, 1903.

Lake of the Ozark News   w   1931-1934
    MoHi: 1932-Jan 23, 1941.
    Became Ozark News 1934, semi-monthly.

ELDON (continued)

Miller County Advocate   w   1932-1937?
    Listed in Ayer 1935-1938.

Miller County News   w   1909?-1911?
    Listed in Ayer 1909-1912.

Modern Farmer and Busy Bee   m   1910
    MoHi: Mar 1910.

News   w   1891-1907?
    In Rowell 1905-1908, Ayer 1905.

Ozark News   sm   1934-1941
    See Lake of the Ozark News.

Register   w   1881
    Listed in Ayer 1882.

Vindicator   w   1894
    Start noted in Missouri Editor, Apr 1894.

EL DORADO SPRINGS (Cedar County)

Cyclone   w   1883
    Consolidated with News 1883, later became Uncle Sam.

Democrat   w   1881-1886?
    In Rowell 1884-1887, Ayer 1887.

Free Press   w   1896-1900
    In Rowell 1897-1900, Ayer 1897-1901.

Gazette   w   1898
    Listed in Rowell 1898-1899.

Herald   w   1882, 1888?-1893?
    Briefly 1882; see Ayer-Rowell 1894.

Mascot   w   1890-1895
    MoHi: Oct 23, 1890.

New El Dorado   w   1891
    Listed in Rowell 1892.

New Tribune   w   1893
    Listed in Rowell 1894.

News   w   1897-1920
    MoHi: 1909-1920. Film, Mar 30, 1905-1908.

People's Advocate   w   1894-1895?
    Death noted in Missouri Editor, Jan 1895; no doubt
    published some in 1894.

Post   w   1894-1895
    In Rowell 1895, Ayer 1895-1896.

Register   w   1922
    Listed in Ayer 1923.

Rural Exchange   w   1920-1955
    Last listed in Ayer 1956.

EL DORADO SPRINGS (continued)

Sun w 1895+
    First listed in Rowell 1896. Masthead for Jan 27,
    1898 has Vol VIII, No 48.

Tribune w 1887-1891
    In Rowell 1888-1893, Ayer 1888-1892.

Uncle Sam w 1881-1891?
    MoHi: Oct 24, 1890. Motto: "The Union Must and
    Shall be Perpetuated."

Watchman w 1894
    In Ayer 1895, Populist paper.

ELLINGTON (Reynolds County)

Courier-Press w 1904+
    See Press.

Press w 1906-1952
    MoHi: 1906-1909; Mar 2, 1911-1944. Film, Jan
    1, 1910-Feb 23, 1911; 1945+. Merged with
    Centerville Reynolds County Courier Jan 3, 1952
    as Courier-Press.

ELLISVILLE (St. Louis County)

Community Press w 1935+
    First in Ayer 1952. Mostly free.

ELLSINORE (Carter County)

Carter County News w 1908-1909, 1919-1925
    Apparently two under this title.

ELMER (Macon County)

Journal w 1906-1917
    Last listed in Ayer 1918.

Sun w 1897-1898?
    Listed in Ayer 1899.

ELMO (Nodaway County)

Echo w 1884
    In Dauchy 1884, founding date 1884.

Enterprise w 1883
    Listed in Rowell 1884.

Register w 1890+
    MoHi: Jly 10, 1896.

ELSBERRY (Lincoln County)

Advance w 1880-1894?
    Last listed Rowell-Ayer 1895.

Democrat w 1900+
    MoHi: 1915-1944. Film, Aug 28, 1903-Mar 18,
    1904; Jan 9-Dec 24, 1914; 1945+.

ELSBERRY (continued)

Gazette w 1899
    Listed in Ayer 1900.

Lincoln County News w 1885-1899
    Also referred to as News. In Rowell 1891-1899,
    Ayer 1891-1900.

ELVINS (St. Francois County)

Argus w 1902?
    In Ayer 1903, no founding date.

Labor Herald w 1902-1910
    In Rowell 1906-1908, Ayer 1904-1911.

Lead Belt Post w 1917-1919
    MoHi: Film, Jly 26, 1918-Jly 4, 1919.

Mining Herald w 1902?-1912
    Apparently continuation of Labor Herald. First
    in Ayer 1912.

Miner's Union Journal w 1912-1915
    In Ayer 1914-1916.

St. Francois County Record w 1912-1917
    MoHi: Feb 2-Mar 31, Apr 28, May 12, Jun 9-23,
    Aug 4, 25, Sep 1, 22, Oct 6-20, Nov 3, 1916;
    Mar 2, Apr 6, May 4, 25, Jun 1, 8, 22, Jly 27,
    1917. Film, Jan 12-Jly 27, 1917.

EMINENCE (Shannon County)

Argus w 1874-1884?
    In Rowell 1879-1885, Ayer 1880-1881.

Current Wave w 1874+
    MoHi: Jun 13, 1901-1905; 1908-1944. Film, Jly-
    Dec 1884; 1886-1887; Jun 1890-1893; 1895-
    1901; 1906-1908; 1945+.
    MoSHi: Aug 13, 1885.
    ICHi: May 10, 1876.

Journal w 1901-1905
    In Rowell 1902-1906, Ayer 1902-1905.

Summerville News w 1930?-1943?
    Listed only in Ayer 1943.

EMPORIA (Daviess County)

New Era w 1880-1881?
    In Rowell-Ayer 1881.

Winston Independent w 1883-1884
    In Rowell 1885.

ENGLEWOOD (Jackson County)

Suburban Items w 1920-1926?
    See Independence.

EOLIA (Pike County)

    News w 1920-1921?
      In Ayer 1922.

    Voice w 1902-1903?
      In Rowell 1902-1905, Ayer 1903.

ESSEX (Stoddard County)

    Leader w 1908-1921
      MoHi: May 5, 1908-1920.
      MoSHi: Jan 6, 1921.

ETHEL (Macon County)

    Courier w 1895?-1921
      Starting dates vary, 1894 to 1896.

    Leader w 1900
      In Rowell-Ayer 1901.

    Leaf w 1895-1898
      In Rowell 1896-1899, Ayer 1896-1898.

EUGENE (Cole County)

    Cole County Enterprise w 1945-1949
      MoHi: Film, Feb 7-Nov 28, 1947; Jan 1948-
      Sep 16, 1949. To Jefferson City 1949.

    News w 1907
      In Rowell-Ayer 1908.

EUREKA (St. Louis County)

    News w 1912-1917
      In Ayer 1913-1918.

    Times w 1907-1908
      In Rowell 1908, Ayer 1908-1909.

EVERTON (Dade County)

    Dade County Journal w 1892-1942
      MoHi: Nov 25, 1898-1899; Jly 1901-Feb 1903
      Jan-May 1904; 1914-1915; Jan 5-27, Feb 10-
      Mar 30, 1916. Subscription list transferred to
      Miller News and Advance.

    Eagle w 1888-1893?
      In Rowell 1889-1894, Ayer 1890-1894.

    General Baptist w 1903-1905?
      MoHi: 1903-1905.

    Journal and Tribune w 1892?-1941
      First in Ayer 1935.

    Rustic-Journal w 1892-1902?
      In Rowell 1900-1903, Ayer 1900-1901.

EWING (Lewis County)

    Hustler w 1910-1912?
      In Ayer 1913.

    Lewis County News w 1911-1919
      In Ayer 1913-1920.

    Zephyr w 1905-1906
      In Rowell 1906-1907.

EXCELSIOR SPRINGS (Clay County)

    Advocate w 1881
      In Rowell 1882 as Excelsior Advocate.

    Banner w 1888-1890
      Ashcraft says later Defender. In Ayer 1888-1889.

    Clay County Call sw 1904?
      Listed in Ayer 1905.

    Call d 1883-1925, w 1911-1925
      MoHi: D, Aug 14, 1903-Aug 11, 1905; Feb 25,
      1906-Dec 1906; Jan-Jun 1907; 1908-Nov
      2, 1918; Dec 21, 1908. Film, Jly 1-Dec 31,
      1907. W, Oct 19, 1911-Oct 1916. Merged
      with Daily News Aug 10, 1925 as Daily News-
      Call.
      KHi: Nov 3, 1922.

    Christian Union Witness-Herald w 1901-1902
      MoHi: Sep 12, 26, Nov 21, 28, Dec 5, 1901; Jan 9,
      16, Feb 13, 20, 27, Mar 13, 20, 1902.

    Democrat w 1934-1942
      First listed in Ayer 1939.

    Excelsior Springs d 1886?-1889
      Listed in Rowell 1890.

    Graphic w 1890-1892?
      Listed in Rowell 1893.

    Herald w 1882-1883
      Listed in Rowell 1883.
      CoD: Jly 12, 1883, Vol 2, No 17.

    Journal w 1886-1907, d 1907-1916
      MoHi: w, Aug 18, 1905-1906; Jly 19, 1907. D,
      Aug 23, 1907-1909; Mar 1913-Sep 1915; Jan
      18-Apr 27, 1916; Jly 5-Aug 22, 1907; Oct
      25, 1890.

    Missouri State Journal w 1926
      MoHi: Jan 30-Sep 18, 1926.

    News d 1923-1925
      MoHi: Jly 17, 1925-Aug 10, 1925. See Call.

    News-Call d 1925-1926
      MoHi: Aug 10, 1925-Jan 7, 1926. Became North-
      west Missourian Jan 7, 1926.
      KHi: Nov 9, 1925.

EXCELSIOR SPRINGS (continued)

Morning News   d   1926
  MoHi: Mar 9-Jun 30, 1926. See Northwest
  Missourian.

Northwest Missourian   w   1926
  MoHi: Jan 7-Mar 4, 1926. Formerly News-Call.
  Became Northwest Missourian Jan 7, 1926;
  Morning News Mar 9, 1926.

Phunn   d   1887-1893?
  Listed in Rowell 1893-1894, Ayer 1887-1892.

Review   w,d   1896-1898
  Listed as d Ayer-Rowell 1897, 1898.

Sentinel of Truth   w   1883-1887
  In Rowell 1884, 1888, Ayer 1887-1888.

Standard   w   1887-1919   tw   1919   d   1919+
  MoHi: w, Jan 2, Nov 27, 1903; 1907-1909; 1913-
  Nov 10, 1919; Sep 5, 1896; May 6, 1935. Pub-
  lished tw Mar 3-Nov 7, 1919. Became d Nov
  10, 1919. MoHi: Nov 10, 1919-Jan 17, 1920;
  Feb 22, 1927-1950. Film, 1923-1926; 1951+.
  KHi: Sep 25, 1927.

Times   w   1888-1892?
  MoHi: Oct 12, 1888.

EXETER (Barry County)

Barry County Beacon   w   1881-1882?
  Greenback paper in Rowell-Ayer 1883.

Barry County Gazette   w   1893
  Listed in Rowell-Ayer 1894.

Barry County News   w   1905
  Listed in Rowell-Ayer 1906.

Booster   w   1928-1936
  Listed in Ayer 1929-1937.

Enterprise   w   1897-1898
  In Rowell 1897-1899, Ayer 1898.

Farmer's News   w   1889-1891
  In Rowell 1890-1892, Ayer 1890-1891.

Index   w   1891
  In Ayer 1891 founding date 1891.

Kodak   w   1894-1898?
  Also spelled Codac. In Rowell 1895-1899.

Republican   w   1879-1882.
  Moved to Panacea Springs 1882.

Speaker   w   1892-1893
  In Rowell 1893-1894, Ayer 1894.

FAIRFAX (Atchison County)

Chief   w   1883
  In Rowell 1884-1885, Dauchy 1884.

Comet   w   1885
  In Rowell 1886.

Forum   w   1892+
  MoHi: Aug 1901-1914; 1919-1944. Film, 1915-
  1918; 1945+.

Independent   w   1882
  Ayer 1882 has 1882 founding date. See Corning
  Eagle.

Independent Chief   w   1882-1887?
  From Corning Eagle. Probably part of Chief,
  Independent history.

Star   w   1889
  In Ayer 1889-1890, Rowell 1890.

Tribune   w   1930-1933
  In Ayer 1933, ended 1933. See Craig Tribune.

FAIR GROVE (Greene County)

Journal   w   1927-1933
  In Ayer 1929-1934.

Times   w   1910?-1912
  In Ayer 1913.

FAIRMONT (Jackson County)

Blue Valley Inter-City News   w   1911-1954
  MoHi: Oct 11, 1929-Oct 2, 1931. Film, 1951-
  1954. Formerly Mount Washington News.
  Blue Valley dropped 1931. See Inter-City
  News.

Jackson County Democrat   w   1911-1950
  MoHi: Film, 1946-1949. See Blue Springs.

Mount Washington News   w   1911-1928
  MoHi: Sep 24, 1926-1928. Became Inter-City News
  Jan 4, 1929; Blue Valley Inter-City News Oct
  11, 1929. Shorter title Oct 9, 1931.

Inter-City News   w   1911+
  MoHi: Jan 4-Oct 11, 1929; Oct 9, 1931-1944.
  Film, 1945-1956. Under Independence in Ayer
  1963.

FAIR PLAY (Polk County)

Advocate   w   1893-1957?
  MoHi: 1919-Sep 2, 1943. Called Advocate Feb
  7-28, 1919; other times Fair Play Advocate.

Chief   w   1889
  In Rowell-Ayer 1890.

FAIR PLAY (continued)

Comet w 1891
    In Ayer 1891, Rowell 1892.

Flag w 1888-1889
    In Rowell 1889, Ayer 1890.

Fling w 1888
    In Ayer 1889.

Rambler w 1953+
    MoHi: Film, Apr 4, 1957+. Formerly Trenton
        Rambler, earlier at Linneus.

FAIRVIEW (Newton County)

Herald w 1909?-1919
    In Ayer 1917-1920.

News Herald w 1920-1922
    In Ayer 1923.

World w 1909-1915?
    In Ayer 1911-1916.

FARBER (Audrain County)

Eye w 1885-1887?
    In Rowell 1886-1888, Ayer 1887.

Forum w 1891-1915
    MoHi: Jly 10, 1896.

FARMINGTON (St. Francois County)

Argus w 1862-1872
    MoSHi: Sep 4, 1873. See Missouri Argus.

Bugle w 1898
    Started April 22, 1898.

Herald w 1865-1872
    MoSHi: Jly 2, 1868; Oct 27, 1870. Formerly
        Missouri Argus. To DeSoto 1872. Rowell
        gives founding date 1868.

Missouri Argus w 1861-1872?
    MoHi: Mar 6, 1862.
    MoSHi: May 30, 1861; Jly 18, Dec 7, 1867.
        Formerly Southern Missouri Argus, later Farm-
        ington Herald.

New Era w 1871-1879
    ICHi: May 18, Jly 6, 1876. Last in Rowell 1880.

News w 1883+
    MoHi: 1919-1924; 1927-1944; Sep 3, 1954. Film,
        1917-Aug 9, 1918; 1925-1926; 1945+.
    MoSHi: Feb 3, Jly 14, 1905; Feb 22, 1907; Apr 11,
        1919; Aug 5, 1921; Jly 14, 21, 1922; Oct 14, 1927.

Post w 1892
    In Ayer 1892, founding date 1892.

FARMINGTON (continued)

Press w 1928+
    First in Ayer 1930.

Progress w 1902-1904?
    In Rowell 1904-1906. See Southeast Missouri
    Progress.

Reveille w 1879
    Listed in Rowell-Ayer 1880.

Southeast Missouri Progress w 1902-1904?
    MoHi: Jan 16, Feb 27, 1903.

St. Francois Herald w 1892-1902
    MoHi: Film, Sep 18, 1901-Aug 6, 1902.

St. Francois County Democrat w 1886-1891?
    MoHi: Oct 25, 1890.
    MoSHi: Jly 19, 1890; Mar 14, 1891.

St. Francois County Republican w 1910-1912
    MoHi: May 10, 1912.

Southern Missouri Argus w 1861-1862
    See Missouri Argus.

Times w 1874-1926
    MoHi: Dec 1898-Feb 1926; Nov 6, 1890. Sold to
        News 1926. Called Times and Herald from Aug
        1902-1906.
    MoSHi: Sep 1, 1881; Mar 16, 1911; Apr 18, 1912;
        Apr 10, May 22, 1913; Sep 24, 1915.
    ICHi: Feb 10, Jly 6, 1876.

Times and Herald w 1902-1906
    See Times.

FAR WEST (Marion County)

Elder's Journal w 1837-1839
    Mentioned by Organ.

FAYETTE (Howard County)

Advertiser w 1840+
    MoHi: Jly 27, 1901-1905; 1908-1944. Film, 1906-
        Dec 19, 1907; 1945+. Called Howard County
        Advertiser until Dec 6, 1916; Advertiser there-
        after.
    Central College Library: Sep 1941+ with scattered
        omissions.

Banner w 1856, 1861, 1889-1891
    MoHi: Mar 11, 1891. In American Newspaper
        Record 1856, American Newspaper Directory 1861.

Boon's Lick Democrat w 1834-1844?
    MoHi: Aug 23, 1836; May 9, 1837. Later became
        Missouri Democrat which ended in 1850.

Boon's Lick Times w 1827-1848
    MoHi: Mar 28, 1840-Sep 30, 1848; Jly 11, 18, Aug
        1, 15, 22, Oct 17, 1840; Mar 13, 1841. Formerly

FAYETTE (continued)

Boon's Lick Times (continued)
Glasgow <u>Missourian</u>. Changed to Glasgow <u>Times</u>
Sep 30,1848.
MoSHi: Dec 19,1840.
DLC: Mar 21,Oct 3,1840.

Democrat   w   1856
Listed in Newspaper Record 1856.

Democrat Banner   w   1873-1874?
MoHi: Apr 9,1870; Dec 23,1892.
MoSHi: Jun 13,1874. In Rowell 1873-1874 under
this title.

Democrat-Banner   d,w   1894-1896   sw   1897?
MoHi: w, Jun 26,1896; sw, Aug 24,1897.
MoSHi: May 12,1893.

Democrat-Leader   w   1874+
MoHi: Dec 8,1898-1899; Jly 11,1901-1944;
Jun 9,Sep 15,1898. Film, 1945+.
Central College Library: Sep 5-Dec 26,1941;
1942-1943; 1944-1945 inc; 1946-1948; 1949
inc; 1950; 1951 inc; Nov 23,1952+.

Globe   w   1897-1904
In Rowell 1900-1905, Ayer 1900.

Hickory Club   w   1840
MoHi: Aug 22,1840.

Howard County Advertiser   w   1840+
MoHi: Sep 10,1863; Jun 17,1864; Aug 16,1866;
Jly 1,1869; Feb 22,1872; Jly 27,1876; Jun 21,
1877; Sep 23,1887; Jun 7,1888; Jan 25,1894;
Jun 10,1898. Film, Jan 11,1877-Dec 24,1891.
See <u>Advertiser</u>.
MoSHi: Mar 26,Sep 3,Oct 23,Dec 25,1863; Jan
8-Feb 19,Mar 11,18,Apr 29,May 20,27,Jun 3,
Jly 15,1864; Aug 31-Sep 28,Oct 12,Nov 2-23,
Dec 7,14,1865; Jan 11-Feb 8,Mar 1-Apr 26,
May 10-24,Jun 14-Jly 5,1866; Aug 20,1868;
Oct 25,1888; Oct 5,1891; Jan 4,Dec 7,1911.
ICHi: Jly 20,1876.

Howard County Banner   w   1848-1864?
MoHi: Jan 26,1854; Aug 8,1861. Name used for
some time for <u>Howard County Advertiser</u>, see
Glasgow.
MoSHi: Nov 18,1858; Jly 18,1861.
U of KC Library: Sep 20,1856.

Howard County Democrat   w   1879-1891
MoHi: Feb 8,1889; Oct 31,1890. Film, Sep
19,1890-Sep 1891.

Howard County Leader   w   1894-1897?
MoHi: Sep 5,1895; May 28,1896. Film, Nov 18,
1897-Nov 28,1901.
MoSHi: Sep 9,1897.

FAYETTE (continued)

Missourian   w   1827-1840
Ct: 1827-1829 inc; Mar 7,1837. Formerly
<u>Western Monitor</u>, later <u>Boon's Lick Times</u>.

Missouri Democrat   w   1844-1850
MoHi: Jan 29,Apr 2-Dec 17,1845; Sep 16,1846-
Mar 21,1848. Formerly <u>Boon's Lick Democrat</u>.
MoSHi: 1846-1847 inc.
MWA: Jly 23,1845.
AzTP: Film, Apr 2-Dec 17,1845.
DLC: Apr 2, Jly-Dec 1845.
KHi: Film, Apr 2-Dec 17,1845.

Missouri Independent   w   1879-1888?
MoHi: Sep 28,1883.

Missouri Intelligencer   w   1819-1830
MoHi: Film, Jun 29,1826-Apr 9,1830. Moved
from Franklin to Fayette Jun 29,1826, to
Columbia May 4,1830. Merged with <u>Boon's</u>
<u>Lick Advertiser</u> May 21,1827.
DLC: Jun 29-Dec 21,1826; Aug 9,18,27; Jun-
Dec 1829; Jan 8,1830.

Missouri Plowman   w   1874
Also known as <u>Plowman</u>.

Semi-Centennial News   m   1906-1907
MoHi: 1906 exc May,Sep; Apr 1907.

Union   w   1856
Listed in Newspaper Record 1856.

Western Monitor   w   1827-1837
MoHi: Feb 21,1829-Dec 15,1830; Jun 14,1836.
Became <u>Missourian</u>, 1837, <u>Boon's Lick Times</u>
1840.
MoSHi: <u>Monitor</u>, Jun 12,1824; <u>Western Monitor</u>,
Mar 15,1836; <u>Western Monitor & Boonslick</u>
<u>Correspondent</u> Sep 22,1827; Feb 2,Jun 14,
1828; Jan 31,1834; Dec 1,1835;
AzTP: Film, Feb 21,1829-Dec 15,1830.
KHi: Film, Feb 21,1829-Dec 15,1830.
DLC: Feb-Dec 1829; 1830.

FERGUSON (St. Louis County)

Blade   w   1915-1916
Listed in Ayer 1916-1917.

Town Talk   w   1923-1960
Merged with Florissant <u>Valley Reporter</u> 1960.

FESTUS (Jefferson County)

Business Index   w   1891
Listed in Rowell 1892.

Crystal Mirror   w   1885-1886
Listed in Rowell 1886-1887.

Freie Blatter   w   1891
Listed in Ayer 1892.

FESTUS (continued)

Jefferson County Jeffersonian   w   1938
    Name used briefly for News.

Jefferson County Press   w   1936
    See Press.

News   w   1903-1942
    MoHi: 1917-1919; Jan-Apr 2,1942. Merged with
    Hillsboro Jefferson Democrat Apr 9,1942 as
    News-Democrat.

News-Democrat   w   1865-1950   d   1950-+
    MoHi: W,Apr 9,1942-1944. Film, 1945-Apr 27,
    1950; D,May 1-Dec 31,1950. Film, 1951+.
    Changed to Daily May 1,1950.

Press   w   1933-1936
    MoHi: Aug 30,1934-Jun 4,1936. Merged with
    Crystal City Press Jun 8,1936 to become
    Jefferson County Press.

Times   w   1890   w   1895
    In Rowell 1891, 1896, Ayer 1891.

Tri-City Independent   w   1907-1952?
    MoHi: Feb 1913-Aug 1916; 1917-1919.

Tri-City Leader   w   1931?-1939
    Also noted under Crystal City.

Twin City Advertiser   w   1935?-1943
    Listed in Ayer 1940-1944.

Twin-City Advocate   w   1931-1934
    Listed in Ayer 1934-1935.

Voice   w   1902
    Listed in Ayer 1903.

FESTUS-CRYSTAL CITY (Jefferson County)

Daily News-Democrat   d   1954
    MoHi: Dec 21,1954.

FIDELITY (Jasper County)

Pioneer   w   1861
    In American Newspaper Directory 1861.

FILLEY (Cedar County)

Cedar County Breeze   w   1899-1900
    Listed in Rowell 1900-1901.

FILLMORE (Andrew County)

Gazette   w   1911-1913
    Listed in Ayer 1913-1914.

Gem   w   1931-1941
    Listed in Ayer 1933-1942.

FILLMORE (continued)

Herald   w   1890
    Listed in Rowell 1891.

Lever   w   1899-1909?
    Last listed in Ayer 1910.

FLAT RIVER (St. Francois County)

Interests   w   1898-1899
    In Ayer 1900, Silver Democrat paper.

Lead Belt News   w   1898+   d   1928
    MoHi: 1920-1944; Dec 3-31,1915; Jan 7-21,
    1916. Film, Jan 5,1917-1919; 1945+. Daily
    in 1928.
    MoSHi: Jun 10,1935; Dec 26,1941. See Desloge
    Sun.

Southeast Missouri Messenger   w   1906
    Listed in Rowell 1907.

St. Francois County Journal   w,bw,tw,d   1932+
    MoHi: tw, Dec 8,1938-Oct 10,1941. D, film,
    Jly 1961+. Listed as sw Ayer 1939; tw 1941;
    d, 1947. Leadwood Press, founded in 1932,
    combined in 1936 with St. Francois County
    Journal, founded in 1935.
    Micro-Photo: Film, 1961+.

Voice of the People   w   1910-1912
    Listed in Ayer 1911-1913.

FLEMINGTON (Polk County)

Sentinel   w   1912-1914
    Listed in Ayer 1913-1915.

FLORIDA (Monroe County)

Monroe County Democrat   w   1882-1884?
    MoHi: Aug 16,1882.

FLORISSANT (St. Louis County)

News   w   1911-1913
    MoHi: Aug 11,1911; Apr 17,24,1912.
    MoSHi: Jan 15,Feb 8,Nov 15,1913.

Times   w   1958-1960
    Florissant Public Library: May-Dec 31,1958; Aug
    1959-Jan 31,1960.

Valley Reporter   w   1950+
    Florissant Public Library: 1950+.
    Microfilm Cen: Film, 1958-1961. Ayer 1963
    lists Reporter, founded 1921.

FORDLAND (Webster County)

Journal   w   1886-1888
    In Rowell 1888-1889, Ayer 1887-1889.

FORDLAND (continued)

Monitor   w   1903?
    Listed in Ayer 1904.

News   w   1894
    Listed in Ayer-Rowell 1895.

Pointer   w   1906-1910
    Listed in Ayer 1909-1911.

Sentinel   w   1901

Times   w   1895-1899
    Listed in Ayer 1897-1900.

FOREST CITY   (Holt County)

Courier   w   1860-1861
    Formerly Monitor.

Expose   w   1869?
    Listed in Rowell 1869.

Holt County Journal   w   1869
    Mentioned by Hammond.

Independent   w   1869-1870, 1892-1894
    In Rowell 1870, 1894, Ayer 1894-1895.

Journal   w   1899
    Listed in Ayer 1900.

Missouri Express   w   1863-1868
    Mentioned by Hammond.

Monitor   w   1858-1860
    See Courier.

News   w   1907-1918
    MoHi: Nov 5, 1909. Film, 1914-1917; Jan-Jly
    26, 1918 inc.

Press   w   1901?-1904
    Listed in Ayer 1905.

Record   w   1897
    Listed in Ayer 1898.

Sentinel   w   1863
    Mentioned by Hammond.

Star   w   1901-1904?
    In Rowell 1902-1905, Ayer 1902.

Sun   w   1891
    Listed in Rowell-Ayer 1892.

FORNFELT   (Scott County)

Tribune   w   1915-1917
    MoHi: Mar 9, 1917.

FORSYTH   (Taney County)

Bull Shoals Gazette   m   1951?
    MoSHi: Jly, Aug 1951.

Home and Farm   w   1881-1885
    Listed in Rowell 1885-1886.

Pioneer   w   1870-1879?
    Rowell 1873 calls it Southwest Pioneer, 1875
    Pioneer Farmer, 1878, Pioneer.
    MoSp: Pioneer Farmer, Jly 7, 1876.
    ICHi: Pioneer Farmer, Jun 2, 1876.

Star   w   1891-1895
    Also called Taney County Star which moved from
    Taney City to Forsyth in 1894.

Taney Enterprise   w   1881-1883
    In Rowell 1883-1884, Ayer 1881-1883.

Taney County Leader   w   1901
    MoHi: Film, May 14-Nov 28, 1901.

Taney County News   w   1887-1891
    MoHi: Film, Feb 17-Nov 24, 1887; Jun 14, 21, Jly
    26, Aug 2-Nov 1, Nov 15-Dec 20, 1888; Jan 10,
    24, 31, Feb 14-Jun 6, Jun 20-Oct 1889; Feb 6,
    27, Apr 3, 17, May 1, 15-Jly 3, 1890; Jun 18, Jly
    2-Aug 13, 27, 1891.

Taney County Republican   w   1895+
    MoHi: May 9, 1901-1908; Nov 1911-1944. Film,
    Nov 28, 1895-Nov 19, 1896; Nov 25, 1897-
    Apr 1901; 1909-Oct 1911; 1945+.

Taney County Sentinel   w   1890-1898?
    Last listed Rowell 1899 as Sentinel.

Taney County Star   w   1891-1895
    See Star.

Taney County Times   w   1887-1891
    MoHi: Film, Nov 17, 1887-1891.

Times   w   1875-1876?
    Listed in Rowell 1876.

White River Herald   w   1879-1880, 1893-1894
    In Rowell 1881, Ayer 1880, 1895.

FOSTER   (Bates County)

Beacon   w   1896?-1899?
    In Rowell 1897-1901, Ayer 1897-1900. Founding
    dates vary.

Breeze   w   1896
    Start noted in Missouri Editor, Feb 1896.

Index   w   1889-1890?
    Listed in Ayer 1890-1892.

FOSTER (continued)

News w 1887-1892?
    KHi: Oct 21-Nov 11, 1892.
    In Rowell, Ayer 1888-1889.

Times w 1893-1895, 1901-1904
    Apparently two. In Rowell 1894-1896, Ayer 1902-
    1905, 1894.

FOWLER (Howell County)

World's Cresset w 1902-1906
    MoHi: Film, Jly 2, 1903-1905. Became Norwood
    World's Cresset 1906. Also published in Trask,
    Pomona, and Brushy Knob.

FRANKFORD (Pike County)

Chronicle w 1878-1936
    MoHi: Feb 6, 1914. To Louisiana 1936, became
    Pike County Chronicle.
    KHi: Oct 24, 1924.

Monitor w 1876-1877?
    ICHi: Jly 8, 1876. In Rowell-Pettengill 1877.

News-Letter w 1908
    Listed in Ayer 1909.

Observer w 1875
    Listed in Rowell 1875.

FRANKLIN (Howard County)

Franklin Courier w 1870
    German paper, short-lived.

Missouri Intelligencer w 1819-1826
    MoHi: Mar 5, Apr 9, 1821; Jan 22, 29, Feb 12,
    Jly 16, 30, 1822; Aug 21, 1824; Jly 29, 1825.
    Film, Apr 23, 1819-Jun 16, 1826.
    DLC: Apr 30, 1819; 1821-Jun 15, 1826.
    Moved to Fayette 1826, to Columbia 1830.
    Full name: Missouri Intelligencer and Boon's
    Lick Advertiser.

FREDERICKTOWN (Madison County)

Advance Guard w 1861?
    MWA: Aug 28, 1861. Publ. by Ill. Volunteers

American Eagle w 1892-1893?
    In Rowell 1893-1894, Ayer 1894.

Bee w 1868-1878?
    MoHi: Sep 11, 1869. Formerly Conservative.

Clarion w 1880
    Prohibition paper, in Ayer 1881.

Conservative w 1862-1868
    Renamed Bee 1868, combined with Plaindealer
    1875, moved to Perryville later as Union.
    Conflicting data.

Democratic Merit w 1898-1900
    In Rowell 1899-1901, Ayer 1899-1900.

FREDERICKTOWN (continued)

Democrat-News w 1870+
    MoHi: 1919-1944; Oct 6-20, 1905; Jan 12, 1906;
    Aug 2, 27, 1901-1918; 1945+.
    KHi: Oct 26, 1916.

Democratic Standard w 1881-1885
    Name shortened to Standard 1885.

Espial w 1847-1849
    Renamed Madison County Record 1849, according
    to Organ.

Farmer & Miner w 1875-1876
    ICHi: Mar 18, 1876.

Furnace w 1854-1858
    To Ironton 1858, according to Organ.

Jeffersonian w 1877
    Listed in Rowell 1878.

Journal w 1855-1861
    MoSHi: Union Journal, extra, Oct 25, 1861.

Madison County Democrat w 1893-1911?
    Last listed in Ayer 1912.

Madison County Press w 1895-1948?
    MoHi: Sep 1932-Mar 1945. Became sw 1948.

Madison County Record w 1849
    To Ste. Genevieve, became Pioneer, 1849.

News w 1895-1898?
    MoHi: Feb 15, 1896. Film, Apr 27, 1895-Oct 24,
    1896.
    MoSHi: Oct 16, 1897.

Plaindealer w 1874-1890
    MoHi: Oct 25, 1890.
    ICHi: Jan 8, Jly 8, 1876.

Republican w 1900
    Listed in Rowell-Ayer 1901.

Standard w 1881?-1890
    In Rowell 1889-1901, Ayer 1887-1890.

Tribune w 1898-1918
    MoHi: 1903-1907; 1910-1912; 1915-Oct 31,
    1918; Jly 28, 1905; Jun 6, 1912. Film, Jly
    26, 1901-1902; 1908-Dec 23, 1909; 1913-1914.

FREEBURG (Osage County)

Enterprise w 1904-1914
    In Rowell 1905-1908, Ayer 1905-1915.

FREEMAN (Cass County)

Herald w 1896-1898?
    Successor to Raymore Tribune. In Rowell 1897-
    1899, Ayer 1897-1898.

FREEMAN (continued)

News w 1915-1916?
Listed in Ayer 1917.

FRUIT CITY (Rreynolds County)

Herald w 1913-1915?
Listed as fortnightly in Ayer 1916.

FULLER (Benton County)

World's Cresset w 1896-1898
Listed in Rowell 1897-1899. Paper listed as Jah-
ville, Mo.

FULTON (Callaway County)

Banner of Liberty w 1839-1842
MoHi: Mar 30, Nov 2, 1839; Jan 11, 1840.
DLC: Mar 30, 1839.
Published under these titles: Callaway Watchman,
Western Star, Telegraph, Missouri Telegraph.

Callaway County Journal w 1892-1915
MoHi: Under Journal Jly 25, 1901-Dec 26, 1902;
Jan 5, 1907-Oct 31, 1915. Film, Jan 2, 1904-
Dec 13, 1906. Called by full title, Jan 1913-
Oct 1915.

Callaway Gazette w 1877-1890
MoSHi: Jun 15, 1877-May 18, 1880; Jun 4, 1880-
May 12, 1882; Jun 2, 1882-May 23, 1884; May
30, 1884-May 31, 1886; May 28, 1886-May 18,
1888.
See Gazette for MoHi listing. Sold to Sun, became
Daily Sun-Gazette Jan 1, 1927.

Callaway Republican w 1882
See Guthrie News.

Callaway Star ?
MoSHi: Jly 22, 1887, page 1 only.

Callaway Watchman w 1842-1844
See Banner of Liberty.

Callawegian w 1878-1879
Hammond says destroyed in 1879 fire.

Courier w 1861
In American Newspaper Directory 1861.

Enterprise w 1873-1881
ICHi: May 26, Jly 14, 1876. In Ayer 1880-1881,
Rowell 1874-1882.

Fair Play w 1871
Listed by Rowell 1872.

Galloway Union w 1861
Listed in G-AN&P.

FULTON (continued)

Gazette w 1877-1926
MoHi: 1902-1918; 1921-1926; Oct 23, 1890.
Film, Jun 8, 1877-1901; 1919-1920. See
Callaway Gazette.
MoSHi: Apr 14, 1899; Jly 22, 1910; Nov 10, 17,
1911; Nov 15, 22, Dec 6-27, 1912; Jan 24-
Feb 21, Apr 11-25, May 2-Sep 12, 26, Oct 3-
Nov 7, 1913; Sep 23, 1915; Aug 3, 1916.
KHi: d, Oct 25, 1924.

Globe d 1889
Listed in Rowell 1890.

Journal w 1892-1915
MoHi: Jly 25, 1901-1902; 1907-Oct 31, 1915;
Dec 13, 20, 27, 1894; Jun 27, 1895; May 14, 28,
1896; Jan 14, 21, Feb 18, Mar 18, Apr 1, 15,
May 20, Jly 15, 1897; Jan 20, Feb 10, 1898;
May 15, 1902. Film, 1904-Dec 13, 1906. See
Callaway County Journal.
MoSHi: May 17, 31, Jun 21, Jly 5, 26, Aug 23,
Sep 13, 1894.

Mail w 1873
In Rowell 1873, founding date of 1873.

Missouri Central w 1887
Listed in Rowell 1888.

Missouri Record w 1904
MoHi: Dec 17, 1904. Published by Missouri School
for the Deaf.

Missouri Telegraph w 1839-1956
MoHi: 1869-May 12, 1899; Aug 4, 1848-Jly 11,
1851; Apr 16, 1852-Oct 31, 1862 inc; Jan 16,
1863-Dec 4, 1868, inc; 1869-1892; 1920-
1944; Jly 20, 1849 as Fulton Telegraph; Dec
6, 1850; Feb 10, 17, 24, Mar 3, 10, 1854; Dec
14, 1855; Apr 9, 1858; Dec 18, 1868; Nov 6,
1890; Feb 12, 1909. Film, 1893-Jly 1895;
Apr 1897-1919; 1945-1956. See Banner of
Liberty.
MoSHi: Dec 14, 1855; Jun 15, 1860; May 17,
1861; Jly 3, 1863; Feb 5, Sep 23, 30, 1864.
Discontinued Oct 25, 1956.
MWA: Nov 15, 1845.
WHi: Apr 7, 1865.

Missouri Telegraph and Weekly Sun w 1909
Name used brief time in 1909.

Monitor w 1856
Listed in Newspaper Record 1856.

News d 1898-1899
Published by firm that printed Telegraph.

Press w 1873
Hammond refers to publication in 1868 but no references in directories to other than 1873 edition.

FULTON (continued)

Reformer w 1840-1841
    MoHi: Mar 25, 1841. Library of Congress has
    Vol 1, No 4, Jun 18, 1840, which says the Re-
    former had purchased office of Banner of
    Liberty.

Saturday Evening Sharpshooter w 1878
    Mentioned by Hammond, county history.

Sun w, sw 1888-1926 d 1888-1926
    MoHi: w, Aug 2, 1901-1909. (SW to 1901, w 1901-
    1903, sw 1904-1905) SW, film, Sep 8, 1891-
    1900. D, 1920-1926; Sep 18, 1903; May 13,
    Nov 29, Dec 6, 1904; Jun 6, 23, 30, Aug 1, 8,
    Nov 21, 30, Dec 5, 27, 1905; Jan 5, 26, 1906;
    Jun 5, 1908. Film, Mar 26, 1888-1919; 1925.
    KHi: d, Aug 26, 1919; Jly 23, 1923; Jun 20,
    1924; Jly 27, 1925; Jan 8, 12, 1926.

Sun-Gazette d 1888+
    MoHi: 1927-1950; Dec 1, 1954. Film, 1951+
    Westminster College: 1940-1944; 1947+
    History traced to 1888 through Sun.

Telegraph w 1839-1956
    ICHi: Aug 18, 1876. See Missouri Telegraph.

Times w 1916?
    MoHi: Mar 2-May 18, Jun 1-29, 1916.

Twentieth Century w 1901-1903
    MoHi: Film, 1902-Aug 28, 1903.

Vox Populi w 1860-1861
    First paper in Missouri with Latin name.

Western Star w 1844-1845
    MoHi: Mar 16, 1844; Mar 26, 1845.

World d, w 1886
    Firm also published New Moon, monthly.

GAINESVILLE (Ozark County)

Bull Shoals Gazette w 1953?
    Listed only in Ayer 1953-1954.

Democrat w 1904-1905
    MoHi: Film, Jun 1904-Nov 1905.

Gazette-Tribune w 1876-1877
    Listed in Rowell 1877-1878.

New Era w 1880-1882
    MoHi: Apr 22, 1882.

Ozark County Democrat w 1914-1916
    Listed in Ayer 1915-1917.

Ozark County News w 1882-1906
    MoHi: Nov-Dec 1903; Jan-Sep 1904. Film, Mar-
    Nov 1883; Mar-Nov 1887; Jan 1889-Oct
    1890; 1891-1899; 1901-1904.

GAINESVILLE (continued)

Ozark County News and Times
    Listed under this title in Rowell 1906-1908. See
    Ozark County Times.

Ozark County Times w 1882+
    MoHi: 1903; Mar 1905-1944. Film, Nov 1901-
    Oct 1907; 1945+. History traced to Ozark
    County News.

Republican w 1900, 1905-1906
    MoHi: Film, Dec 1905-Nov 1906. Earlier Repub-
    lican listed in Rowell 1900-1901.

GALENA (Stone County)

Home Advocate w 1889-1890
    In Rowell 1890, Ayer 1889-1891.

James River Republican w 1911-1914
    MoHi: Jly 9, 1914. Film, Jan 1-Nov 19, 1914.

News w 1903
    Listed in Ayer 1904.

Recorder-Advertiser w 1907-1908
    MoHi: Apr 30, Jun 4, 11, 18, Jly 16-Aug 27, Nov
    3, 1908.

Republican w 1898-1900?
    Listed in Rowell 1900-1903.

Stone County News w 1903-1917
    MoHi: Apr 9-Oct 3, 1903; 1915-May 9, 1917.
    Merged with Stone County Oracle May 16, 1917.

Stone County News-Oracle w 1884+
    MoHi: May 16, 1917-1921; Nov 1924-1934; 1937-
    1944. Film, 1935-1936; 1945+. See Stone
    County News. 1884 date traced to Oracle.

Stone County Oracle w 1884+
    MoHi: May 3, 1902-Feb 1912; Jly 9, 1903; Jly
    1, 15, 1914. Film, 1913-May 9, 1917. See above.

Stone County Republican w 1957+
    MoHi: Film, Jan 1, 1959+.

Signal w 1880
    Greenback paper in Rowell 1881.

Table Rock Times w 1961+

Times w 1878-1887?
    Last listed in Rowell 1888.

Transcript w 1896?
    Listed in Ayer 1900.

GALLATIN (Daviess County)

Daviess County Republican w 1901-1902
    In Rowell 1902-1903, Ayer 1903.

GALLATIN (continued)

Democrat w 1869+
  MoHi: Nov 24,1898-1944; Oct 23,1890. Film,
    1945+.
  DLC: Nov 8, Dec 6,1923; Jan 3,1924.
  ICHi: Sep 14,1876.

Good Citizen w 1897-1898
  Temperance paper in Ayer 1899.

Missouri Sun w 1853-1854
  See Sun. Mentioned by Organ.

Missourian d 1893
  Listed in Ayer 1894.

North Missourian w 1864+
  MoHi: 1911-1944; Dec 20,27,1860; Feb 14,21,
    Jun 20, Jly 27,1867; Jan 28, Jun 24, Jly 22,
    Aug 26, Sep 16,23, Oct 7, Nov 18,25, Dec 9,
    1869; Feb 29,1872; Oct 30,1873; Jan 29,
    Feb 5, Mar 26, Jun 11, Jly 23, Sep 24,1874;
    Mar 25, Apr 1,22, May 20-Jly 22, Aug 12, 19,
    1875; Jly 4, Nov 28,1878; Apr 3, Jun 5,12,
    26,1879; Jan 11,1900; Jan 3-Feb 14,28,
    Mar 7-21, Apr 4-Jly 25, Aug 11,1905; Apr
    17, Jly 17-Sep 4,1908. Film, Sep 15,1864-
    Aug 20,1866; 1867-Aug 1869; Oct 1872-
    Sep 1875; 1886-Sep 15,1887; Aug 19,1892-
    1900; Aug 1,1901-1910; 1945+.
  ICHi: Jly 6, Aug 24,1876.
  MoSHi: May 29,1884; Oct 28,1937.

Observer w 1882
  Listed in Rowell 1883.

People's Press w 1862-1864
  Formerly the Western Register.

Record w 1893
  Survived nine weeks, according to National
  Printer-Journalist, Oct 1893.

Spectator w 1854-1858
  Mentioned by Organ

Sun w 1853-1858
  Originally Missouri Sun. New name 1854.

Torchlight w 1866-1869
  Became Torchlight and Democrat 1869, Democrat
  1882.

Torchlight and Democrat w 1869-1882
  See Torchlight.

Western Register w 1858-1862
  Became People's Press 1862.

GALT (Grundy County)

Herald w 1887-1906
  MoHi: Feb 9,1905.

GALT (continued)

Journal w 1921-1924
  Listed in Ayer 1923-1925.

Sun w 1900-1906
  In Rowell 1901-1908, Ayer 1902-1912.

Sun and Herald w 1900-1921
  Apparently merger Herald and Sun 1906.

Tribune w 1927-1941
  Subscription list sold to Waverly Times.

GARDEN CITY (Cass County)

Enterprise w 1902-1903?
  Listed in Ayer 1903, Rowell 1904.

Garden City w 1891
  Listed in Ayer 1892.

Headlight w 1897
  Death noted in Country Editor, Apr 1897.

Times w 1884
  Listed in Rowell 1885.

Views w 1880+
  MoHi: 1931
  KHi: Apr 26,1923.

GASHLAND (Clay County)

Gladstone News w 1954-1958?
  Sale noted in MPN, Apr 1958.

GAYOSO (Pemiscot County)

Democrat w 1871-1891
  MoHi: Film, Nov 6-Dec 25,1891. Later became
  Southeast Missouri Statesman 1875; renamed
  Democrat 1879; to Caruthersville 1892.

Pemiscot Press w 1895
  In Rowell 1896. See Caruthersville.

Southeast Missouri Statesman w 1875-1878
  ICHi: Jly 22,1876. See Democrat.

GASCONADE (Gasconade County)

Gasconade Breeze sm 1923-1926?
  MoHi: Film, Oct 31,1923-Jly 1926.

GENTRY (Gentry County)

Sentinel w 1900-1922
  Last listed in Ayer 1923.

GENTRYVILLE (Gentry County)

Record w 1875
  Published in office of Albany Ledger.

GEORGETOWN (Pettis County)

Argus w 1856
    Listed in Newspaper Record 1856.

Democratic Press w 1859-1861
    Formerly Pettis County Independent, according to
    Organ.

Journal w 1860-1861
    Mentioned by Organ; California News, Aug 4, 1860.

Pettis County Independent w 1857-1859
    Renamed Democratic Press 1859.

GERALD (Franklin County)

Independent w 1907-1914
    Listed in Ayer 1908-1915.

Journal w 1916+
    First listed in Ayer 1917.

GIBBS (Adair County)

Telephone w 1906
    Listed in Rowell-Ayer 1907.

GIBSON (Dunklin County)

Justice w 1914
    Socialist paper in Ayer 1915.

GIDEON (New Madrid County)

News w 1940+
    See Clarkton News.

GIFFORD (Macon County)

Gazette w 1909-1911
    Listed in Ayer 1911-1912.

South Gifford Comet w 1907
    Listed in Rowell-Ayer 1908.

GILLIAM (Saline County)

Bee w 1890-1900?
    Last listed in Rowell 1901.

Globe w 1900-1925
    Last listed in Ayer 1926.

GILMAN CITY (Harrison County)

Guide w 1896-1931
    MoHi: Jly 26, 1901-Nov 1921; Sep 18, 1903.
    KHi: Jly 26, 1923.

Tribune w 1933-1956
    In Ayer 1937-1956. End noted in MPN, Feb 1956.

Truth w 1898
    Mentioned in Country Editor, Feb 1898.

GLASGOW (Howard County)

Boon's Lick Times w 1840-1861
    Formerly Missourian. Glasgow Public Library,
    Mar 28, 1840-Feb 26, 1852.

Central Missourian w 1879-1891
    MoHi: Jly 1881-Dec 1882 inc; Aug 14, Sep 4,
        11, 25, Oct 2, 9, 16, 23, 30, Nov 27, 1879;
        Jan 29, Apr 22, May 27, Jun 3, 17, Jly 1, 22, 26,
        May 24, 31, Jun 22, Jly 19, 26, Aug 9, 23, Sep
        6, 27, Oct 4, 18, 25, Dec 13, 20, 1880; Jan 3,
        Mar 27, Apr 10, May 15, Jly 3, 1884; May 14,
        28, Jun 11, 25, Jly 9, 16, 23, Oct 8, 1885; Sep
        30, Nov 11, 1886; Feb 3, 17, Mar 24, Apr 28,
        May 12, 26, Dec 1, 8, 15, 1887; Jun 21, 1888;
        Oct 30, Nov 20, Dec 4, 18, 1890; Aug 13, 1891;
        Jun 9, 16, 23, 1892; Jly 12, 1894; Apr 30, 1896;
        Feb 16, Mar 9, 16, 30, Apr 6, 1899; Dec 4, 1900.
    Glasgow Public Library: 1879-1891.

Globe w 1897-1907
    MoHi: Christmas supplement 1897; Nov 10, 1898;
        Mar 2-Apr 13, 1899.

Graphic w 1909-1910
    Listed in Ayer 1911-1912.

Howard County Advertiser w 1839-1848
    Founded as News in Glasgow 1839. Renamed Howard
    County Banner 1848. Later moved to Fayette.

Howard County Banner w 1848-1853
    MoSHi: Nov 6, 1851 (also Banner)
    University of Kansas City Library: Jly 19, 1849
    DLC: Oct 28, 1852.

Howard County Echo w 1898-1904
    MoHi: Film, Jly 25, 1901-Dec 25, 1902.

Howard Union w 1865-1866
    MoHi: Jun 15-Dec, 1865; Jun 29, 1865.

Journal w 1868-1889
    MoHi: Feb 20, Mar 20, 1873; Jan 28, 1875; Apr 6,
        Sep 15, 1876; Mar 30, 1877; Jan 18, Jun 20-Jly
        11, Sep 19, Nov 21, 1878; Apr 10, 17, Jun 5, 19,
        26, Jly 3, Aug 14, Sep 4, 11, 25-Oct 30, Dec 25,
        1879; Jan 16, 29, Mar 11, May 6, 20, 27, Jun 10,
        24, Jly 1, Sep 9, 1880; Feb 3, May 5, Jun 30-Jly
        14, 28, Aug 11-25, Sep 29-Nov 17, Dec 1881;
        Jan 5-Feb 9, 23-Apr 6, 20-Jun 8, 29, Jly 6, 20,
        Aug 3, 10, 24, Sep 7, 14, Oct 5, 12, Nov 16-30,
        1882; Jan 4, Feb 1, 8, 22, Mar 1-22, May 17, 31,
        Jun 28, Jly 5, Aug 2, 9, Sep 20-Oct 4, Nov 8, 29,
        Dec 13, 20, 1883; Jan 3, Apr 10, May 1, Jun 26,
        1884; Feb 26, Mar 26, Apr 30, May 7, 14, 28,
        Jun 4, 11, Jly 2-16, Sep 10, Oct 8, 1885; Aug 19,
        Oct 21, Dec 23, 1886; Apr 28, May 12, Dec 1, 8,
        1887; Jly 5, 1888; Mar 23, 1889.
    MoSHi: Jun 22, Jly 13, Aug 3-24, Sep 7, 1871; May
        9, Nov 7, 1872.
    KHi: Nov 11, 1869.
    ICHi: Jly 28, 1876.

GLASGOW (continued)

Missourian w 1867+
    MoHi: Jly 1901-1912; 1914-1944; Jun 13, 1895.
        Film, 1913; 1945+.
    Glasgow Public Library: 1941+.

News w 1839-1848
    Became Howard County Banner.
    MoSHi: Jun 12, 1845; Jun 24, 1847.

Pilot w 1843-1845?
    Mentioned by Organ, Hammond.

Times w 1827-1861
    MoHi: Sep 30, 1848-Feb 25, 1858; Sep 13, 1849;
        Aug 24, 31, Sep 7, 1866; Oct 1, 1869. Film,
        Mar 11, 1858-Aug 22, 1861. Formerly Boon's
        Lick Times; became Times Sep 3, 1848; sus-
        pended 1861. Restarted Jun 15, 1865 as Howard
        Union.
    Glasgow Public Library: Mar 4, 1852-Aug 22, 1861.
    MoSHi: Jan 23, 1851; Oct 21, Nov 11, 18, Dec 9,
        1852; Mar 17, Apr 7, 14, May 5, 19, 26, Jun 9,
        30, Aug 4, 1853; Apr 10, 1856; Dec 17, 1857.

Western Monitor w 1827-1836
    Apparently name for Times during years cited.

GLENWOOD (Schuyler County)

Criterion w 1870-1892
    MoHi: Jun 8, 1870-1873; 1877-May 29, 1884;
        Jan 8-Apr 30, 1874; Jun 17-Aug 19, Sep 2,
        1875; Dec 14-28, 1876; Oct 31, 1890.
        National issues, Sep 13-27, Oct 25, 1879.
    IaHi: Mar 24-Nov 15, 1876.
    IChi: Jly 21, 1876.

Journal w 1910-1914
    Listed in Ayer 1912-1915.

Missouri State Register w 1884?
    Listed in Dauchy 1885.

National Issue w 1879
    Printed on two pages of Criterion brief time.

Phonograph w 1894-1909
    MoHi: May 21, 1902-1909; May 4, 1900. Sus-
        pended briefly in 1895.
    IaHi: Feb 15, 1895-Jan 17, 1896.

GOLDEN CITY (Barton County)

Echo w 1919-1920
    Listed in Ayer 1921.

Free Press w 1892-1905
    MoHi: Jly 1901-1905; Dec 1, 22, 29, 1898; Jan
        5-Feb 23, Mar 9, 16, 23, Jun 29, Jly 6-27, Aug
        10-31, Sep 14-Oct 19, Nov 24, Dec 1, 1899.
        Name changed to Register May 25, 1905.

GOLDEN CITY (continued)

Herald w 1881+
    IChi: Aug 29, 1889. First in Rowell 1883.

Independent w 1926-1949
    Last listed in Ayer 1950.

News w 1881
    Succeeded by Herald before end of year.

Register w 1892-1912
    MoHi: 1906-1910; Jan 5-26, Feb 9, 16, 23, Mar 2,
        9, 16, 23, 30, Apr 6, 13, 30, May 4-Sep 28, 1911.
        Formerly Free Press.

Tribune w 1914-1916
    Listed in Ayer 1915-1917.

Whirlwind w 1887-1888
    Published by 15-year-old boy, according to MPN
    Jly 1955.

GOODLOE (Taney County)

Taney County Sentinel w 1894-1900?
    In Rowell 1895-1901, Ayer 1896.

GOODMAN (McDonald County)

Press w 1928-1935
    Listed in Ayer 1930-1936.

GORIN (Scotland County)

Argus w 1890+
    MoHi: Mar 12, 1931-1944. Film, 1945+.

Graphic w 1915-1918
    Listed in Ayer 1917-1919.

Missouri State News 1903-1912
    MoHi: Mar 5, 1903-1910. Film, 1911-Dec 19, 1912.

GOWER (Clinton County)

Enterprise w 1905-1937
    Subscription list sold to Plattsburg Leader.

Epitomist w 1897-1904?
    MoHi: Film, Jly 25, 1901-Nov 10, 1904.

Locomotive w 1886-1887
    Listed in Ayer 1887-1888, Rowell 1888.

Monitor w 1891-1894
    Apparently started in Kearney, moved to Gower
    1894.

News w 1883
    Listed in Dauchy 1884.

Rustler w 1838-1943
    Started in Holt. Suspended 1943.

GRAHAM (Nodaway County)

Headlight w 1874-1876?
    ICHi: Jly 7, 1876. In Rowell 1876.

News w 1909-1910
    Listed in Ayer 1911.

Nodaway Valley Spy w 1874.
    Listed in Rowell 1875.

Post w 1890-1908?
    Formerly Reporter. Named Post 1895.

Record w 1911-1914
    Listed in Ayer 1912-1915.

Reporter w 1890-1895
    See Post.

Tribune w 1919-1922
    Listed in Ayer 1920-1923.

GRAIN VALLEY (Jackson County)

Herald w 1913-1918?
    Listed in Ayer 1915-1923.

News w 1922-1923
    Listed in Ayer 1923-1924.

GRANADA (Douglas County)

Times w 1897-1900
    In Rowell 1897-1901, Ayer 1900.

GRANBY (Newton County)

Investigator w 1869-1870
    See Neosho Investigator.

Journal 1881?
    Listed only in Rowell 1882.

Miner w 1873-1877, w 1892-1914
    MoHi: Film, Feb 21,1913-Feb 27,1914; Oct 4,
    1873-Sep 26,1874.
    ICHi: Sep 16,1876.
    Second became Missourian Mar 6, 1914.

Miner and Mechanic w 1873-1880
    One source says paper moved to Neosho 1880.

Miner-Missourian w 1892-1920
    MoHi: 1919-1920. Film, Apr 14,1916-1918. See
    Missourian.

Mining Record w 1882
    Listed in Rowell 1883.

Missourian w 1892-1916
    MoHi: Film, Mar 6,1914-Apr 7,1916. Became
    Miner-Missourian Apr 14,1916.

GRANBY (continued)

News w 1920-1924
    KHi: Dec 17,1925. In Union List, name for News-
    Herald briefly.

News-Herald w 1920-1954?
    Originally appeared as News.

Sentinel w 1892-1894
    In Rowell 1893-1895, Ayer 1894.

Southwest Independent w 1868-1869
    Formerly Neosho Gazette, merged with Granby
    Investigator, 1869.

GRANDIN (Carter County)

Carter County Courier w 1916
    Listed in Ayer 1917.

Herald w 1905-1909
    MoHi: Film, Oct 19-1905-Nov 11,1909.

GRANDVIEW (Jackson County)

Advocate w 1890? +
    MoHi: Film, Jan 1953-May 19,1955. Name
    changed to Jackson County Advocate May
    26,1955. Confusion on founding.

Independent Times w 1930-1935
    Listed in Ayer 1931-1936.

Jackson County Advocate w 1890+
    MoHi: Film, May 26,1955+. First in Ayer 1957.

Jackson County Times w 1890-1955?
    See Times.

Sun w 1913-1915
    Listed in Ayer 1915-1916.

Times w 1925-1928
    Apparently name used for a time for the Jackson
    County Times.

GRANGER (Scotland County)

Enterprise w 1895
    Listed in Ayer 1896.

Gazette w 1903-1904
    In Rowell 1904-1905, Ayer 1904.

News w 1914-1915
    Listed in Ayer 1915-1916.

GRANT CITY (Worth County)

Enterprise w 1867-1869
    MoHi: Feb 13,27,Mar 5,19,Apr 30-May 28, Jun
    11-Aug 6,27-Oct 29,Nov 12-Dec 31,1868;
    Jan 28-Mar 4,1869. Became Star.

GRANT CITY (continued)

Star   w   1867-1922
    MoHi: 1903-Mar 1922; Mar 11-Dec 30,1869;
        Feb 17,24,Mar 10-31,Apr 14-May 12, Jun 2,
        Nov 3,24-Dec 15,1870; Jan 25,Feb 1-Mar 7,
        Apr 4-25,May 2-30, Jun 13-Sep 5,Oct 3,10,
        31,Nov 14-Dec 26,1872; Mar 16,1876; Oct
        14,1886; Dec 20,1888; Jun 22, Jly 13-27,
        Aug 10,Nov 9,23,Dec 7,1888; Jan 3-18,
        Jun 4,1906. Film, 1871; 1873-1885; 1887-
        1895; 1897-1902.
    MoSHi: Aug 7-Dec 24,1913; 1914-1916 inc;
        May 4,11,1921.
    ICHi: Jly 13,1876.
    MnHi: Jan 27,Feb 3,10,Nov 24,1870.

Times-Tribune   w   1867+
    MoHi: 1929-1944. Film, 1945+. Merged 1929.

Worth County Times   w   1872-1929
    MoHi: 1902-Oct 1925; Apr 21,1927-1928. Film,
        Feb 10,1881-May 11,1882; May 19,1892-
        Dec 24,1903; Jan 12,1905-1910. See Times-
        Tribune.
    ICHi: Apr 13,1876.

Worth County Tribune   w   1913-1928
    MoHi: Dec 9,1915-1928. Founded in Worth,
        moved to Grant City 1914.

GREEN CASTLE (Sullivan County)

Blade   w   1900-1901
    Listed in Ayer 1901-1902.

Clipper   w   1891
    Listed in Ayer-Rowell 1892.

Independent   w   1882-1896
    In Rowell 1885-1888, 1894-1896,Ayer 1887,1896.

Journal   w   1904-1933
    MoHi: Sep 16,1904-Jun 8,1932.

GREEN CITY (Sullivan County)

Bugle   w   1884
    Listed in Rowell 1885.

Creamer   w   1886-1889
    In Rowell 1888-1890, Ayer 1887-1889.

Journal   w   1890-1891
    MoHi: Oct 24,1890.

News   w   1891
    In Rowell 1892-1893,Ayer 1892.

Press   w   1893+
    MoHi: Jly 26,1901-1944; Dec 6,1956. Film,
        1945+.

GREENFIELD (Dade County)

Advertiser   w   1954+
    MoHi: Film, Jun 11,1957.

American Standard   w   1855-1857
    Later named Southwest. Data from Organ.

Dade County Advocate   w   1874-1951
    MoHi: Jan 26,1899-1944; Jan 1,1891; Oct 23,
        1890; Mar 12,1908; Jly 2,1914; May 27,
        1875. Film, Dec 24,1874-Dec 16,1875; Jan
        11,1877-Jly 1,1880; Jan 20,1881-Jan 19,
        1899; 1900-Dec 25,1902; 1945-1951. Sold
        to Vedette April 12,1951.
    KHi: Apr 6,1922.
    ICHi: Jly 6,1876.

Dade County Phoenix   w   1872-1873
    Listed in Rowell 1873-1874.

Democrat   w   1898-1899?
    Listed in Ayer 1900.

Dade County Times   w   1872
    MoHi: Aug 30,Sep 27,Oct 18,1872.

Enterprise   w   1888-1895
    In Rowell 1895,Ayer 1896.

Globe   w   1882-1884
    Became Leader, later Times, says Hammond.

Leader   w   1884-1888
    Mentioned by Hammond.

Missouri Army Argus   d   1861-1862?
    MoHi: Nov 22,23,1861. Also appeared in Neosho,
        Cassville, Camp Des Arc, and Arkansas.

Ozark Advance   ?   1884
    MoHi: Jly 1884.

Pointers   w   1888-1894?
    In Rowell 1892-1894,Ayer 1894.

Southwest   w   1857-1859
    IHi: Southwester, Sep 21,1857. See American
        Standard.

Southwest News   w   1891-1898
    In Rowell 1896-1899,Ayer 1897-1899.

Times   w   1888
    See Globe.

Tribune   w   1861?
    In American Newspaper Directory 1861.

Vedette   w   1866-1951
    MoHi: 1903; 1914-1944; Oct 23,1890; Jly 2,
        1914. Film, Jun 6,13, Nov 21,1867; Jan 23-
        Feb 13,1868; Apr 27,1876; May 24,1877;
        May 30,1878; Jun 10,1880; Jun 23-Jly 28,

GREENFIELD (continued)

Vedette (continued)
Aug 11, Oct 6, 13, Dec 22, 29, 1881; Feb 16,
Mar 23-Jun 1, 1882; Jly 12, 1883; Jly 3, 1884;
Jun 18, 1885; 1886-1888 inc; 1889-1899;
1900-Dec 25, 1902; 1945-1954. Bought Dade
County Advocate Apr 12, 1951.
ICHi: Jun 29, 1876.

Vedette and Advocate   w   1866+
See Vedette. Full title in Ayer 1963.

GREEN RIDGE (Pettis County)

Enterprise   w   1883-1890
In Rowell 1884-1891, Ayer 1889-1891.

Local News   w   1891?+
First in Rowell 1893.

Pettis County Enterprise   w   1882-1892
MoHi: Jun 16, 1892.

Rustler   w   1887

GREENTOP (Schuyler County)

Booster   w   1920
Listed in Ayer 1921.

Herald   w   1907-1910
Listed in Ayer 1908-1911.

Reporter   w   1926+
In Ayer 1925-1926, founding date 1924.

GREENVILLE (Wayne County)

Reporter   w   1869-1870   w   1926+
Several. Ayer 1939 list one founded 1907, Ayer
1963 says established 1926. Rowell 1870 lists
first Reporter.

Sun   w   1893+
MoHi: 1908-1944. Film, Jan 2-Dec 17, 1896;
May 19, 1899-1907; 1945+.

Times   w   1873
Listed in Rowell 1874.

Wayne County Democrat   w   1872
Later moved to Piedmont.

Wayne County Journal   w   1877-1919
MoHi: May 8-Dec 18, 1902; 1903; Jan 7-Aug 4,
1904; 1905-Nov 7, 1907; Jan 14, 1909-Dec
11, 1919. Film, Aug-Dec 1904; Nov 1907-Jan
7, 1909. Combined with Piedmont Banner Dec
25, 1919.

GREENWOOD (Jackson County)

Herald   w   1909
Listed in Ayer 1910.

GREENWOOD (Illinois)

Gem
MoHi: Feb 1867-Jun 1868.

GUILFORD (Nodaway County)

Advertiser   w   1900-1902?
In Rowell 1902-1903, Ayer 1902.

Grit   w   1898-1899?
In Rowell 1898-1899, Ayer 1899.

Guide   w   1897-1898
In Rowell 1897-1899, Ayer 1898.

Monitor   w   1894-1895
Listed in Ayer 1896.

Signal   w   1890
Listed in Ayer-Rowell 1891.

Times   w   1905-1931?
Last in Ayer 1932.

GUTHRIE (Callaway County)

News   w   1881
Moved to Fulton. In Rowell-Ayer 1882. See Fulton
Callaway Republican.

Times   w   1905-1907?
In Rowell 1906-1908, Ayer 1907.

HALE (Carroll County)

City Times   w   1884-1898
In Rowell 1885-1896, Ayer 1889-1890.

Hustler   w   1894-1905
MoHi: Jan 1, Mar 11, 1904. Merged with Leader
Feb 17, 1905. Jly 26, 1901-Dec 8, 1903.

Hustler-Leader   w   1905-1923
MoHi: Feb 17, 1905-Nov 30, 1923. Renamed
Leader Dec 15, 1923.

Leader   w   1894+
MoHi: Jly 3, 1903-Feb 10, 1905; Dec 7, 1923-
1944. Film, 1945+.

Times   w   1884-1896
Apparently name at times for City Times. Under
this title in Ayer through 1897. See Chillicothe.

HALLSVILLE (Boone County)

Eagle   w   1903
MoHi: Film, May 24-Dec 25, 1903.

Herald   w   1894-1895
Listed in Rowell-Ayer 1896.

Hustler   w   1894-1895
Populist paper in Rowell 1895, Ayer 1896.

HALLSVILLE (continued)

Journal   w   1923
    Listed in Ayer 1924.

News   w   1907-1909
    MoHi: Jan 15,1909.

HAMILTON (Caldwell County)

Advocate-Hamiltonian   w   1878+
    MoHi: Mar 6,1919-1939; 1941; 1943-1944.
    Film, 1940; 1942; 1945+. See Farmer's
    Advocate for earlier copies.

Farmer's Advocate   w   1890-1919
    MoHi: Feb 4,1904-Feb 27,1919; Jan 12-Feb 2,
    16,Mar 2-30,Apr 13-27,May 11-Jun 15,1898.
    Film, Apr 26,1890-Jan 28,1904. Merged with
    Hamiltonian Mar 6,1919.

Hamiltonian   w   1878-1919
    MoHi: 1911-Feb 1919. Film, Jly 1878-Jun 1901;
    Aug 1901-1910. See Farmers' Advocate.
    Hamilton Public Library: Back to 1880,uncatalogued.

Head Light   w   1885-1889?
    In Union List, founded 1885? No directory.

News   w   1868-1877
    MoHi: Sep 14,21,Oct 5,1876; May 31,Jun 7,
    14, Jly 5,1877.
    ICHi: Aug 31,1876.

News-Graphic   w   1877-1899
    MoHi: Aug 9,1877-Jly 27,1882; Jly 31,1884-
    Jly 14,1892; Oct 24,1890. Film, Jly 21,
    1892-Apr 13,1899.

HANCOCK (Pulaski County)

Ozark Commoner   w   1912-1913
    Listed in Ayer 1913-1914

HANNIBAL (Marion County)

All This For A Dime   w   1868
    MoHi: Mar 5,1868. Church publication.

Chronicle   w   1862-1866?
    Moved to Clarksville as Monitor; later Sentinel.
    MWA: Jan 18,1866.

Citizen   w   1914-1915
    Labor paper listed in Ayer 1916.

Clipper   w   1871-1878   m,sm   1871-1872
         d   1874-1878?
    MoHi: D,Sep 28-Dec 31,1874; Jan 4-Dec 30,
    1875; 1877; Jun 4,5, Jly 1,1878. W,Feb 21,
    1874-Dec 23,1876. Rowell 1872 lists sm;
    1873; 1874 m; 1875 w,d. Hammond says
    merged with Herald 1878. Lost identity when
    merged with Morning Journal 1881.
    ICHi: W, Jly 1,1876. D,Sep 27,1876.

HANNIBAL (continued)

Clipper-Herald   w   1871?-1880   d   1874-1880
    MoHi: D,Nov 26,1878; Jan 6,13,14,Feb 13,
    Sep 8,Oct 14,1879. See Herald.
    NHi: Dec 10,1880.

Commercial Advertiser   w   1837-1839
    MoHi: Jan 4, Jun 22,Sep 18,25,1838; Feb 27,
    1839.

Courant   d   1880
    Listed in Ayer 1880.

Courier   w   1832-1890?   d   1863
    MoHi: D,Oct 31,1872; Feb 21,27,1874; May
    18, Jly 5,1876; Jan 15,May 6,24,27,Dec 6,
    31,1878; Jan 2,Oct 1,14,1879; Nov 15,1881;
    May 15,1882; Sep 30,1883; Apr 6,1884; Jly
    24,1885.
    MoSHi: Jly 2,1886. See Missouri Courier.
    MWA: Jly 27,1865; Sep 7,1871.
    NHi: Apr 30,1878.
    ICHi: W,Sep 14,1876. D,Sep 29,1876.

Courier-Post   w,d   1838+
    MoHi: W,Dec 20,1859. D,Aug 25,1900; Sep 19,
    1901; Jun 3,19,1902; 1906-1917; Oct-Dec
    1918; Oct 1919-1950. Film, Dec 1,1903-
    1905; Apr-Jun 1917; Jan-Sep 1918; Jan-Sep
    1919; 1951+. Sunday Courier, Aug 17,24,
    Oct 4,1884.
    Hannibal Public Library: Jan 1931+ Centennial
    edition Jun 30,1938. Tells of first paper in
    county, Palmyra Missouri Courier 1832. One
    of its publishers founded Comercial Advertiser
    in Hannibal in 1838. Courier-Post and Morning
    Journal combined 1918.
    MWA: Jly 26,1871.
    Micro-Photo: Film, 1906+.

Courier Post & Journal
    MoSHi: Mar 6,1935.
    CSmH: Mar 6,1935.
    IHi: Mar 6,1935.

Democrat   w   1860-1861   d   1883
    See National Democrat. Rowell 1884 lists d.

Gazette   w   1846-1848   d   1859   w   1859?
    MoHi: d,Aug 22,1859; w,Aug 26,1859. Early
    data from Organ.

Great Southwest   w   1881
    W.H.Kerns member of press association 1881.

Headlight   w   1891-1892?
    Single Tax paper in Rowell 1893.

Herald   w,d   1876-1878?
    MoSHi: Hannibal Daily Herald, May 14,1862.
    Sunday Herald also in Rowell 1877-1878.
    Printed at Clipper office.

Independent w 1879-1882
  MoHi: Sep 13, Oct 25, 1879; Sep 9, 1882.

Journal w 1840-1853; 1871?-1915, D 1853?,
      1876-1918
  MoHi: D, Mar 15-Sep 21, 1853 (edited, published
    by Orion Clemens); Feb, Apr, Jun, Sep, Dec
    1900; Jan, Apr, Jun, Aug, Oct, Nov 1902;
    Jan-Mar, Jun-Aug, Nov 1903; Jly 1905-Mar
    2, 1918; Mar 19, Jly 3, Sep 19, Dec 7, 1879;
    Dec 10, 1880; Sep 21, 22, Oct 29, Nov 8, 23,
    29, Dec 1, 1881; Aug 17, 22, Sep 2, 17, 22, 24,
    1882; Apr 12, May 4, Sep 18, 22, 26-29, Oct
    4, 7, 14, 1883; Aug 7, 16, 17, 22, 24, 26, 28, 29,
    31, Sep 2-6, 20, Nov 15, 1884; Dec 8, 1886;
    May 2, 1888; Nov 7, 1890; Feb 15, 19, Mar
    4, 7, 10, 19, 20, 21, 24, 26, 31, Apr 1, 5, 8, 11,
    15, 16, 19, 21-23, 26, May 1, 3, 5, 1896; Jun
    9, 10, 16, 1904; Mar 12, 1904. Film, Jan-Apr,
    Jun-Aug, Oct-Dec 1901. W, Sep 4, 1851-Sep
    15, 1853; 1901; 1903; 1905; Nov 22, 1902;
    Mar 12, 1904. Film, Dec 31, 1846-Jun 27,
    1850.
  MoSHi: Hannibal Journal, Sep 30, Oct 2, 28, Nov
    11, Dec 16, 1852; Mar 31, Jun 30, 1853.
  MWA: d, Dec 10, 1880.
  NHi: d, Dec 10-11, 1880.
  KHi: d, Apr 13, 1916.
  IU: 1917-1918.

Journal and Native American w 1842
  Name used briefly, later Journal.

Journal and Price Current w 1841
  Name used for year.

Labor Advocate w 1885-?

Labor-Press w 1915+
  MoHi: Jan 22, 1937-1944; Mar 4, 1927. Film,
    1945-1954.
  MoSHi: May 16, 1941; Dec 11, 1942; Sep 7, 1945.

Messenger w, tw, d 1852-1865
  MoHi: D, Dec 7, 1858-Dec 6, 1859; Mar 23, 1860;
    Feb 27, 1859. tw, Jly 15, 1852-Oct 13, 1853;
    Nov 8, 1853-Nov 13, 1858. Dec 14, 1854. W,
    Sep 1, 1859; Oct 18, 31, 1861.

Missouri Courier w 1832-1865
  MoHi: Oct 12, 1848-Jun 8, 1854. Film, Jan 18,
    1849-Jan 4, 1855 inc. Name changed to
    True American.
  MoSHi: May 5, Jun 30, 1853; Nov 9, (North
    Missouri Courier) 1865.
  WHi: May 24, 1849-Jan 5, 1855. Also on film.

Missouri State Register w 1919-1921?
  In Ayer 1921-1922. Also called Register.

Monitor w 1876
  ICHi: Mar 11, 1876. In Rowell 1876.

Morning Journal
  MoSHi: Jun 27, 1915.

National Democrat w 1856-1860? d 1861
  MoHi: Oct 2, 1856-Mar 12, 1857. Later Democrat.
    D issued briefly 1861.

National Standard w 1855
  Mentioned by Organ.

News w 1857-1858, d 1895-96
  MoHi: Jan 2, 11, 1861 of Daily Evening News;
    May 3, 1885, Morning News. Such dates
    not listed in directories.

North Missouri Courier d 1863-1871?
          w 1863-1871?
  MoHi: W, Mar 12, Apr 2, Jun 18, Jly 2, 9, 1863;
    Jly 6, 1864; May 16, 1867; Dec 10, 1868;
    Jun 24, 1869. D, Jly 5, 1864; Apr 22, May
    24, Jun 6, 14, Nov 23, Dec 22, 1864; May 9,
    1867.

Pacific Monitor w 1840-1841
  Became Journal and Price Current 1841.

Political Examiner w 1837-1839
  Started in Palmyra.

Post d 1886-1890? w 1887-1889
  MoHi: d, Oct 27, 1890.

Press w 1861
  Mentioned by Hammond.

Times w 1881 d 1872, 1881, 1895
  MoHi: Daily Times, Jly 13, 27, 1872; Sunday Times,
    Oct 6, 23, 1881.

Tribune w 1891
  Listed in Ayer 1891.

True American w 1855-1856 d 1856
  MoHi: d, May 19-Jun 21, 1856, w, Jan 18, 1855-
    Sep 11, 1856.

Union w 1856
  Listed in Newspaper Record 1856.

West and South w 1867?-1870
  MoHi: Feb 17, 1870.

Western Union w 1850-1853
  MoHi: Oct 10, 1850-Aug 28, 1851. Orion
    Clemens, editor.

Whig Messenger w 1851-1859?
  MoHi: Sep 15, 1852-Sep 1, 1859.

HAPPY VALLEY (Harrison County)

Advertiser w 1900-1902
  Listed in Rowell 1901-1903.

HARDIN (Ray County)

Journal   w   1954+
      First in Ayer 1961.

News   w   1888-1953
      MoHi: Jly 25,1901-1910; 1915-Jun 1921; 1924-
      1944. Film, 1911-1914; 1945-1953. Merged
      with Richmond Ray County Herald Oct 15,1953.

HARRIS (Sullivan County)

Herald   w   1913-1938
      Subscription list sold to Milan Standard 1938.

Journal   w   1897,1899,1902-1903
      Apparently three Journals from directories,
      Country Editor.

New Issue   w   1896-1897?
      Listed in Ayer 1896-1898.

Review   w   1888,1908-1910
      In Dauchy 1896, Ayer 1910-1911.

Voice   w   1888-1893?
      In Rowell 1889-1894, Ayer 1890-1892.

HARRISBURG (Boone County)

Zephyr   w   1897-1898
      In Rowell 1897-1899, Ayer 1898.

HARRISON (Boone County)

Boon County Advocate   w   1868
      Listed in Union List. No other data.

HARRISON BRANCH   (?   County)

Western Chronicle   w   1850-1853?
      Mentioned by Hammond.

HARRISONVILLE (Cass County)

Cass County Courier   w   1871-1879
      ICHi: Jly 7,1876. In Rowell 1872-1879. See
      Times-Courier.

Cass County Democrat   w   1881-1954
      MoHi: Jan 1909-Dec 1944; Jun 20,1889; May 8,
      1890; Aug 20,1891. Film, Apr 1881-Feb 1885;
      Apr 1885-Mar 1889; Mar 1890-Nov 1896; Nov
      1898-1908; 1945-1954. Merged with Missourian
      Sep 9,1954.

Cass County Democrat-Missourian   w   1881+
      MoHi: Film, 1954+. See Cass County Democrat.

Cass County Gazette   w   1854-1856
      MoHi: Aug 7,1856. Became Western Democrat
      1856.

HARRISONVILLE (continued)

Cass County Herald   w   1867-1870
      In Rowell 1871 as Cass County Democratic Herald.
      Shorter title in 1870.

Cass County Leader   w   1897?-1926
      MoHi: Apr 5,1906-Aug 6,1925. Became Review
      1926.

Cass County Missourian   w   1891-1892
      In Ayer 1891-1892, Rowell 1892-1893.

Cass County News   w   1878-1917
      MoHi: 1911-Jly 1917. Film, Oct 3,1878-Aug
      1893; Sep 1894-1910. Cass News, Mar 10,
      1882. Name used briefly.

Cass County Republican   w   1889-1890
      In Rowell-Ayer 1890-1891.

Cass County Times   w   1874-1879?, 1896
      MoHi: Aug 23,1877. Two papers.

Democrat   w   1865-1872, w   1861?
      MoHi: Nov 18,25, Dec 2,1865; May 22,Oct 2,
      1867; Jan 15,Nov 11,18,1868; Sep 15,1869.
      Democrat listed at Harrisonville Court House
      in American Newspaper Directory 1861.

Democratic Herald   w   1869?
      Later became Cass County Democrat.

Gazette   w   1856
      Listed in Newspaper Record 1856.

Herald   w   1880
      In Rowell 1880, founding date 1880.

Local Missourian   w   1893-1894
      MoHi: Film, Jan 5-Jun 1,1894. Represents con-
      solidation of Pleasant Hill Local and Harrison-
      ville Missourian.

Missourian   w   1930-1954
      MoHi: Jly 30,1931-1944. Film, 1945-Aug 1954.
      Merged with Cass County Democrat Sep 9,1954.

People's Journal   w   1879-1883
      In Ayer 1883, Rowell 1883-1884, Greenback.

People's Organ   w   1882
      Formerly Vindicator.

People's Record   w   1892-1902?
      In Rowell 1893-1901, Ayer 1896-1900. Ashcraft
      says Populist, ceased 1902.

Retort   w   1901-1903
      MoHi: Film, Jan 9-Jly 31,1903.

Review   w   1926
      MoHi: Jan 22-Apr 29,May 20,1926.

HARRISONVILLE (continued)

Times-Courier   w   1870-1882
    Merged as Times-Courier 1879, absorbed by Cass
    County Democrat 1882.

Western Democrat   w   1856-1863
    MoHi: May 1,15, Jly 10, Sep 18, Dec 18,1858;
    Jly 14,28, Sep 15, Oct 20,27, Dec 8,1860;
    Mar 2,1861.

Vindicator   w   1879-1881
    In Rowell, Ayer 1881-1882, Greenback.

HARTSBURG (Boone County)

Enterprise   w   1895-1896
    Listed in Ayer 1896-1898.

Truth   w   1899-1949?
    MoHi: 1903-1922; Jun 1926-1939. Tri-County
    Truth, May 25,1939-1944. Film, 1945-
    1946; 1948-Feb 1949. Became Tri-County
    Truth May 25,1939.

HARTVILLE (Wright County)

Democrat   w   1889-1929
    MoHi: Jly 1901-1903; 1906-1908; 1910-1919;
    Apr 1920-1925; 1927-Sep 19,1929. Film,
    Nov 25,1898-Sep 15,1899.

Granger   w   1875-1876
    Moved to Pulaski County 1876 says Hammond.

Native   w   1884-1885?
    Mentioned in county history.

News   w   1869-1877?
    Later to Arkansas. Also listed as Southwest News.
    Southwestern News.

Press   w   1889-1897
    In Rowell 1891-1897, Ayer 1890-1898.

Public Opinion   w   1882-1883
    In Rowell 1883-1884, Ayer 1883.

Republican   w   1902-1905
    In Rowell 1906, Ayer 1903,1906.

Southwest Republican   w   1884?-1890?
    MoHi: Oct 24,1889. In Rowell 1889-1891, Ayer
    1888-1891.

Western Granger   w   1874
    Listed in Rowell 1875.

Wright County Clarion   w   1892-1896
    In Rowell 1893-1896, Ayer 1894-1896.

Wright County Home Talk   w   1877-1881
    In Rowell 1878-1882, Ayer 1880-1881.

HARTVILLE (continued)

Wright County Journal   w   1872-1873
    Listed in Rowell 1873-1874.

Wright County Progress   w   1893-1912
    MoHi: Nov 25,1898-1910.

Wright County Republican   w   1885-1957
    MoHi: Feb 3,1911-Aug 7,1930; Mar 12-Sep 10,
    1931; Jan 12,1939-1944. Film, 1945-1954.
    Merged with Mansfield Mirror Apr 4,1957.

HARWOOD (Vernon County)

Citizen   w   1895-1897
    Death noted in Country Editor, Feb 1897.

Hummer   w   1916-1920
    Listed in Ayer 1919-1921.

Record   w   1887
    In Ayer 1887, founding date 1887.

Times   w   1885   w   1925-1928
    In Rowell 1886, Ayer 1927-1929.

HAWK POINT (Lincoln County)

Motor   w   1907-1908
    In Rowell 1908, Ayer 1908-1909.

Transcript   w   1912-1917?
    MoHi: Jan 22,1914. In Ayer 1913-1918.

HAYTI (Pemiscot County)

Argus   w   1898-1907
    MoHi: Film, Jan 13,1905-Jly 5,1907. Last
    in Rowell 1908. See Caruthersville. Also
    known as Pemiscot Argus.

Critic   w   1912-1915
    MoHi: Jan 1-Feb 19, Mar 5-May 7, Jun 11,1915.

Missouri Herald   w   1908+
    MoHi: Mar 3,1922-1944. Film, 1945+. Herald
    until Mar 3,1922.

Herald   w   1908-1922
    MoHi: 1909-Feb 24,1922.

Signal   w   1897
    Listed in Ayer 1898.

HELENA (Andrew County)

Herald   w   1893
    Listed in Ayer 1894.

Sun   w   1905-1907?
    In Rowell 1906-1908, Ayer 1906.

HENDERSON (Webster County)

Record   w   1884-1885
In Rowell 1885, Ayer 1886.

HENRIETTA (Ray County)

News   w   1925-1931?
Listed in Ayer 1927-1932.

Progress   w   1914-1919
Listed in Ayer 1915-1920.

Review   w   1914?-1920
Listed in Ayer 1921.

HERCULANEUM (Jefferson County)

Independent   w   1916-1918
MoHi: Film, Jan 5-26, Feb 16, Mar 30-Apr 6,
Apr 20-Jun 29, Jly 20-Dec 21, 1917; Jan 4-
Feb 8, Mar 29-Apr 5, Apr 19-20, May 17, 31,
Aug 2, 16, 30, 1918.

Times   w   1920-1950
In Ayer 1922-1950. See Crystal City Jefferson
County Press.

HERMANN (Gasconade County)

Advertiser   w   1873-1877
MoHi: Film, Mar 1, 1875-Oct 13, 1876; Jan 5-
Feb 16, 1877. Combined with Gasconade
County Courier Feb 23, 1877.
ICHi: Jly 7, 21, 1876.

Advertiser-Courier   w   1873+
MoHi: 1909-1944; May 30, 1888; Oct 26, Nov 19,
1890; Dec 28, 1904; Oct 18, 1905. Film, Feb
23, 1877-1908; Jan 4, 1945+. Traced to Advertiser 1873.
MoSHi: Oct 15, 1919; May 30, 1952.

Courier   w   1874-1877
See Gasconade County Courier, Organ.

Das Calumet   w   1869
MoHi: Nov 25, 1869. German.

Fortschritt   w   1884
German. Also published Gasconade Democrat.

Gasconade County Advertiser   w   1873-1877
See Advertiser.

Gasconade County Courier   w   1874-1877
See Courier, Advertiser-Courier. Name used
short time.

Gasconade County Tribune   w   1894-1896?
Published in English, German. In Ayer-Rowell 1897.

Gasconade Democrat   w   1878?-1881, 1882
Earlier Independent. Became Gasconade Democrat
1882.

HERMANN (continued)

Gasconade Zeitung   w   1870-1873?
German. In Rowell 1871-1874.

Independent   w   1879-1882, 1930-1956
MoHi: Apr 29, 1938-Mar 24, 1944. Film, 1946-
1956. First Independent became Gasconade
Democrat. Second ceased Jan 6, 1956.

Ledger   w   1888-1896
MoSHi: Dec 21, 1888.

Licht-Freund   m   1840-1842
Philosophical journal advocating abolition of
slavery, says Organ.

Republican-Banner   w   1896-1900
MoHi: Film, Jun 25, 1897-Sep 16, 1898.

Stern   w   1883-1888?
German. In Rowell 1887-1889.

Volksblatt   w   1856-1928
MoHi: Nov 14, 1890; Oct 28, 1898. Dec 30, 1904-
Apr 18, 1928. Film, 1860-Sep 7, 1871; Oct 24,
1872-1904; 1906-1909; 1912-Apr 18, 1928. Also
known as Hermanner Volksblatt. In Rowell 1873
listed as Volksblatt and Gasconade Zeitung.
Publisher of Advertiser-Courier has complete
file.
MoCat: 1917-Aug 2, 1918.
NN: May 18, 1861.
MWA: Jan 6, 1866; Aug 23, 1876.
ICHi: Jly 5, 1876.

Volksfreund   w   1840
Abolitionist paper, brief career.

Wochenblatt   w   1843-1854
MoHi: Mar 13, 1847. Formerly Volksblatt, which
Organ says was founded 1843.

HERMITAGE (Hickory County)

Enterprise   w   1870-1873
MoHi: Mar 5, Apr 30, 1870.

Gazette   w   1895-1899
MoHi: Film, Oct 16, 1895-Sep 7, 1898. See Index-
Gazette.

Hickory County Democrat   w   1898-1901?
1911-1912, 1886
MoHi: Film, Apr 23, 30, Jun 18, Jly 9, 23, Aug 6,
20, 27, Sep 3, 1886 (published 1886 in
Wheatland); Feb 24, Mar 10, Aug 25, 1898;
Aug 9, 1900. Apparently three attempts.
First in Rowell 1898.

Hickory County Herald   w   1882-1886, 1909-1912
MoHi: Film, Mar 20, Jly 17, Aug 1, 8, 29, Sep 5, 19,
Oct 10, 1885. Hammond says Herald moved to
Wheatland, became Hickory County Herald, 188

HERMITAGE (continued)

Hickory County Republican   w   1898-1903?
    MoHi: Film, May 28-Dec 31, 1903.

Hickory County Times   w   1922
    Listed in Ayer 1923.

Index   w   1885+
    MoHi: Mar 28, 1903-1944; Jan 21, 1904; Jun 29,
    Jly 20, Dec 21, 1905; Jan 4-25, 1906; Jun 4,
    1908. Film, Jly 24, 1885-Nov 1898; Jun 15-
    Nov 2, 1905; 1945+. Absorbed Gazette.

Index-Gazette   w   1885-1907?
    MoHi: Film, Nov 23, 1898-Jun 14, 1900; Oct 25-
    Dec 1900; Mar 21-Sep 12, 1901; Oct 30, Dec
    11-25, 1902; Jan-Mar 19, 1903. Under this
    title Rowell 1900-1908.

New Era   w   1876-1880?
    ICHi: Jly 20, 1876. In Rowell 1876-1880, Ayer
    1880. Also called Hickory County New Era.

Republican   w   1903-1907?
    Apparently continuation Hickory County Repub-
    lican. In Rowell 1904-1907.

HIGBEE (Randolph County)

Enterprise   w   1882-1883?
    Listed in Rowell 1883.

News   w   1887-?
    MoHi: May 1926-1944. Film, Jly 5, 1890-1925;
    1945-Mar 5, 1953.

HIGGINSVILLE (Lafayette County)

Acme   w   1895
    Listed in Rowell-Ayer 1896.

Advance   w   1878+
    MoHi: Aug 14, 1903-1944. Film, 1945+. Also
    known as Lafayette County Advance.

Democrat   w   1888-1890
    MoHi: Oct 24, 1890.

Globe   w   1896
    Listed in Ayer 1897.

Jeffersonian   w   1894-1945
    MoHi: Aug 10, 1901-1944. Film, Jan-Mar 22, 1945.
    Robertson Memorial Library, Higginsville, several
    decades, uncatalogued.
    MoSHi: Mar 22, 1917.

Lafayette County Advance   w   1879-1887?
    Name shortened to Advance.

Lafayette County Post   w   1883-1887?
    In Rowell 1884-1887, Ayer 1887.

HIGGINSVILLE (continued)

Lafayette Leader   w   1888-1906
    MoHi: Film, Dec 17, 1898-Jly 27, 1901; Jun 17,
    1905-Sep 1, 1906. Shortened to Leader before
    1905.

Messenger   w   1882
    Listed in Ayer 1883.

Missouri Thalbotte   w   1871-1918
    MoHi: Jan 1-Dec 18, 1903.
    MWA: Aug 26, 1876 (Supp).

Voice   w   1882
    Listed in Ayer 1882.

HIGH HILL (Montgomery County)

Enterprise   w   1906-1911
    In Rowell 1907, Ayer 1907-1912.

HILLSBORO (Jefferson County)

Jefferson County Crystal Mirror   w   1885-1899?
    In Rowell 1888-1899, Ayer 1887-1900.

Jefferson County Leader   w   1866-1869
    MoHi: Film, 1866-Dec 4, 1868. Became Jefferson
    Democrat Jan 1869.

Jefferson County Record   w   1905+
    MoHi: Mar 2, 1911-1944. Film, 1945+.

Jefferson County Republican   w   1885?
    In Ayer 1901 as established 1885.

Jefferson Democrat   w   1866-1942
    MoHi: 1911-1940. Film, Jan 22, 1869-1910.
    Merged with Festus News as News-Democrat
    Apr 9, 1942.
    ICHi: Jly 7, Sep 8, 1876.

New Era   w   1905-1910
    Union List says name used for these years by
    Jefferson County Record.

HOBERG (Lawrence County)

Herald   w   1917
    Listed in Ayer 1918.

HOLBROOK (Putnam County)

Times   w   1889?
    In Rowell 1904, founding date, 1889.

HOLDEN (Johnson County)

Advance   w   1877-1878
    Listed in Rowell 1879.

Democrat   w   1871-1872
    Changed to True Democrat 1872.

HOLDEN (continued)

Democratic Era   w   1872
   Noted by Hammond. Brief career.

Enterprise   w   1865-1937
   MoHi: 1926-Nov 4,1937; Feb 26,1885; Aug
     5,Nov 18,25,1886; Mar 29,Nov 1,1888;
     Jly 25-Sep 12,1901; Sep 17-Oct 29,1925;
     Nov 5,12,Dec 17-31,1926. Film,Mar 19,
     1903-Nov 17,1904.
   ICHi: Jly 6,Aug 17,1876.

Globe   w   1894-1899
   In Rowell 1897-1901. Ayer 1897,1900.

Herald   w   1882-1891
   In Rowell 1883-1892,Ayer 1883-1891.

Independent   w   1890
   MoHi: Dec 4,1890. In Ayer 1890,Rowell 1891.

Johnson County Mirror   w   1894-1896?
   In Rowell 1895-1896,Ayer-Dauchy 1896.

Progress   w   1904+
   MoHi: Jly 1907-1944. Film,Oct 8,1904-Jly
     25,1907; 1945+.

Record   w   1895-1896
   In Ayer 1897. Suspension noted in Missouri
   Editor, Dec 1896.

Republican   w   1876-1877
   Absorbed by Enterprise 1877.

Times   w   1895-1896
   In Rowell-Ayer 1896. Suspension noted in Missouri
   Editor, May 1896.

True Democrat   w   1872-1873
   Formerly Democrat. Equipment to Houston 1873.

HOLLAND (Pemiscot County)

Advertiser   w   1913-1914?
   Listed in Ayer 1915.

HOLLIDAY (Monroe County)

News   w   1908?
   In Rowell 1908. No data.

HOLLISTER (Taney County)

News   w   1911-1918?, 1927
   MoHi: Dec 1,1911-1914. Film, 1915-1918.
   Listed Ayer 1927-28.

White River Bulletin   w   1908-1909
   Listed in Ayer 1909-1910.

HOLT (Clay County)

Register   w   1941
   Data from MPN Mar, Jun 1941.

HOLT (continued)

Rustler   w   1890-1938
   MoHi: Apr 3,1903. Moved to Gower.
   KHi: Jun 1,1923.

HOPKINS (Nodaway County)

Herald   w   1884-1887?
   In Rowell 1885-1888,Ayer 1887-1888.

Journal   w   1875+
   MoHi: 1919-Jan 29,1931. Film,Aug 27,1903-
     1918; 1951+.
   KHi: Dec 13,1923.
   ICHi: Jun 22, Jly 27,1876.

Leader   w   1892
   In Ayer 1892, Rowell 1893.

Wave   w   1906
   Listed in Rowell-Ayer 1907.

HOUSTON (Texas County)

Democrat   w   1899-1906   w   1876-1877?
   MoHi: Film,Oct 29-Dec 18,1903. Formerly Texas
     County Republican until Oct 29,1903.
   NHi: Nov 15,29,1877.
   ICHi: May 25, Jly 13,1876.

Herald   w   1878+
   MoHi: 1910-1944; Apr 18,1888; Oct 22,1890.
     Film,Dec 1,1898-Dec 28,1899; Jan 17,1901-
     1909; 1945+.

Republican   w   1899+
   MoHi: May 6,1909-Jly 1925; Feb 1926-1944.
     Film, 1945+. Formerly Texas County Repub-
     lican, then Democrat.

Texas County Democrat   w   1899-1903
   See Democrat. Earlier listing Rowell 1876-1877.

Texas County Pioneer   w   1868-1875
   MoHi: Dec 11,1869.
   MWA: Apr 25,1868.

Texas County Record   w   1868
   Listed in Rowell 1869.

Texas County Republican   w   1899-1903
   MoHi: Film, Jly 9-Dec 25,1903. Apparently name
     for Republican briefly.

Texas County Sentinel   w   1890-1892.
   MoHi: Oct 23,1890.

Texas County Star   w   1893-1914
   MoHi: Film,Oct 15,1903-Jly 6,1911.

HOUSTONIA (Pettis County)

Banner   w   1885-1889
   MoHi: Feb 8, 1889. In Ayer 1886-1887,
   Rowell 1889.

Houstonian   sw   1906-1914?
   Last listing in Ayer 1915.

Leader   w   1922-1937
   MoHi: Film, Nov 14, 1930-Feb 24, May 19, 1933;
   Oct 16, 1936-Jan 29, 1937.

Spectator   w   1898-1917?
   Last listing in Ayer 1918.

HUMANSVILLE (Polk County)

Advocate   w   1894-1898?
   In Rowell 1895-1899, Ayer 1896-1897.

Bee   w   1888-1890
   Under Union Bee in Rowell 1891.

Chronicle   w   1879
   Listed in Ayer 1880.

Dawn   w   1888
   Listed in Ayer 1889.

Headlight   w   1900-1901
   In Rowell-Ayer 1901, Rowell 1902.

Polk County Review   w   1875
   Founded in Bolivar 1874. Moved to Springfield.

Star   w   1877-1887
   Consolidated with Polk County Leader of Bolivar
   1887.

Star-Leader   w   1877+
   MoHi: 1919-1944. Film, 1913-1918; 1945+.
   Polk County Leader, founded in Bolivar,
   consolidated with Leader 1887.

Union Bee   w   1888-1891?
   At one time Farm Alliance paper. In Rowell 1890-
   1891, Ayer 1891.

HUME (Bates County)

Bates County Globe   w   1894-1895
   MoHi: Feb 21, 1895.

Border Messenger   w   1889+
   MoHi: Sep 17, 1925-1944. Film, 1945+. Border
   Telephone until Sep 17, 1925.

Border Telephone   w   1889-1925
   MoHi: Jly 27, 1901-Sep 10, 1925; Oct 24, 1890;
   Feb 10, 1906.
   KHi: Jun 23, 1921.

HUME (continued)

Chronicle   w   1888
   Earlier called News, Star. In Ayer 1888, founded
   in 1888.

News   w   1881?-1884
   MoHi: Aug 17, Oct 19, 1883; Mar 28, 1884.

Saturday Globe   w   1894
   Start noted in Missouri Editor, Jun 1894.

Star   w   1884-1888
   MoHi: Mar 6, May 8, 1885; Mar 18, 1887; Feb 3,
   1888. Later became Chronicle.

Sun   w   1901
   Listed in Ayer 1902.

HUMPHREYS (Sullivan County)

Advance   w   1884-1885
   Listed in Rowell 1885-1886.

Blade   w   1890
   MoHi: Oct 30, 1890. In Ayer 1890-1891.

Gazette   w   1881-1883
   In Ayer 1883, Rowell 1884.

Leader   w   1892?-1896?
   In Ayer 1889-1897, Dauchy 1896.

North Missourian   w   1887
   In Ayer 1887 with 1887 starting.

Pilot   w   1897
   In Ayer 1898.

Reporter   w   1905
   In Rowell-Ayer 1906.

Searchlight   w   1898
   In Ayer 1899.

Star   w   1916?-1919
   In Ayer 1919-1920.

Tribune   w   1897?-1905?
   In Rowell 1902-1906, Ayer 1903.

Wave of Prosperity   w   1909-1911
   In Ayer 1911-1912.

HUNNEWELL (Shelby County)

Bee   w   1888-1891
   MoHi: Oct 24, 1890.

Echo   w   1883-1884
   MoHi: Sep 28, Oct 5, 1883. To Shelbyville as
   Shelby County Times 1884.

HUNNEWELL (continued)

Enterprise   w   1885-1886, 1882?
    Hammond notes paper with this title 1882.

Graphic   w   1886-1957?
    MoHi: Sep 4, 1903-1906; 1909-1920. Film,
    1907-1908; Jly 12, 1957. One source says
    name used briefly for Enterprise.

Standard   w   1957-1960
    MoHi: Film, Jly 19, 1957-Jan 1, 1960.

HUNTER (Carter County)

Southeast Missourian   w   1913-1928?
    In Ayer 1914-1929.

HUNTSVILLE (Randolph County)

American   w   1861?
    In American Newspaper Directory 1861.

Citizen   w   1856?   1866?
    In Newspaper Record 1856. MPA minutes 1879
    tells of death of Col. Alex Phipps, who started
    Citizen in 1866.

Herald   w   1869-1931   d   1878?
    MoHi: Jan 18, 1871-Jan 7, 1875; Apr 10, 1879-
    1887 inc. 1888-Mar 12, 1931; Jan 14, Apr
    15, Jun 24, 1875; Nov 1, 8, Dec 6, 1877;
    Oct 30, 1890; Jan 4, 1901. d, Feb 21, 1878.
    Formerly North Missouri Herald. 1869-1871.
    Merged with Randolph County Times Mar 19,
    1931 to become Randolph County Times-
    Herald. ICHi: Aug 31, 1876.

Independent Missourian   w   1854-1855
    MoHi: Nov 16, 1854-May 3, 1855. Name changed
    to Randolph Citizen May 10, 1855.

North Missouri Herald   w   1869-1871
    MoHi: Jan 20, 1869-Jan 18, 1871. Became Herald
    Jan 18, 1871.

Randolph American   w   1858-1860
    Forced to suspend by Federal authorities.

Randolph Citizen   w   1854-1875?
    MoHi: May 10, 1855-Aug 1861; 1861 inc; Jan 10,
    Aug 17, 1866; May 16, Oct 25, 1872; May 29,
    Jun 16, Jly 2, 10, 24, Aug 28, 1873; Jan 15,
    1873; Jan 15, 1874; Jan 15, 1875. See Indepen-
    dent Missourian.
    WHi: Sep 27, 1867.

Randolph County Citizen   w   1897
    Listed in Ayer 1898.

Randolph County Times-Herald   w   1911+
    MoHi: Mar 19, 1931-1944. Film, 1945+. Formed
    by consolidation Randolph County Times and
    Herald Mar 19, 1931.

HUNTSVILLE (continued)

Randolph County Times   w   1911-1931
    See Randolph County Times-Herald.

Randolph Democrat   w   1897-1899?
    MoHi: Film, Nov 25, 1898-1899.

Randolph Vindicator   w   1878
    MoHi: Nov 7, 1878. In Rowell 1879.

Recorder   w   1853
    Later known as Randolph Citizen, Independent
    Missourian, according to Organ.

Review   w   1889
    Listed in Ayer-Rowell 1890.

Times   w   1911-1931
    MoHi: Film, Aug 4, 1911-Oct 31, 1916. See
    Randolph County Times-Herald. Shorter title
    used briefly.

Western Sunburst   w   1881-1883?
    Greenback paper in Ayer 1881.

HURDLAND (Knox County)

Echo   w   1897-1898
    Listed in Rowell 1898-1899.

Gazette   w   1892
    In Ayer 1892 with 1892 founding date.

Grit   w   1899
    Listed in Rowell 1900.

Herald   w   1915-1916?
    Listed in Ayer 1917.

Knox County News   w   1926-1947
    MoHi: Oct 11, 1940-1944. Film, 1945-Jan 31,
    1947. Suspended Jan 31, 1947.

News   w   1889-1890, 1897-1898
    MoHi: Oct 29, 1890. Apparently two.

Times   w   1904?
    Mentioned by Williams.

IANTHA (Barton County)

Tribune   w   1911-1915
    Listed in Ayer 1914-1916.

IATAN (Platte County)

Times   w   1913-1914
    Listed Ayer 1914-1915.

IBERIA (Miller County)

Headlight   w   1898-1899
    In Rowell 1898-1899, Ayer 1900.

IBERIA (continued)

Iberian Advocate w 1885
    Listed as Advocate in Rowell 1886.

Impetus w 1885-1905
    MoHi: Film, Jun 23-Jly 28,1905. Became Crocker
        Impetus Aug 4,1905.

Intelligencer w 1893-1898
    In Rowell 1894-1899, Ayer 1894-1898.

Miller County Sentinel w 1905-1959
    MoHi: Film, Apr 2,1953-Mar 26,1959. See Sentinel.

Sentinel w 1905-1959
    MoHi: Apr 14,1932-1944. Film, 1914-1915; Jan
        31-Dec 19,1919; 1945-Mar 1953. Became
        Tuscumbia Miller County Autogram-Sentinel
        Apr 2,1959. Sentinel's name changed to
        Miller County Sentinel Apr 2,1953.

ILLMO (Scott County)

Headlight w 1905-1912
    In Rowell 1906,1908, Ayer 1906-1913.

Herald w 1914
    Listed in Ayer 1915.

Jimplicute w 1914+
    MoHi: Dec 24,1914-1944. Film, Jan 1945-1957.
        Became Tri-City Jimplicute Jly 4,1957.
        Jimplicute in Ayer 1963.

Tri-County Jimplicute w 1914+
    MoHi: Jly 4,1957-1958.

Twin-City Republican w 1910
    Listed in Ayer 1911.

INDEPENDENCE (Jackson County)

Agrarian w 1854-1855
    Noted by Organ.

Blade w 1895-1896, d 1896
    In Ayer-Rowell 1896-1897.

Border Star w 1847 d 1862?
    KHi: D, Aug 11-13,1862; Apr 3,1897.

Chronicle w 1840-1841
    MoHi: Apr 4,1840; Jan 22,1841.
    DLC: Vol 1, No 1, Apr 4,1840.

Daily d 1915-1919
    Listed in Ayer 1916-1920.

Democrat w 1869,1877-1880?
    In Rowell 1870,1877-1881. Apparently two.

Democratic Gazette w 1861
    In American Newspaper Directory 1861, published
        at Independence Court House.

INDEPENDENCE (continued)

Dispatch w 1856
    Listed in Newspaper Record 1856.

Ensign w 1890-1897?
    NN: Feb 14, May 9,1891. In Rowell 1892-1898.
        At times under Zion's Ensign.

Enterprise d 1873
    Listed in Rowell 1873.

Equality w 1909-1911?
    MoHi: Film, Nov 15,1909-Nov 1,1911.

Examiner d 1905+
    MoHi: May 16,1905-1950. Film, 1951+
    MoSHi: Dec 29,1915; May 18,1948.
    MoKc: Feb 1912-Sep 1932.
    Independence Public Library, 1918-1959, exc
        May 27,1924; Sep 25,1924; Sep 14,1929-
        Jan 30,1930; Sep 14,1939-Jan 11,1940.
    See Jackson Examiner for weekly data.

Gazette w 1888-1891 d 1861
    MoHi: d, Apr 27,1861.

Herald w 1859 w 1871-1875
    Wilkie notes 1859 paper; Rowell 1872-1876
        lists second.

International
    T: Oct 30, Nov 26,1891.

Item w 1893
    MoHi: Sep 30,1893

Jackson County Advocate w 1888-1890
    In Rowell 1889-1891, Ayer 1890-1891.

Jackson County Democrat w 1907-1940
    MoKc: Jun 13,1907-Mar 16,1912. See Jackson
        Democrat. Longer title used to 1912?

Jackson County Judge w 1901-1907
    MoHi: Film, 1903.

Jackson County Tribune w 1895-1896
    Listed in Ayer 1896-1897.

Jackson Democrat w 1907-1934?
    Follows Richmond Democrat. Last in Ayer 1935.

Jackson Examiner w 1898-1928
    MoHi: Jly 1901-Feb 3,1928, suspended; Oct 30,
        1903.
    Independence Public Library: 1906-1907.
    MoKc: Jan 3,1908-Jan 27,1928.

Journal w 1844-1845
    MoSHi: Sep 12-Oct 31,1844.
    DLC: Sep 12,1844, Vol 1, No 1.

Letter   d   1898-1905
　　MoHi: Film, Jly 22,1901-Jan 9,1904. Changed
　　　to Daily Record Jan 11,1904. Copies under
　　　latter title, Jun 19-25,27-30,1905.

Leader   w   1928?
　　Listed in Ayer 1933-1934.

Liahona
　　KHi: Jun 20,1916.

Messenger   w   1840?-1870?
　　MoHi: Jun 19,1869. Preceded by Chronicle,
　　　Western Missourian, Western Expositor,
　　　Missouri Commonwealth, Occidental Messenger.
　　　Suspended during Civil War. First listed Rowell
　　　1869, using 1849 founding date.
　　MWA: Jan 22,1841; Dec 10,1853.

Missouri Commonwealth   w   1850-1851
　　Formerly Western Expositor, later Occidental
　　Messenger.

National Crisis   w   1879-1880
　　Called Crisis in Rowell 1881.

News   w   1882   d   1900+
　　MoHi: 1950. Film, 1951+. MPA minutes 1882
　　　lists representatives from News at convention.
　　　First mention of latter News in Ayer, Rowell
　　　1908.

Occidental Messenger   w   1851-1861?
　　MoHi: Dec 10,1853. Follows Missouri Common-
　　　wealth. Stopped during Civil War, published
　　　briefly after that.
　　KHi: Sep 3,1859.

Pictorial News   w   1939+
　　See Ayer 1963.

Primitive Christian   w
　　KHi: Sep 27,1894-1901.

Progress   w   1881-1899?   d   1898-1899?
　　MoHi: Nov 1,1890; Sep 13,1884.

Record   d   1898-1905?
　　MoHi: Jun 19-25,27-30,1905. Film, Jan 11,1904-
　　　Jun 17,1905. See Letter.

Saturday Blade   w   1896-1897?
　　See Blade. In Ayer 1898, founding date 1895.

School-Girls' Casket   ?
　　IHi: Jun 26,1856.

Sentinel   w   1866-1957   d   1866-1936?
　　MoHi: Nov 1898-1902; Aug 5,1876; Feb 7-21,
　　　1903. Film, Nov 1,1949-1961.

Star   w   1832-1834, 1911-1914?
　　MoHi: Jun 1911-1913; Feb-Jly, Oct-Nov 1914.
　　　Film, Jun 1832-Sep 1834.
　　MoKc: Jun 1832-Sep 1834.

Suburban Items   w   1919?-1940?
　　Conflicting dates. First in Ayer 1929. Partly free
　　　distribution. See Englewood.

Tribune   w   1895,   w   1934-1936
　　MoHi: Mar 9,1895. Two under this title.

Upper Missouri Advertiser   w   1832
　　MoHi: Jly 11,1832. Mentioned by Organ.

Western Dispatch   w   1854
　　KHi: Jan 13,1854.

Western Expositor   w   1843-1849
　　MoHi: Jan 31,1846. Formerly Western Missourian,
　　　later Missouri Commonwealth.

Western Missourian   w   1841-1843
　　MoKc: Sep 3,1842.

INDIAN SPRINGS (McDonald County)

Chief   w   1887-1888
　　In Rowell 1888-1889, Ayer 1888.

Echo   w   1881-1882
　　KHi: Mar 10,1882. In Ayer 1882, Rowell 1883.

IONIA (Benton County)

Independent   w   1906-1907?
　　In Ayer 1907, Rowell 1907-08.

IRONDALE (Washington County)

Gazette   w   1901-1905
　　Also called Washington County Gazette, 1905.
　　Later title in Ayer-Rowell 1906.

Lead Miner   w   1901
　　Listed in Ayer 1902.

IRONTON (Iron County)

Arcadia Valley Enterprise   w   1904-1941
　　MoHi: May 10,1906-Dec 24,1908; Jan 4,1913-
　　　May 31,1916; 1917-1919; Jan 30,1925-Aug
　　　8,1941. Film, Dec 31,1908-1912. Sold to
　　　Annapolis Mountain Echo, Aug 8,1941, sus-
　　　pended.

Bland Register   tw   1861
　　WHi: Jly 9,1861.

Farmer   w   1861
　　In American Newspaper Directory 1861.

IRONTON (continued)

Forge w 1863-1866
  MoHi: Film, Oct 4, 1865-Apr 26, 1866. Later
    became Southeast Missouri Enterprise.

Furnace w 1858-1861
  Formerly published in Fredericktown.

Herald w 1884
  Listed in Rowell, Dauchy 1885.

Iron County Eagle w 1897-1903
  MoHi: Film, Jly 25, 1901-May 7, 1903.

Iron County Register w 1867+
  MoHi: Jly 25, 1901-1916; 1919-1944; Dec 24,
    1874; Jan 6, 1876. Film, Jly 1867-1901;
    1917-1918; 1945+.
  WHi: Mar 1893-Jun 1901.
  ICHi: Jly 6, Aug 3, 1876.

Iron County Republican w 1897-1899?
  In Rowell 1897-1899, Ayer 1900.

Lauman's Own w 1861?
  ICHi: Aug 21, 1861.

Liberal w 1870
  MoSHi: Jly 23, 1870. In Rowell 1871.

Missouri Commonwealth w 1874
  Listed in Rowell 1875.

Mountain Echo w 1937+
  MoHi: Film, Sep 8, 1944+. Formerly at Annapolis;
    to Ironton Sep 8, 1944.

Normal Picket w 1861-1862
  IHi: Film, Dec 24, 1861; Feb 12, 1862.
  WHi: Jan 15, 1862. Edited by Illinois Volunteers.

Ozark Record w 1927-1947
  MoHi: Film, 1939-1943; 1945-Sep 18, 1947.
    Merged with Mountain Echo 1947.

Prospect w 1860-1861
  MoSHi: Apr 13, 1861. Founded in Arcadia 1859.

Review w 1866
  Became Iron County Register 1867.

Republican w 1896
  Listed in Ayer 1897.

Southeast Missouri Enterprise w 1866-1875
  MoHi: Jan 1869-Mar 1870; Sep-Nov 1871;
    May-Sep 1873.

Truth w 1890-1891
  In Ayer-Rowell 1891, Rowell 1892.

Van-Guard w 1862?
  IHi: Film, Jan 20, 1862.

IRONTON (continued)

Western Privateer w 1871
  Listed in Rowell 1872.

JACKSON (Cape Girardeau County)

Advocate and Jeffersonian w 1852-1854
  Moved to Cape Girardeau, according to Organ.

Cape County Post w 1886-1962
  MoHi: Jly 1918-1919; Aug 1925-1938. Film,
    1951+. Consolidated with Missouri Cash-Book
    to become twice-weekly Jackson Pioneer May
    10, 1962.

Comet w 1894-1897
  People's Party paper in Rowell 1895-1897, Ayer
    1896-1898.

Courier w 1853-1861?
  MoHi: Feb 4, 1854.
  MoSHi: Oct 7, 1854.
  MWA: Jun 28, 1823; Jun 19, Jly 3, Aug 25, 1824;
    Sep 14, 1850. Formerly Jeffersonian, according
    to Organ.

Deutscher Volksfreund w 1886-1921?
  MoHi: May 17, 1912.
  MoCaT: 1917-1919.

Democrat w 1856
  Listed in Newspaper Record 1856.

Eagle w 1831-1835
  MoHi: Mar 24, Dec 22, 1832. Earlier called
    Mercury. Later equipment used for Cape
    Girardeau Southern Advocate and State
    Journal.

Examiner w 1898-1927?
  Not in Rowell or Ayer. See Union List.

Herald w 1897-1910
  MoHi: Film, Jly 25, 1901-Dec 4, 1910.

Independent Patriot w 1820-1826?
  MoHi: Dec 23, 1820-Nov 16, 1822; Feb 8, 1823-
    Oct 8, 1825; Mar 4-Dec 15, 1826; Apr 16, 1825.
    Later became the Mercury.
  MoSHi: Sep 27, 1823; Jan 5, 1828.
  AzTP: Film, Dec 23, 1820-Dec 13, 1826.
  KHi: Film, Dec 23, 1820-Dec 13, 1826.
  Micro-Photo: Film, 1821-1826.
  DLC: Dec 23, 30, 1820; 1821-Nov 16, 1822; Feb
    8-Dec 1823; 1824-Dec 13, 1826.

Items w 1910-1916
  MoHi: Jun 13, 1912. Published by Cape County
    Post.

Jackson Pioneer tw 1962+
  See Cape County Post.

JACKSON (continued)

Jeffersonian w 1852-1853
  MoHi: Jan 8, Apr 9, Jly 16, 1853. Later became
    Courier.
  MoSHi: Jun 11, 1853.

Mercury w 1828-1831
  MoHi: Dec 31, 1831. Later became the Eagle.
    See Missouri Herald.
  DLC: Dec 13, 1828; Oct 3, 1829.

Missouri Cash-Book w 1871-1962
  MoHi: Dec 10, 1908-1944; Apr 24, 1884; Oct
    30, 1890; Apr 12, 1900; Aug 11, 1871. Film,
    Aug 4, 1871-1908; 1945-1961. Consolidated
    with Cape County Post May 10, 1962 to be-
    come Jackson Pioneer.
  ICHi: Jly 6, 1876.
  KHi: Jly 26, 1923.

Missouri Herald w 1819-1825
  MoHi: Aug 13, 1819-Aug 26, 1820.
  DLC: Aug-Dec 1819; Jan-Aug 1820.
  KHi: Film, Aug 13, 1819-Aug 26, 1820.
    Later Independent Patriot. One source says
    became Mercury, Cape Girardeau Farmer.

Pioneer bw 1871+
  See Missouri Cash-Book.

Review w 1845-1849
  MoHi: Apr 5, Jun 21, Jly 12, 1845; Jun 6, Oct
    24, 1846; Dec 2, 1848. Formerly Southern
    Advocate, later same title resumed.

Sentinel w 1876
  ICHi: Jly 29, 1876.

Southern Advocate w 1835-1850
  MoHi: Jan 20-Dec 29, 1838; Jly 6, 1839; Jly
    11, 25, Aug 29, 1840; Jly 22, 1843; Jly 13,
    Sep 14, 1844. Formerly Southern Missouri
    Advocate. Took shorter name Mar 2, 1838,
    says Organ.
  MoSHi: May 15, 1836.
  DLC: 1838.

Southern Democrat w 1850-1852, 1834-1845?
  MoHi: Aug 3, 10, 1850; May 10, Oct 4, 1851;
    May 15, Jun 5, 1852. Listed 1836 in Madison
    County Probate files, noted as sold 1845,
    became Review.
  MoSHi: Apr 26, 1851; Jan 24, 1852.

Southern Missouri Advocate w 1835-1838?
  KHi: Film, Jan 28-Dec 29, 1838. See Southern
    Advocate.

JACKSONVILLE (Randolph County)

News w 1911-1914
  Listed in Ayer 1913-1915.

JAMESON (Daviess County)

Gem w 1913-1942
  MoHi: 1919-Feb 13, 1941. Film, Sep 25, 1913-
    1918.

Journal w 1897-1900
  In Rowell 1897-1901, Ayer 1900.

Laconic w 1891-1897
  In Rowell 1892-1898, Ayer 1891-1897.

Reporter w 1884-1885
  Listed in Rowell 1885-1886.

Review w 1889
  Listed in Rowell 1890.

JAMESPORT (Daviess County)

Gazette sw, w 1877-1944
  MoHi: w, 1903-Aug 26, 1915; Jly 1922-Apr 13,
    1944. Was sw until Aug 7, 1913. Suspended
    Apr 13, 1944. Sw, Dec 11, 1900; Jan 5, 1904.

Gazette-Herald w 1891?
  Under this title in Ayer 1892. Separately in 1890.

Herald w 1888-1891
  MoHi: Film, Dec 5, 1889-Dec 4, 1891. Merged
    with Gazette to form Gazette-Herald.

Independent w 1876
  In Rowell 1876 with 1876 founding date.

Journal w 1886-1887
  Called Joe's Journal (Joe H. Wright, E&P) in
    Rowell 1888.

News w 1944-1959?
  First in Ayer 1948. Last 1960.

Natural Gas w 1899
  Listed in Ayer 1900.

Republican w 1888
  In Ayer 1888 with 1888 founding date.

Telephone w 1895-1896
  Listed in Ayer 1896-1897.

Tri-County Weekly w 1944+
  First listed under News.

JAMESTOWN (Moniteau County)

Enterprise w 1915-1916
  Listed in Ayer 1916-1917.

Home Messenger w 1888-1900
  In Ayer-Rowell 1900-1901.

Journal w 1899-1907
  In Rowell 1901-1907, Ayer 1902-1908.

JASPER (Jasper County)

Bee   w   1890-1897?
    In Rowell 1891-1898, Ayer 1891-1897.

Constitution   w   1896-1897
    Listed in Ayer 1898.

Enterprise   sm   1887
    In Ayer 1887 with 1887 founding data.

Gazette   w   1905
    Listed in Ayer 1906.

Guard   w   1883
    In Rowell-Dauchy 1884.

Herald   w   1895
    Listed in Ayer 1896.

Jasper County News   w   1888+
    See News. Full title in Ayer 1963.

News   w   1898+   w   1884
    MoHi: 1906-1910; 1915-1944; Dec 22, 1904.
    Film, Jly 26, 1901-1905; 1911-1914; 1945-
    1955. Also listed as Jasper County News.
    Rowell refers to brief, earlier News.

Round   w   1888-1889
    W.C. Simonson, publisher, also printed, Bee in
    1890.

JEFFERSON BARRACKS (St. Louis County)

Convalescent   w   1865?
    WHi: Oct 28, 1865.

JEFFERSON CITY (Cole County)

Capital City Weekly Journal   w   1899
    Listed in Rowell 1900.

Capital News   d   1910+   w   1915-1940?
    MoHi: D, 1919-1920; Jly 1922-1950. Film, Oct
    1915-1918; 1921-Jun 1922; Jan-Mar 1930;
    1951+.
    Micro-Photo: film, 1949+.
    DLC: d, Oct-Dec 1941; Jan-Aug, Oct-Dec 1942;
    1943-1952.
    KHi: d, Oct 25, 1924.

Catholic Missourian   w   1912+
    MoHi: Film, Jly 19, 1959-1960.

Central Missouri Review   w   1934-1935
    MoHi: Jan 25-Mar 8, 1935. Changed to Missouri
    Review Mar 15, 1935.

JEFFERSON CITY (continued)

Cole County Daily Democrat   d   1902-1910
    MoHi: Jly 31, 1903. Film, Apr 1900-Jly 1901;
    Apr 22-Dec 24, 1902; 1904-Sep 1906; Jan-
    Aug 1907; Oct-Dec 1907; Jan-Apr 1908.
    Merged with Tribune Feb 9, 1910.

Cole County Democrat   w   1884-1910   d   1902-1903
    MoHi: Jun 6, 1884-May 1893; May 16, 1895;
    May 14, 21, 1896; Sep 15, 1898; Jun 5, 19-
    Jly 3, 17, 24, Aug 14-28, Sep 25, Oct 3, 23, Nov
    20, Dec 4, 1902; Feb 4, 19-Mar 5, Apr 2, 9, 1903.
    D, Apr 22, 24, 26, May 4, Sep 12, 19, Dec 25, 27,
    28, 31, 1902; Jly 31, 1903. Film, w, Apr 1900-
    Jly 1907.

Cole County Enterprise   w   1946-1954
    MoHi: Film, Feb 7-Nov 1947; 1948-1950; Jly
    20, 1951-Nov 29, 1952; 1953-Mar 5, 1954. At
    Eugene prior to Sep 28, 1949. Became Missouri
    Observer Mar 12, 1954.

Cole County Rustler   w   1897-1927
    MoHi: 1919-1926. Film, Jan 7-Jly 8, 1927. In
    Russellville 1907-1918?

Courier   w   1896-1898?   d   1894-1899
    MoHi: Dec 17, 1897-Mar 1898. Formerly Repub-
    lican Courier. Name changed Dec 17, 1897.
    D, film, Dec 10, 1894-Dec 9, 1895; Feb 28,
    1898-May 16, 1899.

Democrat   w   1902?-1910
    MoHi: Jly 1913-Mar 4, 1915. Jan-Jun 1918;
    Jly-Dec 1919. Film, Feb 9, 1910-Jun 1913;
    Jly 1918-Jun 1919. Became Democrat-Tribune
    May 5-1915-Nov 30, 1924.
    KHi: d, Jan 3, 1924; 1920-Nov 29, 1924.
    WHi: 1917-1919.

Demokrat   w   1853
    Listed in G-AN&P.

Eclipse   d, w   1878-1882
    MoHi: d, Nov 3, 1879-Jan 6, 1881.

Enquirer   (See Inquirer)

Examiner   d, w   1852-1865?
    MoHi: d, Jan 12, 19, 20, 23, Feb 1, 7, 13, 14, 16,
    1855.
    DLC: May 24, 1853, Vol I, No 37. See Jefferson
    Examiner.

Fortschritt   w   1866-1875?
    MoHi: Jun 9, 1869. Followed by Missouri Volks-
    freund.

Herald   w   1892-1893, 1913-1915?
    MoHi: Jly 1913-Aug 1914. Single Tax paper earlier.

Honest Laborer   w   1885
    Started April 16, 1885.

Inquirer w,tw,d 1838-1854
   KHi: d, Dec 19,1850-Mar 2,1851. See *Jefferson Inquirer*, name used after 1854. Second paper in city.

Jefferson Examiner d,w 1852-1862
   MoHi: d, Jan 6,18,Feb 4,5,10,11,Mar 3,10, 11,Nov 30,Dec 1,3,13,14,22,1859; Jan 12, 1860. W,Sep 14,1852-Sep 6,1853; Jan 4, 1855-1857; Apr 24,1858-Oct 1,1859; Dec 24, 1859; Apr 14,28,Sep 15-Oct 20,Nov 10,1860; Sep 13-27,Oct 11,Nov 1-Dec 13,1862. Film, Sep 14,1852-Sep 6,1853; Apr 24,1858-Oct 1, 1859.
   MoSHi: Supplements,Oct 1860; Jun 2,1862.
   DLC: w,May 24,31,Jun 21,28,1853; 1855-1857.
   IHi: Film,Aug 29,Sep 19,1857.

Jefferson Inquirer w 1838-1861 d irregular
   MoHi: w,1855; Jan 20,27,Feb 3,17,Mar 3,Dec 1,8,1855; Jly 24,1852; Dec 23,1854. Film, Sep 10,1840-1849; Feb 23,1850-Oct 14,1854; 1856-Sep 29,1859; Jun 10,1860-Jan 26,1861. D,May 27-Aug 28,1856; Jan 2-Jun 17,1857; Jan 1-Mar 14,1859; Jan 1-28,1861; Jan 9,19, 20,23,26,27,31,Feb 3,13,16,17,1855; Mar 18,1857; Jan 14,Feb 11,1859.
   MoSHi: d,Mar 4,1841; Jun 10,25,26,1845; Jun 15,1850; Jun 30,Feb 21,1853; Dec 15,1852- Feb 25,1853.
   MWA: w,Apr 11,Aug 1,Oct 17,1844; Jly 31- Aug 7,Sep 18,Nov 13-Dec 31,1845; Jly 3- 10,Oct 23,Nov 6,27-Dec 18,1847; Oct 21, Dec 23,1854.
   DLC: Apr 17-Dec 1845; 1846-1849; 1851-1853; 1855-1857.
   IHi: Film,Dec 26,1857. Published during Legislature sessions.

Jeffersonian w 1825-1844
   MoHi: Sep 9,1826.
   MoSHi: Dec 25,1826; May 18,1827; Aug 7-21, 1830; Mar 9,1831; Apr 10,1832; Apr 29,1833.
   DLC: Jan 1,1830. Founded in St. Charles 1825; renamed *Jeffersonian Republican* 1827. Moved to Jefferson City 1826.

Jeffersonian Republican w 1825-1844
   MoHi: Apr 30-Dec 17,1831; 1833-Aug 10,1844; Mar 9,1839. Film,May 27,1843-Aug 10,1844.
   AzTP: Film,Apr 30,1831-1840.
   DLC: Apr-Dec 1831; 1833-1840.
   CSmH: May 1,1830.
   KHi: Film,Apr 30,1831-Dec 26,1840.
   Micro-Photo: Film, 1831-1840.

Lake News
   MoHi: Jly 15,1935.

Metropolitan w 1846-1852
   MoHi: Oct 1846-Sep 1847; Apr 23,1847. Film, Nov 1847-Sep 1848; Oct 1849-Sep 1850.

Metropolitan (continued)
   MoSHi: Oct 6-Dec 29,1846; 1847-1848; Jan 2, 30,1849; Jan 27,Aug 31,1852.
   DLC: Oct 5,1847.
   MWA: Feb 1,1848.

Missouri Call w 1898-1899?
   In Ayer 1899,Rowell 1898-1899.

Missouri Capital w 1844
   Noted by Organ, Hammond.

Missouri Farm Bureau News w 1921-1957, M 1957+
   MoHi: Nov 1921-1944; May 15,1957 changed to monthly. Film, 1945-May 1957. Formerly in Columbia, moved Mar 31,1922.
   KHi: Aug 10,1923.

Missouri Herald w 1845-1846.
   MoSHi: May 10, Jun 7, Jly 8,1845. Became *Metropolitan* 1846.

Missouri Review w 1934-1936
   MoHi: Mar 15,1935-Sep 18,1936. See *Central Missouri Review*.

Missouri Observer w 1954-1957
   MoHi: Film,Mar 12-Dec 1954; 1955-1956. Suspended Nov 11,1957. Changed from *Cole County Enterprise* Mar 12,1954.

Missouri State Journal w 1920-1924
   MoHi: Jan 17,1920-Apr 5,1924.
   MoSHi: Mar 20,Apr 3,17,24,May 15-Jun 19, Nov 6,1920.
   KHi: Sep 23,1922.

Missouri Staats Zeitung w 1878-1882?
   In Ayer 1880,Rowell 1882.

Missouri State Times w,d 1862-1872?
   MoHi: D, Jan 20,26,1864. W, Jan 3,1863-Dec 1864; 1869; May 13-Dec 20,1870; May 17, 1872. Film, w, 1863-Jly 1868; Jan 8,1869- 1870.
   MoSHi: d,Mar 1-17,1871. W,Jun 1,Dec 12,1863; Aug 27,1864.
   DLC: d, Jan 24,1867; Mar 7,1871.
   ICHi: w,Sep 22,Nov 10,24,1865.
   WHi: d,Feb 20,1865.

Missouri State Tribune w 1866 d 1875
   See *Tribune, State Tribune*.

Missouri Trade Unionist w
   MoHi: Film,Jun 1924-Nov 1927; Apr 1932-Oct 1938; 1942-Jly 1944. Published in Joplin to Mar 23,1921.

Missouri Volksfreund w 1876-1927?
   MoHi: Film, 1913-Mar 1917; Oct 29,1890.

Missouri Watchman w 1838
  DLC: Apr 26, 1838, Vol 1, No 1; Jun 7, 1838.

Monitor w 1890
  Reform paper, according to Ashcraft.

Mosby's Missouri Message w 1918-1922
  MoHi: Jan 11, 1918-1921. Film, Jan 6, 20-Jly
    28, 1922.
  MoSHi: Apr 1, 1921.

News w 1888-1889
  MoHi: Oct 12-Dec 1888; Jan 4, 11, 25, 1889.

News and Tribune S 1932+
  See Capital-News, Post-Tribune.

People's Tribune w 1865-1885
  MoHi: Dec 19, 1866-1883; Jan 22, Feb 26, Mar
    12, 1879. Film, Oct 4, 1865-Dec 12, 1883.
  ICHi: Sep 20, 1876. In 1885 became Tribune.

Post d 1908-1927
  MoHi: Feb 3, 1913-Sep 1917; Dec 6, 1924-Jun
    30, 1926. Film, Jly 1, 1926-Feb 2, 1927.
    Merged with Tribune Feb 2, 1927, becoming
    Tribune-Post, later Post-Tribune. A German
    Post listed Ayer 1896-1912.
  KHi: Apr 28, 1924.

Post-Tribune d 1871+
  MoHi: 1928-1950. Film, May-Dec 1927; 1948;
    1951+.
  MoKc: Oct 1910-Dec 1932.
  Micro-Photo: Film, 1949+.

Press w, d 1899-1902
  MoHi: Jun 7, 1899. Film, Jun 1899-Apr 1902 inc.
    Sunday, Oct 27, 1901. W, Oct 31, 1901. Film,
    Jun 7, 1900-May 23, 1901.

Republican d, w 1900-1905
  MoHi: Jan 7, Mar 18, 1901; Jly 23, Aug 4, 5, Oct
    13, Dec 23, 1902; Oct 22, 1904. Film, Aug
    1900-Dec 1902; Jan-Aug 1904; 1905. Became
    Republican-Review Dec 18, 1905.

Republican Courier w 1895-1898
  MoHi: Jun 5, 1896; Jun 19, 1896-Dec 10, 1897.
    Became Courier Dec 17, 1898. In Missouri
    Editor consolidation in mid-1896.

Republican-Review d 1900?-1907
  MoHi: Film, Dec 18, 1905-Jun 29, 1907. Last in
    Ayer 1907 under this title.

Spy w 1844
  Whig campaign paper, Jun-Nov 1884.

State Eclipse
  See Eclipse.

State Journal d 1873-1886? w 1872-1886?
  MoHi: d, Sep 9, 1873-Mar 1874; Sep 9, 1874-
    Jun 1879; 1880-Jun 1881; Jan-Jun 1882;
    1883; Jan-Jun 1884. W, Dec 27, 1872-1882;
    1885-Aug 6, 1886; Feb 9, 1877; Apr 25, Jly
    4, 1879; Sep 3, 1880. Film, 1883-1884.
  MoSHi: Jly 30, 1875.
  ICHi: w, Aug 25, 1876. D, Sep 10, 1876.

State Republican w 1871-1896?
  MoHi: 1890-Mar 1896.

State Sentinel w 1844-1845
  MoHi: Dec 14, 1844.
  MoSHi: Feb 1, 1845 inc.
  DLC: Nov 2, 1844 (Vol I, No 2).

State Times w 1872, 1865
  DLC: Jan 24, 1867 (Vol II, No 16).
  MoHi: Aug 13, 1886-Oct 5, 1888. See Missouri
    State Times.

State Tribune w 1865 d 1870
  MoHi: Film, 1899-1904. Bound, Jan 11, Jun 2,
    3, 5, 8, 15, 1899; Mar 29, Apr 15, 1901; Oct
    2, Nov 26, Dec 5, 6, 8-10, 1902; Jan 31, 1904;
    1905-Apr 1, 1909. (See Tribune: Under Post-
    Tribune, film, Sep-Dec 1927; 1958; 1951+.)
    See People's Tribune, 1865-1883. W, Mar-Oct
    1909; Mar 5, May 2, 1884; Jly 20, 1887; Jun
    3, 1891; May 20, Sep 30, Nov 18, 1896; Jun 1,
    Sep 21, Dec 7, 1898; Jan 11-Feb 1, Jun 22, Dec
    21, 1899; Jun 21, Jly 21, Nov 15, Dec 20, 1900;
    Jly 10, 1903; Mar 9, 1906; Apr 2, 1908.

Tribune d 1871
  MoHi: Dec 1871-Mar 1872; Jan-Mar 1873; 1874-
    1879; Jly 1880-May 1881; Jly 1882-1884; Jly
    1913-Jun 1918; Jly-Dec 1919; 1928-1947;
    1949-1950.

  Various titles of Tribune (d):

Daily Tribune	Dec 6, 1871-Jan 2, 1899
State Tribune	Jan 3, 1899-Dec 1904
Jefferson City Tribune	Jan 1, 1905-Apr 1, 1909
Jefferson City Daily Tribune	Apr 2, 1909-Feb 7, 1910
Daily Democrat-Tribune	Feb 8, 1910-May 4, 1915
Democrat Tribune	May 5, 1915-Nov 30, 1924
Jefferson City Tribune	Dec 1, 1924-Feb 2, 1927
Jefferson City Tribune-Post	Feb 3, 1927-May 4, 1927
Jefferson City Post-Tribune	May 5, 1927-Dec 31, 1953

Volksfreund w 1876-1927?
  See Missouri Volksfreund.

Western Messenger w 1901-1917
  MoHi: 1914-Nov 1917.

Western Monitor 1829?
  MoCaT: Extra, Apr 27, 1829.

JEFFERSON CITY (continued)

West-Chronik ? 1843-1844?
    Listed in G-AN&P.

JERICO SPRINGS (Cedar County)

News w 1882-1887
    In Rowell 1884-1888, Ayer 1883.

Optic w 1888-1937
    MoHi: Jly 26, 1901-Jun 1935; 1936-Feb 1937;
        Nov 7, 1890; Feb 10, 1905.
    IHi: Film, May 3, 1889.

Sentinel 1897
    Country Editor notes death, Apr 1897.

JONESBURG (Montgomery County)

Free Press w 1878
    Short-lived, according to Hammond.

Journal w 1879-1942
    MoHi: Aug 1901-1908; 1913-Nov 1922. Film,
        Jan 16, 1909-Dec 19, 1912. Subscription list
        sold to Montgomery City Standard 1942.

Message w 1928-1940
    MoHi: Aug 1928-1929; 1932-Aug 22, 1940. Film,
        1930-1931. Became Montgomery County News
        Aug 29, 1940.

Montgomery County Leader 1872-1873?
    Moved to Mexico after year or two.

JONESTOWN (Bates County)

Enterprise w 1904
    Listed in Ayer 1905.

JOPLIN (Jasper County)

Advance w 1895
    KHi: May 10, 1895, Vol 1, Nov 1.

American d 1906
    Listed in Rowell-Ayer 1907.

Bulletin w 1874-1876?
    In Rowell's 1876 Centennial Book.

Democrat w 1874, 1924
    Apparently two Democrats. See Rowell 1875,
        Ayer 1925.

Dispatch w 1881
    Greenback paper, notes Hammond.

Free Press w 1912-1914?
    MoHi: Jan 17-May 9, May 23-30, Jun 26, Jly 11,
        25, Aug 8, 15, 29, Sep 12-Oct 3, 1914. Not in
        directories.

JOPLIN (continued)

Friday Advertiser w 1899-1900
    In Ayer 1900, Rowell 1900-1901.

Globe d, w 1896+
    MoHi: d, 1906-1950; Sep 19, 1903; Feb 20, 1906;
        Dec 4, 1908; Jly 23, 1914. Film, Mar 1897-
        Aug 1898; Dec 1898-Nov 1899; Dec 1900-
        1905; 1951+. W, Film, Dec 1898-1899.
    Joplin Public Library: 1904+.
    Micro-Photo: film, 1950+.
    KHi: d, Sep 1, 1921+.
    NcD: Jan 31, 1904.

Harpoon w 1896
    Start noted in Missouri Editor Feb 1896.

Herald d 1877-1900
    MoHi: Aug 23, 1878. Merged with News Mar 4,
        1900.
    MoSp: Apr 15, 1877 (Sunday).

Index d 1872
    County history says lasted less than year.

Jasper County Journal w 1889-1890?
    In Ayer-Rowell 1890-1891.

Mining Journal w 1873-1874?
    Listed in Rowell 1874-1875.

Mining News w 1872-1900
    Weekly edition of News.

Missouri Trades Unionist w 1909-1918
    MoHi: Film, 1911-1918. See Jefferson City.
    KHi: Jan 13, 1908.

News d 1876-1900
    MoHi: May 16, 1899-Mar 3, 1900. See Herald.
    NcU: Aug 2, 1878.
    ICHi: Sep 26, 1876.

News-Herald d 1872+
    MoHi: Mar 4-Oct 1, 1900; 1901-1950; Jly 22,
        1914. Film, 1951+. News and Herald merged
        Mar 4, 1900.
    Joplin Public Library: 1904+.
    Micro-Photo: Film, 1950+.
    KHi: Oct 24, 1919-Oct 27, 1920 inc.

Penny Democrat d 1891
    Listed in Rowell 1892.

Plain Dealer w 1886-1887?
    In Ayer 1886, Ayer-Rowell 1887.

Socialist w 1912-1916
    Listed in Ayer 1915-1917.

Southwestern w 1936-1961
    MoHi: Jun 12, 1936-1944. Film, 1945-Mar 20,
        1961. Ceased Oct 2, 1961.

JOPLIN (continued)

State Line Herald   d   1877-1880
    Name used for Herald for brief time.

Times   d   1900-1912?
    MoHi: Sep 1, 1908-Sep 30, 1910. Film, Nov 8,
    1906-Aug 31, 1908.

Tribune   d   1911-1913
    MoHi: Feb 9-Apr 11, 1913 when suspended.

Tribune   w   1902?-1915?
    Listed in G-AN&P. An edition of Wichita, Kan.,
    Der Herold.

Uplift   w   1926-1933?
    Last listed in Ayer 1934.

Voice   w   1893-1894
    People's Party. In Ayer-Rowell 1894.

World   w   1915-1917?
    Listed in Ayer 1917-1918.

KAHOKA (Clark County)

Clark County Courier   w   1895+
    MoHi: 1896-1897; Dec 2, 1898-1944; Feb 10,
    1905; Jly 21, 1911. Film, Jan-Nov 1898;
    1945+.

Clark County Democrat   d   1878-1880
    MoHi: Film, Mar 9, 1878-Mar 13, 1880.

Clark County Gazette   w   1871-1888
    MoHi: May 14-28, Jun 18, 1874. Film, Mar 12,
    1874-May 31, 1877; Oct 12, 1882-Dec 24,
    1885; Jan 7, 1886-Dec 27, 1888.
    ICHi: Aug 3, 1876.

Democrat   bw   1878-1880?
    MoHi: Oct 8-25, 1879; Aug 7, 1880.

Free Press   sw   1910-1946
    MoHi: Film, 1929-Jun 1946.
    KHi: Jly 24, 1928.

Gazette-Herald   1870+
    MoHi: Jly 1901-1944. Film, Jan 9, 1891-Dec 13,
    1901; 1945+.

Herald   w   1881-1886
    MoHi: Aug 31, Sep 21, 1882; Nov 19, 1884; Jun
    3, 1885.

Independent   w   1891-1892
    Reform paper, brief, notes Ashcraft.

Journal   w   1880
    Listed in Ayer 1881.

KAHOKA (continued)

Review   w   1888-1905
    MoHi: Dec 7, 1898-1900; May 13, 1903; Nov 16,
    1904; Aug 23, 1905. Film, 1901-1905.

Tribune   w   1888-1890?
    Last listing in Rowell 1891.

KANSAS CITY (Jackson County)

Advertiser   w   1865-1869
    Noted by Hammond.

Advocate   w   1885
    Listed in Rowell 1886.

American Citizen
    IU: 1941-1943.

Appeal   w   1893-1898?
    Reform paper also known as Appeal to Reason.
    Under longer title MnHi has Jly 11, 1896. Copy
    dated Apr 18, 1896 marked as No 34, no volume
    number.

American   w   1902, 1928-? 1933?
    MoHi: Jun 21, 1928-1929; 1930-Jan 12, 1933.
    MoKc: Film, Aug 14-Oct 30, 1902.

Arbeiter-Zeitung   1894?
    Listed in G-ANAP.

Barnhart Flyer   m   1909?
    MoHi: Jly 1909. Published by type foundry.

Bee   w   1895
    KHi: Feb 8-Oct 12, 1895 inc.

Blue and Gray
    MoHi: Film, Jan 23-Mar 6, 1902.

Blue Valley Press   w   1902-1938?
    Also known as Sheffield Press.

Border Star   w   1855-1868
    See Westport. Formerly Border Times, later
    Star of Empire. Suspended during Civil War,
    revived 1867 briefly. University of Kansas City
    Library has film, Dec 31, 1858-Dec 22, 1860,
    Vols 3-5.

Border Times   w   1855-1868
    NHi: Extras for May 20-23, 1856. Formerly
    Frontier News. See Border Star.

Bulletin   d,w   1868-1872?
    MoKc: w, Jan 25-Dec 26, 1872.

Call   w   1919+
    MoHi: Jly 25, 1952. Film, Jly 1949+ Negro.
    MoJcL: Film, Aug 6, 1943-1950; 1956-1959.
    KHi: Aug 21, 1925.
    Micro-Photo: Film, 1954+.

Camp's Emigrant Guide   m   1875-1888?
    KHi: 1880-1888.
    NHi: Aug 1879.

Catholic Register   w   1899-1939
    MoHi: 1903-1910; 1913-Sep 14,1939. Film, 1911-
      1912. Became Register Sep 24, 1939. Catholic
      Reporter since 1939.
    KHi: Jan-Jun 1937. Also, Catholic, 1896;
      Catholic Tribune, May 31,1873.

Cattle Trail   w   1873-?
    CoD: Sep 13,1873, Vol 1,No 29.
    KHi: Aug 16,1873.

Centropolis   w   1883-1888?
    MoHi: Film,May 19,1883-Nov 24,1887.

Chief   w   1886
    Listed in Rowell 1887.

Christian   w   1870?
    Formerly Christian Pioneer, published in Chillicothe
    until 1870.

Chronicle   d,w   1874-1890?
    Originally non-political, later agricultural.

Colored Messenger   w   1900-1901?
    In Rowell 1901-1902, Ayer 1901.

Coming Republic   w   1892-1902?
    In Rowell but not in Ayer.

Commercial Advertiser   d   1864-1869
    D edition of Advertiser, in Rowell 1869.

Commercial Indicator   w   1878-1881
    Name used briefly for Livestock Indicator.

Conservator   w   1896
    In Missouri Editor, Feb 1896.

Courier   d,w   1875-1878
    German paper, in Rowell 1877-1878.

Cosmopolita (El)   w   1914-1919
    MoHi: Film,Aug 22,1914-Nov 15,1919.
    MoSHi: May 15,1915.
    MoKc: Aug 22,1914-Nov 15,1919.
    NmSM: Film,Aug 22,1914-Dec 1,1917; Mar 23,
      Dec 14,1918; Dec 8,1917-Nov 15,1919 inc.
    KHi: Nov 27,1915.
    LNT-MA: Film,Aug 22,1914-Dec 1,1917; Dec 8,
      1917-Nov 15,1919; Mar 23-Dec 14,1918 inc.

Democrat   d   1926-1940
    MoHi: Jun 29,1926-Sep 10,1940, when ended.
    MoKc: Jun 10,1926-Sep 10,1940.

Dispatch   w   1886-1889
    Negro. In Rowell 1887-1891, Ayer 1887-1890.

East Side News   w   1939?
    Mentioned in MPN, Jly 1939.

East Side Progress   w   1888
    Listed in Ayer 1889.

East Side Visitor   w   1896
    Listed in Ayer 1897.

Enquirer and Star   1860-?
    DLC has Vol 1,No 1,Apr 19,1860, which states
      Enquirer will "rise from ashes of its predecessor,
      the Metropolitan."
    MoHi: Film,Dec 8-22,1860.
    MoKc: Film,Dec 8-22,1860.
    MWA: May 24,1860.

Enterprise   w   1854-1857
    MoHi: Nov 10,1855-Oct 3,1857. Film,same.
    MoSHi: Nov 10,1855-Sep 27,1856; Oct 11,1856-
      Oct 3,1857.
    MoKc: Nov 10,1855-Oct 3,1857.
    AzTP: Film,Nov 10,1855-Oct 3,1857.
    WHi: Film,Nov 10,1855-Oct 3,1857.
    Micro-Photo: film,1855-1856.
    KHi: Film,Nov 10,1855-Oct 3,1857; Oct 28,1854
    DLC: Film,Nov 10,1855-Oct 3,1857.
    Became Western Journal of Commerce Nov 1857

Examiner   w   1946?
    Listed in Ayer 1952.

Exchange Journal   w   1890
    KHi: May 8-29,1890.

Exodus   w   1880
    Listed in Ayer 1880.

Express   d   1880
    Listed in Rowell 1881.

Eye   w   1889-1890?
    KHi: Jly 10-Sep 18,1890. Firm also issued four
      Kansas papers.

Farm   w   1883
    In Dauchy 1884 as neutral paper.

Free State Republican   w   1860-1861
    In American Newspaper Directory 1861.

Frontier News   w   1855
    See Border Times.

Future State   w   1892-1893?
    Sunday paper, in Rowell 1893-1894, Ayer 1894.

Gate City Press   w   1880-1889?
    KHi: Sep 8,1888. Rowell 1887 refers to as Press-
      Sentinel.

Gazette w 1880
In Rowell-Ayer 1880 with 1880 starting date.
Micro-Photo: Film, 1899, 1901-1905.

Globe w 1889-1909
MoKc: Film, Feb 10, 1889-Apr 28, 1891. Sunday
edition, Apr 1-Jly 29, 1900.
KHi: Feb 10, 1889; Apr 19, 1891.
Also referred to as Grain Valley Globe. Daily
issued briefly.

Greenwood Gazette w 1898
Listed in Rowell 1898-1899.

Herald w 1886-1889
MoHi: Film, Sep 11, 1886-Jly 12, 1889.
MnHi: Oct 23, 1886.

Herold d,w 1880-1884
In Rowell 1880-1884, Ayer 1880-1881.

Herold des Westens 1878?
Listed in Rowell 1879.

Illustrated Public Press w 1875-1886
Listed in Ayer 1887. Successor to King's Illustrated
Life, 1875.

Independent w 1899+
MoHi: Jly 1901-1950. Society paper. Called
Newsbook briefly.
KHi: Aug 9, 1924-1936.

Industrial Liberator w 1873?-1882?
In Rowell 1882, Greenback paper.

Interstate Alliance Echo w 1891-1894?
Farmers' Alliance paper.

Jackson County Democrat w 1911?-1936
MoHi: Nov 9, 1934-Sep 18, 1936. In Ayer 1936.

Jackson County Tribune w 1895-1898?
Listed in Rowell 1896-1899.

Jeffersonian w 1902?-1942
First in Ayer 1939. 1902 date uncertain.

Jewish Chronicle w 1920+
NN: 1951-1953.

Journal w,d 1854-1942
MoHi: D, May 28, 1878-1889; Mar 1890-Aug 1894;
1895-Aug 15, 1896; 1920-Oct 3, 1928; Oct 3,
1938-Mar 31, 1942; May 11, 1879; Jly 17, 1881;
Apr 4, 1882; Mar 29, 1883; Oct 28, 1890. Film,
Jan-Feb 1890; Oct-Dec 1894; Aug 16, 1896-
1919. W, Jan 19, Jun 24, 1877; 1880-1887; Jan-
May 1920; May 6, 1920. Film, 1880-1919.
MoSHi: May 15, 1883; Dec 27, 1885; Aug 29, Dec
12, 1886; Sep 7, 12, 13, 15, 18, 20, 1901; May 10,
1903.

Journal (continued)
MoKc: 1901-Mar 1942. Film, Dec 17, 1858-Dec
11, 1859; Jun 15, 1860-Aug 21, 1861; Mar 18,
1862-Jun 30, 1865; Jan 16-Nov 7, 1877; Jan
1878-Feb 8, 1897; Feb 9, 1897-Dec 1900.
(Under various titles).
ICU: film, Nov 10, 1855-Oct 3, 1857, including
Enterprise.
CSmH: Oct 28, 1854.
DLC: d, Oct 19, 23, 1884; Jan 1, 1888. W, Jly 30,
1885.
IU: w, 1920-1926.
KHi: d, Dec 31, 1882; Jan 1, 1887; Jan 16, 1879;
Aug 31-Oct 3, 1928; Sep 16, 1879; Jan 31,
1886; Jan 1, 1887; Apr 27, 1916. Sunday, Jan
31, 1886. W, Nov 12, 1896; May 22, 1924;
Jan 2-Jun 19, 1879; Dec 26, 1878-May 26,
1898 inc.
MWA: Oct 14, 1854.
MnHi: Jly 6, 1900.
Weekly called Journal-Agriculturist from Nov
22, 1883-1884. Merged with Missouri and
Kansas Farmer Jun 3, 1920. D formerly Daily
Journal of Commerce; became Journal-Post
Oct 4, 1928. Renamed Daily Journal Oct 3,
1938. Suspended Mar 31, 1942.

Journal-Post d,w 1854-1942
MoHi: Oct 4, 1928-Oct 3, 1938. See Journal.
KHi: Sep 1, 1928-1942.
MWA: Apr 14, 1876; Jan 1, 1889.

Journal and Missouri and Kansas Farmer w 1884-1920
MoHi: Jun 3, 1920-1923; 1925-1927. See Journal.

Journal of Commerce w, tw, d 1954-
MoHi: d, Dec 13, 1859-Jun 15, 1860; Jan-Jun 1864;
Jly 4, 1865-1871; Jan-Jun 1873; 1874-May 26,
1878. Film, Dec 17, 1858-Dec 11, 1859; Jun 15,
1860-Aug 21, 1861; Mar 18, 1862-Jun 1865. W,
Dec 7, 1867-Nov 8, 1872; 1874-Jan 12, 1877;
Jly 6, 1877-Dec 1878. TW, Jly 16, 1876.
MoSHi: w, Jan 17, Jun 28, Jly 12, 16, 1872.
MoKc: See Journal listings.
CoU: Film, Dec 17, 1858-Jun 30, 1865.
DLC: d, film, Oct 17-Dec 1857; Dec 17-31, 1858;
Jan-Dec 11, 1859; Jan 15-Dec 1860; Jan-Aug
21, 1861; 1863-Jun 1865; Jly 11, 1876. W,
film, 1859-1861; Apr 25, 1863-Jun 23, 1866 inc.
ICU: Apr 25, 1863-Jun 23, 1866.
IHi: Film, Apr 18, 1865.
KHi: w, film, Dec 17, 1858-Dec 11, 1859; Jun 15,
1860-Aug 21, 1861; Mar 18, 1862-Jun 30, 1865;
(Western) Oct 17, 1857-Feb 28, 1861; Apr 25,
1863-May 20, 1865; Aug 12-Dec 30, 1865; Apr
14-Jun 23, 1866. D, Mar 21, 1865; Jly 13, 1873;
Feb 28, Dec 24, 1874; Jan 14, 1877; Jan 10,
1878. TW, Apr 18, 20, 1865; (Review) Jan 1877;
Jan 5, 1877-Dec 19, 1878 inc.
NcD: d, Oct 9, 1877.
WHi: d, Feb 7, 1865.

Journal of Commerce (continued)
Name changes include:
Kansas City Daily Western Journal of Commerce,
Jun 15, 1858-Dec 11, 1859; Daily Kansas City
Journal of Commerce, Dec 13, 1859-Aug 2,
1860; Daily Kansas City Western Journal of
Commerce, Aug 3, 1860-May 24, 1863; Daily
Journal of Commerce, May 26, 1863-May 26,
1878; Daily Journal, May 28, 1878.

Kansas Citian w 1911
Noted in Union List.

Kansas and Colorado Gazette m 1877-1879
CoD: Vol 1, No 4, 1877.
KHi: Kansas and Colorado Monthly, Apr 1878-
Apr 1879 inc.
NHi: Jun 1879

Kansas and Colorado Illustrated Monthly Newspaper
CoD: May 1878.

Kansas Courier d 1875-1876 w 1877?
Rowell 1876 said "Only German Democratic
daily west of St. Louis."

Kansas-Missouri Enterprise w 1881?-1884?
Listed in Dauchy 1885. Negro.

Kansas Pacific Homestead & Colorado Tourist ?
KHi: May 1, 1880.

Kaw's Mouth w 1893
Listed in Ayer, Rowell 1894.

Kaw's Journal w 1884
Listed in Dauchy 1885.

Kings & Queens of the Range m ?
KHi: Jan 5, 1898; 1899-Jun 1901; May 1902.

King's Life w 1884-1886?
MoHi: May 16, 1886

Labor Exchange w 1893-1894?
KHi: Dec 16, 1893-Mar 20, 1894.

Labor Herald w 1904-1940?
MoHi: Mar 17, 1909-Sep 27, 1940. Film, Jan 31,
1908-Jan 28, 1910; Feb 3-Mar 17, 1911.
MoKc: 1904-Jan 20, 1939.
KHi: May 13, 1910; Oct 13, 1911-Oct 4, 1912.

Labor Beacon w 1954+
Listed in Ayer 1959.

Labor News w 1919-1938?
MoHi: Mar 7, 1924-Mar 27, 1938. See Missouri
Mule.
KHi: Apr 5, 1929-1936.

Labor Journal w 1939-1957 q 1957+ w 1885
MoHi: Sep 25, 1942-1944. Film, 1945-1957. Be-
came quarterly Jly 1957.
KHi: Jun 20-Sep 17, 1885 inc.

Lancet w 1896
Noted in Missouri Editor, Feb 1896.

Leader w 1890-1915?
MoHi: Jan 1904-1912. Film, Jly 2-Dec 24, 1903.
Formerly Mexico The State Leader. Moved to
Kansas City Jly 2, 1903.
MoKc: Sep 21, 1905-Mar 6, 1913.
KHi: May 30, 1907.

Ledger w 1851-1856?
MoKc: Jly 4, Aug 29, 1851. Listed as Public Ledger.
First in Kansas City.

Liberator w 1901-1910
MoHi: 1903. Negro.

Livestock Indicator w 1878-1903?
MoSHi: Mar 28, 1894; Mar 29, 1895; Apr 29, 1896.
MoKc: Apr 4, 1878-1892.
KHi: Film, Mar 9, 1882-1892. Dec 22, 1887; Dec
1892-1904. Jan 1-Jly 30, 1903.

Livestock Record w 1872?-1889?
MoHi: Apr 16, 1885.
KHi: Oct 2, 1884-Feb 21, 1889 inc.

L'Observatore w 1908-1915
MoHi: 1914-Aug 4, 1915; Oct 11, 1912. La Voce
Dell'Imigrante merged with L'Observatore
Aug 11, 1915. Italian.
MoKc: Jun 1914-Aug 1915.

Mail d 1875-1882, 1892-1901? w 1895-
MoHi: Mar 10, 1894. Earlier paper under this title
absorbed by Star in 1882. Later paper listed
Ayer 1900. Film, W, May 14, 1895-Oct 9, 1900.
D, film, Jan 3, 1899-Oct 4, 1902.
MoKc: D, film, Mar 22, 1875-Mar 21, 1876; Sep
19, 1877-Aug 20, 1878; Aug 21-Sep 30, 1878;
Oct 1-11, 1878; Oct 15, 1878-Oct 24, 1881;
Jly 11, 1892-Oct 11, 1902. (Under various
titles.)
NbHi: Dec 27, 1898.
KHi: d, Aug 28, 1877; Feb 26, 1880; Mar 23, 1892-
Oct 4, 1902.

Mercurio (El) m 1883-1884?
KHi: Aug 1883-Jan 1884.

Marlborough News and Dodson News w 1922-1926?
Listed in Ayer 1925-1927.

Messenger w 1894-1900
DLC: Film, Jan 26, 1900. In Rowell 1900 as
Missouri Messenger. Negro.

Mid-Continent   w   1880-1884?
    Originally independent, later evangelical.

Mirror of Progress   w   1879-1882?
    KHi: Oct 4,1879-Apr 23,1881; Feb 28,1880-
    Dec 3,1881. Greenback paper.

Missouri Blatter   1895-1909
    MoHi: 1909.

Missouri Democrat   w   1925-1940
    MoHi: Oct 16,1925-Dec 20,1940 when it
    suspended.

Missouri Post   w   1850-1861,1862-1872
    German paper. To Kansas 1861, back 1862. Daily
    in 1865. Consolidated with Tribune in 1872 as
    Post und Tribune. Presse bought Post und Tribune
    1896.

Missouri Staats-Zeitung   w   1894-1918
    MoHi: Film,Nov 25,1898-Dec 27,1907; Jan 1,
    1909-Dec 7,1917. German paper. Suspended
    Feb 1918, subscription list taken over by
    Presse. See Staats-Zeitung.
    MoKc: 1899; 1909-1917.

Missouri and Arkansas Farmer
and Fruitman   w,m   1888-?
    MoHi: Jan,Aug 1896; Apr 1897.
    KHi: Mar 1896-Feb 1906.

Missouri and Kansas Farmer   m,w   1884-?
    MoHi: Film,Nov 25,1884-Nov 1886; 1890-Dec
    15,1899. See Journal.
    KHi: m, Jan 1903-Dec 1912.

Missouri Mule   w   1919-1923
    MoHi: Aug 16,1919-Jun 8,1923. See Labor News.

Modern Argo   w   1872-1883
    CoD: Dec 23,1882, (Vol 10,No 13); Dec 30,
    1882; Jan 13,1883.

Monday Morning Gazette   w   1880
    Listed in Ayer 1880.

Monday Morning Herald   w   1872
    Listed in Rowell 1873.

National Mirror   w   1885-1917?
    Negro. In Ayer 1915-1918.

Neue Kansas Staats-Zeitung   w   1894-1918
    MoHi: Dec 4,1908. Film, Jan 9,1914-Feb 8,1918.
    MoKc: 1914-Feb 1918.

New Era   w   1892
    Listed in Ayer 1892.

New Missouri   w   1894-1898?
    Negro. In Rowell 1896-1899,Ayer 1896-1897.

News   d   1869-1876?, 1881,1885-1889?
    Apparently two, at least, News in Kansas City.
    Rowell 1870 lists one starting 1869. Rowell 1882
    lists one starting 1881. Ayer 1890 lists one starting
    1885.
    MoSHi: Daily News,Dec 13,1886.
    MoKc: Evening News, film, Mar 17,1887-Oct
    1888; Jan 22,1889-Oct 3,1890.
    KHi: Sep 10,1888-Jly 8,1889; Evening News,
    May 12,1888-Oct 8,1890.

News and Kansas City World   d   1894-1908
    MoKc: Film, Jan 11,1894-Apr 11,1908, except
    Mar 26-Apr 7,1908. Some of these also in
    bound volume. See World. Apparently name
    used for this period.

Newsbook   w   1908
    Listed in Ayer 1909.

News-Press   w   1914+
    Known earlier as South City Press, South Kansas
    City Press.

Neue Westen   w   1885-1889
    Sunday edition Post und Tribune.

Northeast News   w   1932-1951?
    Last listed in Ayer 1952.

Observer   w   1896-1901?
    DLC: Film, Jan 27,1900. Negro. In Ayer 1897-
    1900.

Oil Press   ?
    MoSHi: Sep 15,1919; Apr 1,1920.

Oil Times   bm   1917-1919?
    MoHi: Oct 1,1919. Specialized referring to
    Kansas City as "Gateway to the Oil Fields."

Omnibus   w   1869-1870
    German. In Rowell 1870-1871. Sunday edition of
    Post.

Our Country   w   1912-1916?
    KHi: Mar 13,1915. In Ayer 1917, national topics,
    agriculture.

Out-Look   w   1876-1879
    Listed in Rowell 1879-1880.

Packer   w   1893+
    MoHi: film, Jan 2,1932-Feb 17,1934. Publisher
    had similar papers in New York, Chicago,
    Cincinnati, and on Pacific Coast.
    IaHi: Oct 19,1893-Jan 2,1896.
    KHi: Oct 24,1895-Jly 22,1899 inc; Mar 30,
    Apr 20-Dec 1907; Oct 19,1907-Dec 19,1908.

Passing Show   w   1895
    Missouri Editor, Sep 1895, says a "New and un-
    pleasant paper."

Penny Post   d   1886-1889?
   Rowell 1889 list: Sunday edition called Illustrated
   Sunday World.

Penny Press   d   1887-1890?
   KHi: Feb 15-Jun 19, 1890. In Rowell 1887-1888,
   Ayer 1890.

Pioneer   w,d   1873-1881? 1890?
   MoHi: d, Jly 25, 1879. W, film, Jan 3-Dec 18,
    1880. In Ayer 1891.
   MoSHi: Jun 5, 1880.
   KHi: Jun 18, 1881; Oct 23, 1878.

Post   d   1906-1928   w   1962+
   MoHi: Apr 6, 1906-1915; 1920-Oct 3, 1928. Film,
    1916-1919. Merged with Journal Oct 4, 1928.
    New weekend Post started Sep 8, 1962.
   MoKc: Mar 14, 1906-Oct 2, 1928.
   KHi: d, May 14, 1906-Aug 31, 1928.
    A d German paper 1859-1892; w 1868-1897.

Post und Tribune   d   1858-1896, w   1872-1896?
   MWA: w, Aug 20-Sep 17, Oct 1, 15, 29, Nov 19-
    26, 1859; Jan 14, 1860. D, Aug 25, 27, 1876.
    Long, confused history. See G-AN&P.

Presse   w,d   1883-1941
   MoHi: Film, Jan-Mar 1914; Oct 1915-Dec 1921;
    Nov 18, 1890. D ceased 1918?
   MoKc: Jan 1898-May 1929.
   CoU: Jly 24, 1940.
   KHi: Jly 18, 1918-May 16, 1932 inc.

Price Current   w,d   1873-1882?
   ICHi: Aug 11, 1876.
   KHi: Jun 25, 1880-Oct 28, 1881. Rowell 1883
    lists d, commercial.

Progress   w   1888-1890?
   In Rowell-Ayer 1890-1891.

Record   d   1888+
   MoHi: Feb 9, 1906. Court, real estate.
   MoSHi: 1947 inc.
   MoKc: Jan 1901+.
   KHi: Jan 7, 1890-1893.

Recorder   w   1882?
   E.Y. Kilgore of Recorder MPA member 1882.

Reform   d,w   1890-1909
   MoHi: Film, Mar 17, 1900-1907; Jan-Jun 1909.
   MoKc: Mar 1900-1907; Jan-Jun 1909. Formerly
    in St. Louis; German/English.

Record-Searchlight   w   1908?-1927?
   Negro. In Ayer 1927-1928.

Register   w   1899+
   MoHi: Sep 24, 1939-1944. Film, 1945-Nov 27,
    1959. Prior to Sep 24, 1939 was Catholic
    Register. Became Catholic Reporter Jan 4,
    1959+.

Reporter   w,d   1873-1874   w   1959+
   MoKc: May 21, 1873-Jan 16, 1874.
   KHi: d, Feb 3, 1874. First in Rowell 1873-1874.
    Later is Catholic Reporter.

Review   w   1880?
   Theo. S. Case of Review MPA member 1880.

Rising Sun   w   1896?-1919?
   MoHi: Film, Jan 16, 1903-1908.
   MoSHi: Aug 30, Oct 4, 1902; 1903 inc; Jan 1,
    15, 22, 29, 1904.
   MoKc: Film, Jan 16, 1903-1907.
   DLC: Film, Jan 27, 1900; 1903-1907.
   WHi: Film, Jan 16, 1903-1907.

Saturday Evening Herald   w   1879-1882?
   In Rowell 1880-1883.

Saturday Night   w   1913-1914?
   In Ayer 1914-1915.

Saturday Truth   w   1897

Searchlight   w   1908?-1927?
   See Record-Searchlight.

Secret Society Herald   w   1897
   MoHi: Jan 16, 1897. Fraternal paper.

Sheffield Press   w   1902-1928
   Also known as Blue Valley Press.

Sheffield Sun   w   1898
   In Rowell 1898-1899. Firm also printed Grain
    Valley Globe, Greenwood Gazette.

Signal   w   1908?-1911?
   Negro. In Ayer 1909-1912.

Son   w   1908-?
   KHi: Dec 7, 1912.

South City Press   w   1914-1918
   Union List says under this title for News-Press
   years indicated.

Southwest   w   1924-1936
   Listed in Ayer 1930-1936.

Southwest News   w   1958+
   First in Ayer 1959.

Southwest Postal News d 1910-1911?
   MoHi: Oct 10-12, 1910。Survived only several
     issues, "lack of funds, lack of experience,
     lack of talent." Started again?
   KHi: Sep 1911.

South Kansas City Press w 1919-1923
   Union List says name used for News-Press for
   years indicated.

Spectator 1895
   Listed in Dauchy 1896.

Squib w 1886
   Listed in Rowell 1887.

Star d,w 1880+
   MoHi: D, 1909-Sep 30, 1918; 1919-May 31, 1949;
     Sep 18, 1880; Apr 3, 5, 6, 1882 (Death of Jesse
     James); Dec 14, 1899; Mar 20, Jly 31, 1901;
     Jly 28, Aug 4, Oct 3, 1915; May 3, 1916; Mar
     13, Apr 4, Jly 28, 1917; Feb 6, 1924. Film, Sep
     18, 1880-Dec 31, 1908; Oct 1-Dec 30, 1918;
     Jun 1, 1949+ W, film, 1924-Feb 26, 1930.
   MoSHi: Aug 31, 1919; Jun 4, 1950. Sunday mag-
     azine for Sep 6-Dec 27, 1925; Jan 3-Aug 29,
     1926. Formerly Evening Star Sep 18, 1880-
     Sep 18, 1885. Times became morning edition of
     Star Oct 26, 1901. Jun 1949 to date filmed with
     Times for same dates.
   MoKc: D, film, Sep 18, 1880+ w, 1949-1951.
   MWA: d, Sep 18, 1880; Aug 7, 1921; Aug 9, 1925;
     Sep 18, 1930. w, Feb 2, 1915.
   IHi: Film, Jan 23, 1890.
   IaHi: Mar 27, 1890-Jun 1, 1892; Jun 23, 1892-Jly
     18, 1894; Jan 30, 1901-Jly 16, 1902; Aug 27,
     1902-Sep 23, 1903; Jun 4-30, 1928.
   NbHi: Nov 5, 11, 1884; Sep 14, 1907; Sep 30, 1920.
   WHi: d, Sep 18, 1880-May 31, 1908; Nov 14, 1913-
     Nov 30, 1923; Jun 1, 1949-Jly 31, 1957. Film,
     1880-1908; 1947-1957.
   KHi: d, Oct 11, 1881; Nov 23, 1881; Aug 19, 1886+.
     Film, 1950+ w, Sep 16, 1891+ inc.
   IU: 1909-1949. Film, 1949+.
   DLC: Dec 22-31, 1891; 1892+. Film, 1958+. W,
     1933-1937.
   MnHi: Jly 6, 1900.

Star and Times
   MoKc: d, Sep 22, 1885-Sep 17, 1886; Oct 1887-
     Mar 1891; Sep 18, 1891+.
   Micro-Photo: Film, 1880+.

Star of Empire w 1855-1868
   See Border Star。

Star Farmer w
   MoKc: Film, 1952-May 24, 1961.
   Micro-Photo: Film, 1949+

Staats Zeitung w ?
   KHi: 1917-Feb 8, 1918.

Sun w 1880-1881?, 1908-1924?
   MoHi: Jan 10, 1914-Jun 7, 1924. Negro.
   KHi: w, Mar 3-May 4, 1889. Sunday, Feb 9, 1896.
     Apparently another Sun founded 1889. Rowell
     lists one founded 1880.

Sun-Herald d 1950-
   Catholic.

Suburban News w 1922?-1929?
   In Ayer 1929-1930, founding 1922, 1923.

Sunday Graphic w 1883-1884
   Listed in Rowell 1884-1885.

Sunday Mail w 1892
   KHi: Feb 21-Mar 20, 1892.

Sunday News w 1896
   Noted in Missouri Editor, Jun 1896.

Sunday Sun w 1889-1897?
   Rowell 1893 says this was edition of Chicago
   Sunday Sun.

Svenska Veckoblandet ?
   MoHi: Nov 21, 1890. Ayer 1889-1890 notes
     Svenska Weckobiadet, founded 1883; others
     quote in Union List.

Svenska Harolden w 1878?
   MnHi: May 17, 31, Apr 5, 12, Jly 19, 1882; Jan 31,
     Feb 21, Mar 7, May 9, 23, 30, Apr 4, 18, Jun 6,
     1883.

Svenska Tidningen 1891?
   MnHi: Aug 16, 1895-Feb 3, 1898.

The Other Side w 1895-1896
   Reform paper, short lived.

Times d,w 1868+
   MoHi: Jun-Jly, Sep-Oct 1893; Mar-Apr 15, 1894;
     Jun 16-Aug 15, 1896; Oct 1896-Aug 15, 1897;
     Sep 16, 1897-Feb 1898; Mar 16, 1898-Sep 30,
     1899; Dec 1899-1900; Jun 1908; Nov 1908-
     Oct 1911; Mar-Jun 1912; Sep 1912-1914;
     Mar 1915-Jan 16, 1947; Feb 3, 1947-May
     1949; Jun 5, 1875; 1876 Mammoth Review
     ed; Jun 1877 Premium Distribution Sheet;
     Jun 23, Oct 13, Nov 9, 1881; Mar 19, 1882;
     Mar 15, 1888; Oct 14, 1893; Sep 2, 1900;
     Jan 13, 20, Feb 10, 17, Mar 3, 17, Apr 5, Jun
     2, 16, 23, 1902; Oct 31, 1912; Dec 22, 1916.
     Film, Oct 1, 1901-May 30, 1908; Jly-Oct
     1908; Nov 1911-Feb 1912; Jly-Aug 1912;
     Jan-Feb 1915; Jun 1949-1954; 1955+。
   MoKc: Evening Times, Oct 9, 1890-Dec 12,
     1891. Film, Aug 20, 1871-Dec 1873; Jan 18,
     1873; Jun 21, 1874; Jly 1-Nov 13, 1874 inc;
     1875-Dec 20, 1877; 1878-Jun 14, 1879; Jly
     1874-Oct 19, 1901.

Times (continued)
MoSHi: w, Apr 6, 1882; Dec 15, 1885; Mar 23,
Nov 20, 30, 1886; Aug 15, 1945. D, May 26,
1878; Dec 20, 1891 inc.
DLC: Jly 16, 1877; Dec 20, 1886.
IU: Oct 1908-1919; Aug 21, 1926+.
IaHi: w, Mar 29, 1877-Mar 21, 1878; Nov 30,
1882-Apr 10, 1884; May 3-Oct 18, 1901.
TW, Jan 2, 1900-Apr 26, 1901.
KHi: Jly 1, 1874+. Film, 1949+.
NbHi: d, Mar 30, 1882; Dec 31, 1909. W, Sep
22-Oct 6, 27, Dec 8, 1881; Mar 30, 1882.
NcD: d, Dec 14, 1883.
McHi: d, Jly 5, 1900; Jly 1, 4-5, 1921. W, Jan
3, 1884.
T: w, Apr 13, 27, May 4, 25, Jun 29, Oct 12, 19,
1882; Jly 31, 1884.
WHi: d, Nov 14, 1913-Jun 30, 1915; Jun 1, 1949-
Jly 31, 1957. Film, Jun 1, 1949-Jly 31, 1957.

Tribune   w   1868-1871?, 1896, 1921-1928?
Early edition German, later merged with Post.
Missouri Editor, Feb 1896, tells of new Tribune.
Ayer 1927-1929 list another Tribune, founded
1921.

Tribunen   w   1892-?
MoHi: Film, 1903-Oct 1914. Swedish.
MoKc: Jan 1903-Oct 1914.
MnHi: Jun 24, 1904; Dec 21, 25, 1905; May 23,
1907; Dec 9, 1909; Jly 22, Sep 9, Dec 30,
1910; Jan 20, Feb 11, Mar 31, May 12, 26,
Jly 21, Aug 4, 11, 25, Oct 6, 13, Nov 13, 30,
Dec 7, 1911; Mar 14, 28, Apr 4, 25, May 23,
24, 1912; Mar 6, Aug 6, Oct 30, 1913; Mar
12, Jun 4, Jly 9, 16, 1914.

Traveler   d   1888-1889?
KHi: Jun 13, 1888-Dec 21, 1889.

True American   w   1893-1898
Populist paper. In Ayer 1896-1897. Ashcraft notes
1898 ending.

Truth   w   1882-1884, 1903-1905?
MoKc: Apr 4, 1903-Jan 5, 1905.

Uncle Sam   w   1890
Society humor paper. Editor also with Sunday
Graphic.

Unsere Zeit und Kansas City   w   1874
Listed in Rowell 1875.

Vorwarts   w   1885-1890
May have been printed in O'Fallon too.

Voce (La) dell 'Emigrante   w   1909-1915
MoHi: Aug 11, 1915-Oct 1917. Merged with
L'Observatore Aug 11, 1915.
MoKc: Aug 1915-Oct 1917.

Wednesday Magazine   w   1937+
Mostly shoppers' paper.

Western Argus   w   1891
Negro paper in Ayer 1892.

Western Chronicle   w   1883-1887?

Western Cultivator   w   1878?-1882
In Rowell 1882-1883.

Western Farm & Home   w   1878?-1884?
Non-political paper, in Rowell 1884.

Western Christian Recorder   w   1892-1899?
MoHi: Film, Oct 26, 1911-Sep 16, 1915. Official
organ of African Methodist Church.
WHi: film, Feb 26, 1898-Aug 19, 1899.

Western Hub   w   1890
Listed in Ayer 1890-1891.

Western Illustrated World   w   1879?-1887?
Listed in Rowell 1887-1888.

Western Journal of Commerce   w, d   1854-?
MoHi: w, Oct 24, 1857-Oct 2, 1858; Oct 1859-
Sep 27, 1860; Jly 21, 1866-Nov 6, 1867. Film,
Oct 17, 1857-Jun 23, 1866. Formerly Enterprise
until Oct 1857. Became Weekly Journal of
Commerce Nov 1867. See Journal.
MoSHi: d, film, Dec 17, 1858-Dec 11, 1859; Jun
15, 1860-Mar 7, 1861; May 15-Aug 21, 1861;
Mar 18, 1862-Jun 30, 1865. W, film, Oct 24,
1857-Oct 2, 1858; Oct 16, 1858-Feb 28, 1861;
Apr 25, 1863-Jun 23, 1866.
MoKc: Film, Oct 17, 1857-Jun 23, 1866.
AzTP: Film, Oct 17, 1857-Jun 23, 1866.
WHi: Film, Oct 17, 1857-Jun 23, 1866.
ICU: Film, Oct 17, 1857-Feb 28, 1861.

Western Metropolitan   w   1858-1861?
DLC has Vol 2, No 9, Aug 18, 1859; Mar 8, 1860.
Later became Enquirer, suspended during Civil War.

Western Newspaper Union   ?
MoSHi: Nov 23, 1889; Jan 11, Apr 12, 1890.

Western Messenger   ?
MoHi: Aug 1918-Feb 1921.

Western Wealth   w, m   1889-1892?
MoHi: Jly 1889. Rowell 1890 lists as m.

Western Woman   1895
Noted in Missouri Editor, Jun 1895.

Westliche Volkszeitung   d   1871-1873
Daily merged with Post und Tribune.

Westport Examiner   d, w   1892-1899?
United with Sentinel.

KANSAS CITY (continued)

Westport Sentinel   d   1892-1894
   United with Examiner to form Sentinel-Examiner.

Westport Sentinel-Examiner   w   1893?-1899?
   Union List says name Examiner used 1893?-Jun 9,
   1894; Sentinel 1892-May 1894?

World   d   1894-1908
   MoHi: Feb 1-Jun 30, 1897; Sep 2, 1901-1902;
      1904-Jun 30, 1907; Oct 30, 1895. Film, 1903.
   MoSHi: Jan 4, 1903 inc.
   MoKc: Film, Jan 11, 1894-Apr 11, 1908 inc.
   IaHi: Oct 23, 1901-Jan 1, 1903.
   KHi: Jly 11, 1895; Aug 28, Sep 9, 1896; Sep 11,
      1895-Jun 29, 1907; Jan 1-Apr 11, 1908. See
      News and World.

Word and Way   w   1896-?
   MoHi: Film, Jly 9, 1896-Jun 26, 1902; Jly 4,
      1907-Jun 26, 1913. Baptist.

Wochenblatt der Kansas City Press
   See G-AN&P.

Zeitung   w   1899-1908?
   Weekly German, Catholic paper.

(KHi, Topeka, also has other specialized publications
   that originated in Kansas City).

KEARNEY (Clay County)

Clipper   w   1894-1918?
   MoHi: Oct 8, 1904. Film, 1913-Oct 26, 1917.
      May have been one in 1883.
   MoSHi: Aug 2-Dec 20, 1884.

Courier   w   1932+
   First in Ayer 1935.

Echo   w   1924-1925
   In Ayer 1925-1926.

Herald   w   1883-1888?
   In Rowell 1889.

Monitor   w   1891-1894
   See Gower Monitor.

Sentinel   w   1875
   In Rowell 1875, with 1875 founding date.

Sun   w   1894?
   In Ayer 1920. Founding date vague.

KENNETT (Dunklin County)

Clipper   w   1877-1893?
   MoHi: Oct 23, 1890. Film, Apr 19, 1888-Jun 15,
      1893. Under Kennett-Malden Clipper, MoHi
      has film, Jan 14, 1881-Dec 26, 1884.

KENNETT (continued)

Dunklin County Advance   w   1877-1880
   In Rowell 1878-1880, Ayer 1880.

Dunklin County Democrat, Dunklin Democrat
                              d, w   1888+
   MoHi: 1906-1955; May 22, 1903; Dec 25, 1908;
      Mar 16, 1916. Film, Jun 22, 1893-1905; Jan 2,
      1945-Mar 29, 1956. Daily, Film, Apr 2, 1956+.
      Became Daily Dunklin Democrat Apr 2, 1956.
   Micro-Photo: film, 1956+.

Dunklin County Herald   w   1907-1910
   MoHi: Jan 7, Feb 11, 1910. Film, 1907-1909.

Dunklin County Mail   w   1900-1905?
   MoHi: Jan 12, 26, Mar 2-Apr 27, 1905.

Dunklin County News   w   1916-1931
   MoHi: 1919-May 22, 1931. Film, Aug 4, 1916-
      1918. Sold to Dunklin Democrat May 22, 1931.

Dunklin County Republican   w   1907-1910
   MoHi: Feb 18-Apr 22, 1910.

Dunklin Dispatch   w   1912-1914
   See Ayer 1913-1915.

Dunklin Tribune   w   1936-1941
   Earlier in Kennett. Subscription list sold to
   Dunklin Democrat.

Free Press   w   1937-1939?
   Start noted in MPN, Oct 1937. In Ayer 1939.

News   d, bw   1925
   Editor & Publisher Jun 20, 1925 reported evening
   edition had suspended, and a twice-a-week paper
   would take its place.

Justice   w   1912-1914
   MoHi: Film, Jan 9-Nov 13, 1914.

Southeast Advertiser   w   1873-1875
   ICHi: Jun 10, Jly 15, 1876. See Clarkton Advertiser.

Southeast Missouri Republican   w   1910
   MoHi: Film, Apr 29-Dec 23, 1910.

Times   w   1900-1906
   MoHi: Film, Jly 21, 1905-Dec 21, 1906.

KEYTESVILLE (Chariton County)

Chariton County News   w   1866-1869?
   Under Chariton County Union as name used for
   these years.

Chariton County Union   w   1866-1872
   MoSHi: Oct 19, 1867; Jun 12, 1868.
   MWA: Aug 31-Sep, Oct 12, 26, Nov 30, 1867.
      Conflict on names, dates. Rowell 1870 says
      started 1866. Became Herald 1872.

KEYTESVILLE (continued)

Chariton Courier   w   1872+
    MoHi: Jun 1878-1883; 1911-1944; Oct 23,
        1890. Film, 1884-1900; Jly 26, 1901-1910;
        1945+.
    MoSHi: Dec 4, 1908. Formerly Herald, name changed
        Jun 1878.
    MoHi: Sumner Editions, w, Mar 17, 1939-1944. Film,
        1945-1951. Moved to Keytesville from Sumner
        Mar 17, 1939.

Chariton Recorder   w   1905-1918
    MoHi: Nov 22, 1907-Feb 1, 1918.
    MoSHi: Dec 4, 1908. Sold to Chariton Courier
        Feb 1, 1918.

Democrat   w   1881-1885
    In Ayer-Rowell 1886, conflicting dates. One has
    1881, other 1883.

Herald   w   1872-1878
    MoHi: Mar 1872-May 1878.
    MoSHi: Jan 9, 16, Jly 17, Oct 2, 1875; Nov 8, 1876.
    ICHi: Jun 24, 1876. See Chariton Courier.

Northwestern News   w   1951-1953?
    MoHi: Film, 1951-Nov 1953.

Signal   w   1893-1905?
    Ayer 1905 lists Chariton County Signal.

KIDDER (Caldwell County)

Dispatch   w   1886-1900
    Listed in Ayer 1901.

Enterprise   w   1914-1917?
    Listed in Ayer 1915-1918.

Free Press   w   1914-1918?
    In Ayer 1919, established in 1914.

Independent   w   1903-1913?
    MoHi: Jun 10, 1904. Film, Mar 11, 1910-1911.

Institute   w   1941-?
    At one time printed by Cameron Progress.
    Mentioned in MPN, Feb, Oct 1941.

Optic   w   1886-1899?
    MoHi: Oct 23, 1890; Jun 13, 1895; Jan 27, 1898.

Rustler   w   1914-1920?
    Listed in Ayer 1920-1921.

Star   w   1921-1925
    Listed in Ayer 1922-1926.

KING CITY (Gentry County)

Chronicle   w   1880-1947
    MoHi: Jly 26, 1901-1944; film, 1945-Jan 31,
        1947. Sold to Tri-County News, Feb 1947.
    KHi: Jun 8, 1923.

KING CITY (continued)

Democrat   w   1892-1918
    MoHi: Nov 25, 1898-Jun 30, 1899; 1903; 1905-
        Sep 1918; Dec 25, 1908.

Times   w   1892?
    In Ayer 1919. Founding date uncertain 1892 used
    here.

Tri-County News   w   1920+
    MoHi: Jun 11, 1920-1944. Film, 1945+.

KINGSTON (Caldwell County)

Banner of Liberty   w   1864-1866
    Press formerly used to print Caldwell County Beaco

Caldwell Citizen   w   1873-1878?
    ICHi: May 25, Jly 6, 1876. In Rowell 1874-1879.

Caldwell County Banner   w   1864-1866?
    MoHi: Film, May 1864-Feb 1866 inc.

Caldwell County Beacon   w   1860-1864
    MoHi: May 3, 1861. Advocated secession. See
        Banner of Liberty.

Caldwell County News   w   1921-1953?
    Listed in Ayer 1923-1953.

Caldwell County Sentinel   w   1867-1887
    MoHi: Jan 7, 1876; Apr 29, May 6, 20, 1881;
        May 19, 1882; May 4, Jun 8, 22, 29, Jly 6,
        Oct 12, 19, 26, Nov 2, 9, 1883. Film, Apr 2,
        1886-Aug 26, 1887. Purchased by Times Aug
        1887.
    ICHi: Jly 7, 1876.

Caldwell Republican   w   1894-1898?
    MoHi: Feb 1, 1895.

Hampton's Mercury   w   1895-1921
    MoHi: Nov 7, 1902-Oct 30, 1903; Nov 4, 1904-
        Sep 28, 1917; Aug 12, 1904; Mar 25, 1910.
        Became Kingston Mercury Oct 5, 1917. Under
        this name MoHi has Oct 5, 1917-Apr 1921.

Times   w   1885-1901?
    MoHi: Feb 11, 1886-1889; 1891-1899; Feb-Sep
        1901; Aug 8, 9, 10, 11, 1899; Oct 24, Aug 1,
        1890. D, for brief time?

KINGSVILLE (Johnson County)

Expositor   w   1894-1896
    In Rowell 1895, Ayer 1896-1897.

Herald   w   1897-1899?
    In Rowell 1897-1899, Ayer 1898-1899.

Kodak   w   1900
    Listed in Ayer 1901.

KINGSVILLE (continued)

Missouri Star w 1869?
Listed in Rowell 1869.

Star m 1866-1868?
MoHi: Sep 1866; Mar 15, 1868.

KIRKSVILLE (Adair County)

(NOTE: Pickler Memorial Library, Northeast
Missouri State Teachers College, has many Kirksville
papers but lacks personnel to prepare listing.)

Adair County Farmer w 1890-1894?
IaHi: Sep 19, 1891-Aug 6, 1892; Aug 20, 1892-
Mar 10, 1894. Farm Alliance publication.

Adair County Herald w 1868-1870?
Listed in Rowell 1869-1870.

Advocate w 1890-1899?
In Rowell 1899 as Farmer's Advocate, Ayer 1900
as Advocate.

Democrat w,d 1870-1914 w 1858-1860?
MoHi: W, Jly 26, 1901-1914; Jly 3, 1879; Sep 21,
Oct 9, 1882; Sep 27, Oct 11, 1883; Oct 23,
1890; Jly 9, 1897; Feb 10, 1905. D, film, Aug
30-Dec 31, 1915. Earlier Democrat for brief
time. See Enterprise.

Echo tw 1904-1905
Listed in Ayer, Rowell 1906.

Enterprise w 1856-1859
First in county, campaign sheet. Merged with
Democrat 1859.

Express d 1901-1922
MoHi: Film, Jun 11, 1906-1960. In Ayer 1924
listed under Express and News.
MoSHi: Aug 6, 1912; Sep 9, 28-30, Oct 1, 2, 4, 7-9,
12-15, 18, 20-22, 25, 30, Nov 1-6, 8-12, 15-20,
22-24, 29, 30, Dec 1-4, 6-11, 13-18, 20-24, 27-
31, 1920; Jan 1, 2-8, 11-15, 17-19, 1921.
KHi: Aug 1, 1913.

Express and News d 1901+
MoHi: Film, Jun 11, 1906+.

Farmer's Advocate w 1890-1899
See Advocate. Missouri Editor, Apr 1894, reported
Adair County Farmer sold, name changed to
Farmer's Advocate, Populist.

Graphic w 1880-1953
MoHi: 1903-1908; 1911-1944; Aug 29, 1884; Apr
17, 24, May 1, 8, 15, 1908. Film, May 1880-Mar
1897; Apr 1898-Mar 1899; Mar 30, 1900-1902;
1909-1910; 1945-Feb 12, 1953, date of suspension.

Herald w 1867-1870
Possibly Adair County Herald. Listed by Hammond.

KIRKSVILLE (continued)

Journal w 1865-1925 d 1926
MoHi: W, Aug 1, 1901-Sep 11, 1925; Nov 10, Dec
1, 1881; Oct 23, 1890. Merged with Brashear
News Sep 11, 1925, became Kirksville Journal-
News. D, Mar 1-Nov 26, 1926. Bought by
Daily Express Nov 25, 1926.
ICHi: w, Sep 14, 1876.

Journal-News w 1925-1926
MoHi: Sep 11, 1925-Jan 28, 1926. See Journal.

News d 1897, 1913-1922
MoHi: Film, Jan 6-Dec 30, 1915. Earlier News
listed as e, latter m.
KHi: Nov 25, 1922. Morning News Aug 2, 1913.

North Missouri Register w 1870-1879
MoHi: Dec 8, 1870-Nov 30, 1871; Mar 9, 1876;
May 23, 30, 1878; Jan 23, Mar 20, 1879; Jly
11, 1872. Formerly North Missouri Tribune.
Became Register Dec 8, 1870.
ICHi: Jly 6, 1876.

North Missouri Tribune w 1870
MoHi: Dec 1, 1870. Started Aug 25, 1870,
became North Missouri Register Dec 8, 1870.

Patriot w 1864-1865
MoHi: Dec 15, 1864. Equipment used by Journal.
MWA: Aug 17, 1865.

Pell-Mell Greenbacker w 1881
In Ayer 1881. Also dated at Edina.

Saturday Mail w 1899?
Listed in Ayer 1900.

Star-Republican w 1879?
R. B. Grossman attended meeting of Press Association
1879 as representative of Star-Republican. No
other mention.

Tattler w 1875
MoHi: Film, Jan 23-Jly 27, 1875.

Times tw 1906
Listed in Ayer 1907.

Theocrat 1904?
Listed by Walter Williams in 1904.

Vanguard w 1912-1913?
Listed in Ayer 1913-1914.

KIRKWOOD (St. Louis County)

Advertiser w 1946+
Kirkwood Public Library, 1955+. First in Ayer 1952.

American w 1895
Listed in Rowell 1895.

KIRKWOOD (continued)

Courier w 1902-1919
MoHi: 1903-1912. Film, 1915-1918. Changed to
St. Louis Countian Jan 20, 1919.

Leader w 1886-1894
MoHi: Jun 4, 1887. Known later as Surburban
Leader.

Mail w 1877-1878
MoHi: Jan 31, 1877-Feb 20, 1878.
MoSHi: Feb 14, 21, Oct 17, 24, 31, Nov 14, Dec 5,
1877; Feb 27, Mar 14, Apr 4, 1878.

Messenger w 1923-1959
Kirkwood Public Library, 1949-Sep 17, 1959.
MoHi: Film, Apr 7, 1955-1959. Suspended Sep
17, 1959.

Monitor w 1915-1947?
MoHi: 1919-Jly 14, 1944.
MoSHi: Jly 10, 1925; Aug 14, Oct 9-Nov 27,
Dec 11, 1936; Oct 20-Dec 29, 1939; Jan 5,
1940. See Tablet.

News w 1889-1890?
In Rowell 1890, Ayer 1889-1890.

Record w 1889-1890
In Rowell 1891.

Royal Priest sm 1889-1890?
MoHi: Oct 29, 1890. "Bible study."

Star-Republican w 1879
In Ayer 1880.

St. Louis Countian w 1902-1955
MoHi: Jan 24, 1919-1944. Film, 1945-Apr 1955,
when ended. Formerly Courier.
MoSHi: Mar 6, 1931.
Kirkwood Public Library: March 1950-?

St. Louis County Messenger w 1923-1925
See Messenger.

St. Louis County News w 1907-1914
MoSHi: May 3-31, Jun 14, 28, Jly 5-Sep 30,
1912; Aug 7, 15, Sep 25, Oct 2-Nov 1, 1914.

St. Louis County Republican w 1878-1879?
Apparently name used briefly for Star-Republican.
Rowell 1879. Star-Republican Rowell 1880.

Suburban Leader w 1886?-1898?
First in Rowell-Ayer 1896. See Leader.

Tablet w 1907-1912?
MoSHi: Jun 27-Dec 26, 1908; 1910-1912 inc.
MPN, Dec 1914, tells of death of John Jacaty,
of Monitor. Said he bought equipment of Tablet
1915, started Monitor.

KISSEE MILLS (Taney County)

Taney County Times w 1887-1890
In Ayer 1888-1889, Rowell 1888-1890.

KNOBNOSTER (Johnson County)

Electric Light w 1882-1885?

Gazette w 1870
MoHi: Jun 25, 1870.

Gem w 1870-1948
MoHi: May 31, 1878-May 19, 1882; May 23,
1884-Jly 11, 1890; 1920-1944. Film, 1914-
1919; 1945-Sep 17, 1948, when ended. Called
Will Carr's Gem May 23, 1884-Jun 27, 1890.

Item w 1950+
In Ayer 1959-1963.

Missouri Farmer w 1873
In Rowell 1874.

News w 1869-1870?
MoHi: Sep 18, Oct 9, 1869. Rowell 1870.

Register w 1871-1874
In Rowell 1872-1875.

Review w 1881-1882
In Rowell-Ayer 1882.

Taylor's Local w 1874-1876
In Rowell 1875-1876.

Will Carr's Gem w 1884-1890
See Gem.

KNOX CITY (Knox County)

Bee w 1893-1913
MoHi: 1904-1905.

Enterprise w 1914-1917
Apparently name used briefly for Bee.
Enterprise in Ayer 1915-1918.

Herald w 1860-1861
Mentioned in county history.

Independent w 1885
Moved to Edina 1886 as Knox County Independent.

Mirror w 1893
In Ayer 1894.

News w 1922+
In Ayer 1924 with 1922 founding date.

Rebel and Copperhead Ventilator w 1861?
Issued irregularly during Civil War.

KOSHKONONG (Oregon County)

Oregon County Leader   w   1902-1916
    MoHi: Jly 16,1908; Feb 4,11,25,Mar 4-Apr 1,
    22-Jun 3,17-Oct 21,1908. Film, Jly 10,1903-
    Sep 16,1904; 1912-Dec 17,1914. Became
    Oregon County Times-Leader 1916.

Oregon County Times-Leader   w   1902-1953
    MoHi: 1919-1944; Jly 17,1952. Film,1917-Oct
    18,1918; 1945-Nov 1953.

Times   w   1914-1916
    In Ayer 1915-1916. See Oregon County Leader.

KRAKOW (Franklin County)

Polish Eagle   w   1870-1873?
    Moved to Union before 1874.

LABADIE   (Franklin County)

Herald   w   1913?-1916
    Listed in Ayer 1917.

LA BELLE (Lewis County)

Journal   w   1878-?
    Hammond says survived 21 weeks, material taken
    to Monticello, used on Lewis County Journal.
    Name in Rowell 1880, but no data.

Star   w   1883+
    MoHi: Aug 16,1901-1944; Oct 3,1884. Film,
    Apr 14,1883-May 7,Oct 22,1886-Sep 27,
    1901; 1945+.
    KHi: May 5,1922.

LACLEDE   (Linn County)

Blade   w   1890-1945
    MoHi: Jly 12,1902-1944; Oct 25,1890; Sep 10,
    1904; Aug 22,1908. Film,1945.
    MoSHi: Jun 23,1916.

Centennial   w
    ICHi: Apr 6,1876.

Blade and Messenger   w   1946-?
    Merged with Meadville Messenger 1946.

Laconic   w   1883-1889?
    In Rowell 1884-1889,Ayer 1887.

Linn County News   w   1881
    Listed in Ayer-Rowell 1882.

Lynn County Centennial   w   1876-1877
    Spelling "Linn" in Rowell 1877. Last listing.
    See Centennial.

Progress   w   1880-1881
    Listed in Rowell-Ayer 1881.

LACLEDE   (continued)

Reporter   w   1877
    Listed in Rowell 1878.

Republican   w   1871?-1874?
    In Rowell 1872-1875,no founding date.

Review   w   1883?-1888?
    Listed in Ayer 1889.

LADDONIA (Audrain County)

Easter Tidings   1897
    MoHi: Apr 17,1897. Published by local church.

Enterprise   w   1882-1884
    MoHi: Mar 4,1884.

Herald   w   1884-1945
    MoHi: Nov 25,1898-1907; 1913-Aug 17,1945;
    Oct 30,1890; Jly 9,16,1903; Aug 10,1905.
    Merged with Vandalia Press Aug 23,1945,
    became Vandalia Press and Laddonia Herald.

Light   w   1891-1894?
    Single Tax publication, in Rowell 1893-1894,
    Ayer 1894.

LA GRANGE (Lewis County)

Bulletin   w   1853-1858
    Mentioned by Organ.

Democrat   w   1872-1891
    MoHi: Jly 4,1872-Jun 1882; Jun 14,1884-Dec
    16,1886; Feb 17,1888-Jly 1891; May 10,31,
    1878; Jan 17,1879; Aug 31,1882; Sep 27,
    1883; Jun 12,19,26, Jly 3,7,Aug 14-Oct 2.
    30,Nov 13,20,1884; Apr 2,May 21,Jun 8,
    1885; Nov 7,1890.
    ICHi: Sep 8,1876.

Free Press   w   1846-1851
    Became Missourian 1851, later Bulletin.

Herald Democrat   w   1889-1895
    In Rowell 1892-1896,Ayer 1891-1897.

Indicator   w   1893+
    MoHi: Nov 24,1898-1944. Film, 1945+.

Lewis County Herald   w   1889-1891
    In Ayer-Rowell 1890-1891.

Missourian   w   1851-1853
    See Bulletin, Free Press.

National American   w   1857-1872
    MoHi: Aug 29,1857-Oct 20,1860; Jan 5,Feb 2,
    Mar 9,Apr 20,27,May 25,1861; Jan 30-Mar
    5,Aug 11-Sep 22,Oct 13,1864; Mar 2,30,
    Apr 6-20,1865; Feb 20,Mar 5-May 7,21,28,
    Jun 4,18, Jly-Aug,Dec 1868; Jan 15, 22,Feb

LA GRANGE (continued)

National American (continued)
19,26,Mar–May 7,21,1869; Jan 7,21,Mar 25,
May 6,Jly 15,Sep 2,Oct 7,14,Nov 4,1870;
Jan 20,1871. Film,Aug 29,1857-Oct 20,1860.
MWA: Feb 8,1866.

North Missourian   w   1871-1872
In Rowell 1872.

Tribune   w   1900-1909?
In Rowell 1901-1908,Ayer 1903,1909-1910.

LAMAR (Barton County)

Banner of Truth   w   1869
MoHi: Nov 30,1869.

Barton County Advocate   w   1873-1886
MoSHi: Jly 1873. Press to Galena.
ICHi: Mar 11,1876.

Barton County Democrat   w   1870-1882?
Hammond says called Progress 1881, later Democrat.

Barton County Progress   w   1881-1883
MoHi: Sep 1,1882. Film,Sep 1882-May 12,1883.
Became Democrat May 17,1883.

Barton County Republican   w   1894,1951
In Rowell 1895,Ayer 1951-1952.

Democrat   w   1871   d   1900+
MoHi: w,Sep 1903-1904; 1908-1944; Jly 23,
1914. Film,May 17,1883-Sep 3,1903; 1905-
1907; 1945+. Formerly Barton County Progress.
Changed name May 17,1883. D,Jan 16,Jly 1,
25,1914.
KHi: Jan 20,1923. Nameplate for Mar 19,1885
is Vol V,No 1.

Flag of the Free   w   1867
Union List says copy Mar 15,1867 at Henry County
Historical Society, Newcastle, Ind.

Hummer   d   1895   w   1890
In Rowell 1896. W named Industrial Leader.

Independent   w   1873-1880
In Rowell 1874-1881,Ayer 1880.

Industrial Leader   w   1890-1909?
MoHi: Jly 26-Nov 8,1901. Listed at different
times as weekly under Hummer and Leader.

Industrial Union   w   1890-1895?
Ayer 1892 calls it Farm and Labor Union paper.

Journal   d   1950-1954
First listed in Ayer 1951.

LAMAR (continued)

Leader   w   1890-1951?   d   1895,1896-1910
MoHi: W,Oct 1902-Apr 1912; Jan-Feb 1913;
Jan-Jly 1914; Feb 9,Aug 10,1905; Jly 16,
1914.

Political Review   w   1893-1894
Reform paper, noted by Ashcraft.

Republican   w   1868-1950   d   1896   1932-1950
MoHi: W,Aug 8,1901-Sep 18,1902; 1903; Jun
17,1920-Sep 6,1934. Changed name to
Republican-Sentinel. Renamed Republican
Jun 17,1920. Missouri Editor, Mar 1896,tells
of start of daily, apparently short-lived. Name
of daily changed to Journal and weekly to
Barton County Republican in 1950. Nameplate
for May 18,1899 is Vol XVIII,No 39.

Republican-Sentinel   w   1867-1920
MoHi: Nov 28,1907-Jun 10,1920; Jly 23,1914.
MoSHi: Jun 26-Dec 25,1913; 1914; 1915-Feb
28,1918.

Rustler   d   1883-1884
Listed in Dauchy 1884. Slogan of "Positively the
Only Reliable Paper on Earth."

Sentinel   w   1899-1905
After 1905 under Republican-Sentinel.

Silver Hummer   d   1895-1896
Listed in Ayer 1896-1897.

South-West Missourian   w   1868-1874   w   1881-1898
MoHi: Jun 10,1869. Film,Feb 17,1870-Oct 15,
1874.
NHi: Dec 12,1872.

Star   w   1897
Mentioned in Country Editor,Aug 1897.

Universe   w   1857-1861
First in county. Starting date uncertain. Stopped
at start of Civil War,according to Organ.

LAMONTE (Pettis County)

Record   w   1880-1944
MoHi: Aug 9,1901-1928; Oct 30,1908; Feb 22,
1929. Film, Jan 4-Jly 26,1929. Sedalia Times
and LaMonte Record merged Mar 3,1944.

Star   w   1927-1929
Listed in Ayer 1929-1930.

LANCASTER (Schuyler County)

Democrat   w   1887-1905?   1859-1861
Earlier Democrat follows Herald, according to
Organ.

LANCASTER (continued)

Excelsior   w   1866+
     MoHi: Mar 15,1866-Apr 8,1882; May 2,1902-
          1944; Jly 30,1870; Nov 30,1878; Jan 18,
          Mar 15, Aug 23,30, Sep 6, 1879; Nov 26,1881;
          May 5, Oct 6,13,1883; Apr 24,1908; Mar 12,
          1909; Jan 10,1880; Mar 19,1897. Film,1945+.
          Herald consolidated with Excelsior 1899?
          Schuyler County Republican merged with paper
          1935.
     IaHi: May 23,1891-Jun 25,1892.
     ICHi: May 27,1876.

Excelsior-Republican   w   1866+
     Name used several years. See Excelsior.

Herald   w   1856-1859
     First in county. Renamed Democrat 1859. Ceased
     at beginning of Civil War.

Republican   w   1887-1896?
     MoHi: Oct 25,1890.

Schuyler County Avalanche
     Union List says name used briefly for Schuyler
     County Republican.

Schuyler County Herald   w   1895-1899?
     In Rowell 1897-1899, Ayer 1896-1899.

Schuyler County Republican   w   1899-1934
     MoHi: Apr 4,1902-1916; Oct 1922-Nov 1934;
          Jun 30, Dec 8,1905; Jan 19,1906. Suspended
          Nov 29,1934.

LA PLATA (Macon County)

Advocate   w   1874-1876
     In Rowell 1875-1876. Published in Macon.
     Missouri Grange office.

Globe   w   1871
     Listed in Rowell 1872.

Home Press   w   1876+
     MoHi: Feb 1913-1944; Jan 25, Feb 22, Mar 8, Aug
          30, Oct 11,1879; Nov 25,1881; Sep 1,1882;
          Sep 28,1883; Aug 8,15, Oct 11,1884. Film,
          May 1876-Sep 1892; Apr 1898-1907; 1909-
          1913; 1945+. Published as Moberly Signal
          May-Jly 1876.
     LaPlata Public Library: 1878+.

Record   w   1940
     Suspension noted in MPN Jan 1940.

Republican   w   1892-1925
     MoHi: 1913-Jly 9,1925; Dec 23,1904.

LAREDO (Grundy County)

Grindstone   w   1888
     Listed in Ayer 1888.

LAREDO (continued)

Herald   w   1904?
     Listed by Williams 1904.

Tribune   w   1900-1924
     MoHi: Film, Jan 13-Dec 29,1905.

LA RUSSELL (Jasper County)

Enterprise   1905?
     In Rowell 1906, no other data.

Spring River News   w   1916-1920
     MoHi: 1919-1920; Film, Mar 15,1917-1918.
          Moved to Miller, became News-Herald Jan 1,
          1920.

LATHAM (Moniteau County)

Leader   w   1900-1905
     In Ayer 1902, Rowell 1901-1905.

LATHROP (Clinton County)

Advertiser   w   1935
     Listed in MPN Dec 1935.

Golden Era   w   1883-1884?
     Brief career, apparently temperance paper. In
     Rowell-Dauchy 1884.

Herald   w   1896-1906
     MoHi: Jan 7-Nov 8,1906. Film, Jun 6,1901-
          1905. Merged with Monitor Nov 15,1906.

Jeffersonian   w   1885-1886?
     Listed in Rowell 1885-1886.

Monitor   w   1869-1906
     MoHi: Jan-Nov 8,1906; Jun 4,1886; Jly 9,
          1903; Jly 13,1905. Film,1903-1905. Merged
          with Herald Nov 15,1906.
     ICHi: Sep 8,1876.

Monitor-Herald   w   1906-1913
     MoHi: Nov 15,1906-Jly 1913. See Herald.

Optimist   w   1909+
     MoHi: 1919-1944; Jun 26,1952. Film, Feb 6,
          1913-Sep 9,1915; 1945+.

Rustler   w   1890
     Listed in Ayer 1891.

Times and Mirror   w   1869?-1882
     In Ayer 1883, founding date 1869.

Tribune   w   1895
     Listed in Missouri Editor, Sep 1895.

LAWSON (Ray County)

Courier w 1888-1892
In Rowell 1889-1892. Union List says name used for Review.

Gazette w 1881-1884
Followed in 1884 by New Era, in 1887 by Lawsonian, according to Hammond.

Journal w 1899-1900
In Ayer 1900, Rowell 1900-1901.

Lawsonian w 1887-1889.
See Gazette.

Leader w 1888-1899?
Under Review as name used several years.

New Era w 1884-1887
See Gazette.

Ray County Review w 1888+
MoHi: Nov 13, 1902-May 4, 1916; Aug 20, 1908. Name changed to Review May 11, 1916.

Review w 1888+
MoHi: 1916-1944; film, 1945+. Conflict over founding date, some listings to 1880.

LEADWOOD (St. Francois County)

Lead Belt Banner w 1906-1911?
Last listed in Ayer 1912.

News w 1940
Listed in MPN, Oct 1940.

Press w 1932?-1936?
Micro-Photo: Film, 1930-1936. See Flat River St. Francois County Journal.

LEBANON (Laclede County)

Anti-Monopolist w 1873-1881
ICHi: Aug 4, 1876. Greenback paper, in Rowell 1875-1881, Ayer 1880.

Champion w 1883-1884
Renamed Graphic, brief career.

Chronicle w 1868-1874
In Rowell 1869-1875.

Clipper w 1869
In Rowell 1870.

Graphic w 1883-1889
See Champion. Last in Rowell 1889.

Herald w 1952?
Death of co-publisher, Paul Page, Sr., noted in MHR, Apr 1952.

LEBANON (continued)

Index w 1882
In Rowell 1883.

Journal w 1873?-1882
ICHi: Jan 21, 1876. Conflicting dates, 1873, 1874, 1875. Last in Ayer 1882.

Laclede County Leader w 1870-1872, 1878-1879
Apparently two within decade.

Laclede County Republican w 1889-1935
MoHi: 1919-Feb 15, 1935; Nov 14, 1890. Film, Aug 11, 1911-1918. Republican to Aug 11, 1911. Became Rustic-Republican Feb 22, 1935.

Laclede County Sentinel w 1873-1907
MoHi: Dec 2, 1898-1907.

Laclede Journal w 1861
In American Newspaper Directory 1861.

News d 1936-1945?
Ayer 1947 lists as Record and News.

Record d 1945+
MoHi: Feb 9, 1948-1950. Film, 1951+. W referred to as Laclede County Record. MoHi May 1937-1944. Film, 1945-Aug 9, 1946. Rustic-Republican and Record merged Aug 9, 1946 as Rustic-Republican.

Republican w 1897-1911, 1889-1894?
MoHi: Dec 4, 1908. Film, Aug 9, 1901-Aug 4, 1911. Became Laclede County Republican Aug 11, 1911. Earlier Republican in Rowell 1894; similar data under Review Rowell 1895.

Review w 1882, 1889
Rowell 1895 says founded 1889; Dauchy 1896 says 1882.

Rustic w, sw 1873-1935
MoHi: 1913-Feb 17, 1935; Sep 20, 1894; Aug 10, 1905; Jan 25, Feb 1, 1906; Apr 23, 1908. Film, Jly 2, 1903-1912; Jan 1, 1891; Nov 22, Dec 27, 1900; Feb 7, 1901. See merger above.

Rustic-Leader w 1873-1883? d 1879
See Rustic, Rustic-Republican.

Rustic-Republican w 1873+
MoHi: Feb 22, 1935-1944. Film, 1945-+. Consolidation of Rustic, Laclede County Republican, and Times Feb 22, 1935.

Shield and Advocate w 1877, 1882
Apparently 1877 paper was temperance publication. G. J. Bradfield of Advocate member of MPA 1882.

Times w 1934-1935
See Rustic-Republican.

LECOMA (Dent County)

Messenger   w   1883
    Listed in Rowell 1884.

LEE'S SUMMIT (Jackson County)

Democrat   sw   1932-1937
    MoHi: Mar 3, 1933-Jan 5, 1937, when it suspended,
    sold to Journal.

Journal   w   1881+
    MoHi: Nov 25, 1898-1944. Film, 1945+.
    MoKc: Jan 1907-Dec 1932. Conflict over starting.
    Sources list 1882, 1883.

Ledger   w   1873-1874
    Listed in Rowell 1873-1875.

Register   w   1907-1909?
    In Rowell 1908, Ayer 1908-1910.

LEETON (Johnson County)

Independent   w   1896-1898
    In Ayer-Rowell 1897-1898. Rowell 1899.

Times   w   1896-1943
    MoHi: Film, Oct 19, 1922-Aug 12, 1943.

LEHIGH (Jasper County)

Miner   w   1884
    Listed in Dauchy 1884.

LEONARD (Shelly County)

News   w   1913-1915
    Listed in Ayer 1915-1916.

LEWISTOWN (Lewis County)

Courier   w   1905
    Listed in Rowell-Ayer 1906.

Journal   w   1895-1897
    In Rowell-Ayer 1896-1898.

Leader   w   1895-1905
    Last listing in Rowell 1906.

Lewis County Journal   w   ?
    In Ayer 1928 under Lewistown as w established
    1877. Ayer 1929 refers to Monticello.

News   w   1928-1954
    Consolidated with Monticello Lewis County Journal
    1954.

Record   w   1914-1931
    Consolidated with Maywood Journal.

Times   w   1905-1915
    In Rowell 1906-1908, Ayer 1907-1916.

LEXINGTON (Lafayette County)

Advertiser   w   1845   d   1899-?   w   1888+
    MoHi: d, Jly 1931-Jun 1932. First Advertiser had
    brief career. 1845. Ayer 1923 first to list
    Advertiser as daily, founded 1899. Ayer 1926
    listed weekly founded 1924. Ayer 1932 has
    founding date for weekly as 1888. See
    Advertiser-News.

Advertiser-News   w,d   1888+
    MoHi: d, Oct 3-Dec 31, 1932; Sep 16, 1936-1950;
    Apr 1, 1952. Film, 1951+. Advertiser and News,
    dailies, consolidated in 1931. For some time
    published w edition called Intelligencer.

American Citizen   w   1855-1857
    MoHi: Film, Sep 4, 1855-Jan 21, 1857. American
    Party paper, short-lived.

Appeal   w   1846-1850
    MoSHi: Apr 7, 14, 1847; Feb 15, May 9, 16, 23,
    1848.

Caucasian   w   1840-1875
    MoHi: 1874-Aug 1875; Nov 1, 1873; Jan 11, 1868.
    Film, 1866-Mar 1869; 1870-1873. Published
    under various titles.
    MWA: Oct 24, Dec 12, 1840; Jan 16, Feb 6, Mar 6,
    20-Apr 3, 1841; Nov 30, 1853.
    NcU: Jun 22, 1872.

Central Union   w   1862-1866
    Equipment formerly used for Express. Paper renamed
    Express 1866.

Citizens Daily Advertiser   w   1860
    Mentioned by Hammond.

Constitution   w   1850
    Mentioned by Organ.

Democratic Journal   w   1848-1850
    Renamed Western Chroncile 1850, ended 1855.

Dispatch   w   1873
    Mentioned in county history.

Express   w   1840-1861, 1866
    MoHi: Jly 6, 13, 20, 27, Oct 26, 1853; Oct 14, 21,
    Nov 4, 18, Dec 2, 23, 30, 1865; Jun 9, Jly 7, 14,
    Aug 4, Sep 1, 22, 1866. Film, Jly 30, 1844-Jun
    9, 1846; Aug 18, 1852-Jan 24, 1855; Aug 27,
    1859-Sep 15, 1860.
    Lexington Public Library: Feb 2, 1842-Jun 4,
    1844; Jly 1844-May 23, 1845; Jun 10, 1845-
    Jun 2, 1846; Aug 1852-Jan 1855; Sep 4,
    1855-Jan 21, 1857; Aug 27, 1859-Sep 19,
    1860; Jan 1866-Nov 24, 1866. Also Jan-Nov
    24, 1866 of Caucasian and Express. Pioneer
    paper of county. See Central Union. In 1866
    renamed Caucasian.

First Kansas   w   1862
    KHi: Jan 18, 1862.

Harry of the West   w   1844
    MoHi: Aug 2, 1844. Published by Express.
    MWA: May 3, 17-Jun 21, Jly 19-Aug 9, 23-30,
        Sep 27, Oct 18, 1844. Campaign paper.

Herald   w   1889-1894, 1896
    MoHi: Feb 21, 1894. Brief revival of Herald 1896.

Intelligencer   w   1871-1950   d   1898-1943?
    MoHi: d, Apr 10, 1909. w, Sep 1875-1876; 1879-
        1944; Sep 23, 1882; Jun 5, 1897; Oct 25, 1890;
        Jly 27, 1895; Jun 1, 1901; Sep 9, 30, 1905.
        Film, Jan 10, 1872-1873; 1877-1878; 1945-1950.
    KHi: w, Apr 18, 1919; Dec 19, 1924; Mar 22, 1928.
    ICHi: Aug 19, 1876.

Jefferson Republican   w   1894
    Cited in Missouri Editor April 1894.

Journal   w   1856, 1864
    In Newspaper Record 1856. Another Journal started
    Jun 9, 1864, office raided by Price before end of
    year. Material used to issue Lafayette Advertiser
    1865.

Lafayette Advertiser   w   1865-1867
    Renamed Missouri Valley Register 1867?, Register
    1881.

Lafayette County Pionier   w   1860
    Mentioned by Organ. Also known as Lafayette
    Pioneer. German paper.

Lafayette County Post   w   1883-1889?
    Listed in Ayer 1888-1889.

Lafayette County Republican   w   1896
    Listed in Ayer 1897.

Lafayette County Sentinel   w   1873-1881
    MoHi: Film, Aug 16, 1878-Mar 4, 1881. Formerly
        in Waverly. Moved to Lexington Aug 16, 1878.

Lexingtonian   w   1909-1915
    MoHi: 1910-1914; Jan 7-Feb 4-May 27, 1915.

Miner's Journal   w   1895
    Published few months in 1895 by a strike leader.

Missouri Cumberland Presbyterian   w   1850
    Listed as newspaper by Organ, short-lived.

Missouri Expositor   w   1856-1861
    Equipment taken to Kansas by First Kansas
    Volunteers 1861.

Missouri Valley Register   w   1866-1869
    MoHi: 1866-Jun 24, 1869. Film, Jan-Apr 19, 1866.
        Became Register Jly 1, 1869.

Missouri Thalbote   w   1871-1880
    ICHi: Sep 2, 1876. German paper, in Rowell
        1875-1880, Ayer 1880.

News   w   1889-1932
    MoHi: 1918-1921; Feb 1924-1929; Apr 7, Dec 29,
        1892; Sep 21, 1893; May 14, 1896; Mar 25,
        1897; Apr 11, Oct 24, 1895; Jan 25, 1900.
        Film, Apr 11, 1889-1907; Jan 5, 1922-Jan 2,
        1924; Jan 2, 1930-Dec 1932. Merged with
        Advertiser as Advertiser-News Oct 3, 1932.
        In Ayer through 1945, weekly.

Post   w   1883-1888
    MoHi: Film, Nov 25, 1887-Nov 16, 1888. In
        Rowell 1888-1889.

Register   w   1869-1890?
    MoHi: Jly 1, 1869-Apr 28, 1870; Jan 7, 1875-
        Sep 9, 1879; May 4, 1876-Nov 14, 1878; May
        9, 1878-Apr 22, 1880; Jan 3, 1888-Mar 20,
        1890; Jly 1, 1869; Oct 10, 1889. Film, May
        12, Dec 8, 1870-Dec 27, 1876; Jan 22, 1885-
        Dec 30, 1886. Formerly Missouri Valley
        Register, name changed Jly 1, 1869.
    ICHi: Jly 20, 1876.

Reporter   w   1852
    Short-lived anti-Benton paper.

Saturday Herald   w   1880?-1894?
    Start given as 1877, 1880, 1889 in Ayer-Rowell.

Telegraph   w   1845-1846
    Later renamed Appeal, ended 1850.

Times   w   1863
    MoHi: Sep 5, 1863.

Union   w   1861-1865
    MoHi: Film, Jan 3, 1862-Jly 8, 1865 inc.   t in
        starting date. DLC has copy Vol 2, No 5 dated
        Aug 22, 1863.

Western Chronicle   w   1850-1855
    Formerly the Journal. Suspended 1855.

LIBERAL (Barton County)

American Idea   w   1887
    Free Thought paper, Rowell-Ayer 1888.

Barton County Enquirer   w   1887
    Listed in Ayer-Rowell 1887.

Commercial   w   1891
    Listed in Ayer 1892.

Ensign   w   1887
    Listed in Ayer 1887.

LIBERAL (continued)

Enterprise   w   1892-1913
    MoHi: Jly 26, 1901-1906; 1909-Jly 1913. Film,
    1907-1908.

Head-Light   w   1883
    Listed in Dauchy 1884.

Independent   w   1891-1905
    MoHi: Film, Sep 16, 1904-Aug 18, 1905.

Liberal   w,m   1879-1885?
    MoSHi: Jun 6, 1883; Jan 8, 1885. Listed as
    infidel publication.

Messenger   w   1888
    Listed in Ayer-Rowell 1889.

News   w   1910+
    MoHi: Feb 25, 1910-1944. Film, 1945+.

West Barton Globe   w   1890
    Listed in Ayer 1890.

LIBERTY (Clay County)

Advance   w   1875-1959
    MoHi: Nov 22, 1901-1918; 1926-1944; May 12,
    1882; Oct 31, 1890; Oct 23, 1908. Film,
    Feb 4, 1875-Feb 1877; Jan 1884-Dec 1897;
    Jan 1899-Dec 1901; 1919; 1924-1925; 1945-
    1959.
    MoSHi: May 20, 1875-Dec 13, 1877; Feb 8, 1878-
    Nov 12, 1880; Jan 9-Mar 27, Apr 17-May 8,
    May 22, 29, Jun 19, 26, Jly 3-Sep 5, 1885;
    Jly 2, Aug 13, Sep 24, Nov 12, 1886; Dec 31,
    1909; Jan 28, Apr 15, 1910; Feb 4, 1916.
    William Jewell College Library: 1939-1946; 1954+
    Also copies in Frank Hughes Memorial Library,
    but not catalogued. Combined with Tribune
    Dec 28, 1959.
    ICHi: Jun 15, 1876.

Banner   w   1843-1844, 1875?
    MoHi: Mar 3, 22, 1844.
    William Jewell Library: Mar 3, 1844.
    MoSHi: Feb 9, 1844. Ayer 1889 lists Banner,
    founded 1875.
    WHi: Film, Mar 3, 1844. Vol 1, No 44.
    KHi: Film, Mar 3, 1844.

Chronicle   w   1933-1943
    MoHi: Apr 27, 1933-Sep 2, 1943.
    MoSHi: Aug 18, 25, Sep 1, 1938; Sep 14-Dec 14,
    28, 1939; Jan 4, 11, 25, Feb 1, Mar 7, Jun 20,
    Jly 4, Aug 1-Dec 26, 1940; Jan 2, 16, 30-
    Mar 6, 27, Apr 3-Oct 30, Nov 20-Dec 25, 1941.
    William Jewell Library: 1938-1940; 1943.

Clay County Democrat   w   1870-1871, 1895-1905?
    MoHi: Jly 25, 1901-1903; Jly 23, 1903.
    MoSHi: Jly 13, 1870-Sep 27, 1871.

LIBERTY (continued)

Clay County Flag   w   1860-1861
    MoSHi: Jly 18, 1860-May 8, 1861; Mar 13, 1861.

Clay County Progress   w   1888-1894
    MoHi: Oct 22, 1890.

Democratic Aclalde   w   1911
    Listed in Ayer 1912.

Democratic Platform   w   1853-1855?
    KHi: Mar 23-Oct 5, 1854 as Democrat Platform.
    In Newspaper Record 1856.

Far West   w   1836-1839?
    MoHi: Aug 11, 18, 25, Sep 8, 15, 22, 29, Oct 6, 1836.
    William Jewell Library: Same issues, loaned to
    MoHi for photostats. Paper sold 1839, no record
    beyond that.
    WHi: Film, Aug 11-Oct 6, 1836.
    KHi: Film, Aug 11-Oct 6, 1836.

Herald   w   1841-1842, 1895-1899
    First mentioned by Organ, second in Ayer 1898-
    1900.

Missouri Enquirer   w   1835?
    MoHi: Jun 16, 1835.

News   w   1910
    Listed in Ayer 1911.

Progress   w   1888-1899
    Ayer 1890 lists Clay County Progress.

Searchlight   w   1894-1896
    People's Party paper. In Rowell 1895, Ayer 1896.

Spotlight   w   1957
    Mentioned in MPN, Oct 1957.

Tribune   w, tw   1846+   d
    MoHi: Apr 1846-Apr 1853; 1903-1910; 1913-
    1919; 1921-1944; Nov 18, 1887; Oct 30,
    1908; Jan 29, 1909; Apr 4, 1846; Jun 9,
    1854; May 7, 1869; Oct 30, 1887; May 1,
    1896; Film, Apr 1853-Apr 1886; May 1887-
    May 1891; May 1893-Apr 1903; 1911-1912;
    1920; 1945+.
    William Jewell Library: 1939; 1944; 1951-1952;
    1955-1956; 1846-1886; 1908-1913. Film,
    Apr 1853-Apr 1886; May 1887-Apr 1903; Jan
    1911-Dec 1912; Jan 1920-Dec 1920.
    MoSHi: Apr 4, 1946; Jun 1, 8, 1860; Nov ?, 1871;
    Feb 20, 1880; Aug 11, 1882; Sep 28, Oct 5,
    Nov 16, 23, 30, 1884; Jun 26, Jly 3, Aug 7, 21,
    1885; Jan 8, Feb 5, 12, Jly 23, Dec 10, 1886;
    Jun 17, 24, Jly 22, Aug 26, Oct 14, Dec 9, 23,
    30, 1892; Nov 10, 17, Dec 15, 1893; May 24,
    1895; May 1, 1896; Aug 6, 13, 28, 1897; Feb
    24, Apr 14, May 5, 1899; Jun 30, 1905; Jan
    22, 29, 1909; Apr 15, 1910; Dec 10, 24, 1915;
    Feb 4, 1916; Nov 14, 1919. W, May 23, 1846-

LIBERTY (continued)

Tribune (continued)
Nov 23,1849; Apr 12-Sep 6,Nov 15,1850;
Dec 24,1852; Jan 14,1853-Dec 21,1855; 1856-
Dec 16,1859; Jan 6,Dec 26,1862; Jan 9,1863-
Dec 22,1865; 1860-Dec 25,1868; Jan 8,1869-
Oct 27,1871; Jan 10,1868-Dec 23,1870; 1872-
1874; Jan 8,1875-Dec 21,1877; Jan 4,1878-
Dec 25,1880; 1881-Mar 9,1883; Jan 11,1884-
Apr 23,1886.
MWA: Nov 18,1853.
AzTP: Film,Apr 4,1846-Mar 3,1849; Apr 6,1849-
Apr 9,1852.
KHi: Film,Apr 4,1846-May 21,1875.
WHi: Film,Apr 16,1852-Apr 8,1853.
Micro-Photo: Film,1846-1849.

Union w 1867-1869
MoSHi: May 10,1867-May 6,1869.

Upper Missouri Enquirer w 1834-1840
MoSHi: Jan 25,1834 inc.
DLC: Jan 11,25,1834.

Western Journal w 1838-1844
MoSHi: Jly 22,1842. Called Star 1838,Western
Journal 1841 says Organ.

Western Pioneer w 1844
MoSHi: Nov 1,1844.
DLC: Jun 21,1844,Vol 1,No 1.

Western Star w 1838-1841
MoHi: Jun 7,1839. See Western Journal.
MoSHi: Feb 5,May 28,1841.
DLC: Jun 15,1838; Apr 9,1841.

LIBERTYVILLE (St. Francois County)

New Era w 1871
In Rowell 1872. To Farmington, later to Marble
Hill.

LICKING (Texas County)

Ledger w 1878-1879
In Pettengill 1878.

News w 1893+
MoHi: Film,1958+.

LILBOURN (New Madrid County)

Banner w 1929-1937
MoHi: Oct 27,1927-1928; 1930-Sep 2,1937
when it became Semo News.

Herald w 1912-1927?
MoHi: Apr 10,1925-1926; Feb 28,1919. Film,
1914-Oct 25,1918.

Ledger w 1910-1911
In Ayer 1911-1912.

LILBOURN (continued)

Risco Reporter w 1943-1948
In Ayer 1945-1949.

Semo News w 1927+
MoHi: Sep 1937-1944. Film, 1945+. See Banner.

Southeast Missouri News w 1927-1956
Under Semo News Ayer 1956.

LIMA (Carroll County)

Herald w 1884-1905?
In Rowell 1904-1905.

LINCOLN (Benton County)

Advance w 1885

Central Missouri Reflector w 1895-1896
Populist paper. In Ayer 1896.

Chronicle w 1907?-1919
In Ayer 1915-1920.

Home News w 1892-1897
In Rowell 1897-1898,Ayer 1898.

Independent w 1906-1913?
In Ayer 1909-1914.

New Era w 1962+
First new paper there in 40 years.

Plain Dealer w 1891-1900
In Rowell-Ayer 1899 with 1891 founding.

Rail-Splitter w 1891-1897?

Republican w 1893-1906
MoHi: Mar 31,Jun 2,Jly 7,Sep 1,8,1905; Jan
29,1906. Film,Aug 19,1903-1906.

Times w 1892-1896
In Rowell 1893-1896,Ayer 1892-1896.

LINDLEY (Grundy County)

Christian Pioneer w 1854-1864
Formerly Western Pioneer, later in Chillicothe.

LINN (Osage County)

Liberalist w 1879-1889
Listed in Ayer 1888-1890.

Osage County Advocate w 1866-1875
Hammond says named Osage County News in 1875,
Unterrified Democrat 1883.

Osage County News w 1875-1881
See Osage County Advocate.

LINN (continued)

Osage County Observer   w   1954+
    Mentioned in MPN, Sep 1962.

Osage County Republican   w   1882+
    MoHi: 1903-May 1921; 1925-Sep 1, 1927. Film,
    Jly 24, 1901-1902.

Queen State   w   1895
    Noted in Missouri Editor, May, 1895.

Unterrified Democrat   w   1866+
    MoHi: Apr 19, 1906-1944. Film, 1945+.
    KHi: Dec 8, 1927.

LINN CREEK (Camden County)

Camden County News   w   1902-1904
    MoHi: Dec 18, 1902-Dec 1903.

Camden County Rustic   w   1874, 1901-1903?
    MoHi: Dec 31, 1902-Dec 20, 1903. In Rowell 1875.

Camden County Sentinel   w   1889-1890
    See Osage Valley Sentinel.

Democrat   w   1895-1899
    Listed in Ayer 1900.

Enterprise   w   1876-1878
    Pettengill 1878 calls it Enterprise and Farmer.

Journal   w   1899
    Formerly Stoutland Journal. Moved 1899 to Linn
    Creek.

Messenger   w   1888
    Listed in Rowell-Ayer 1889.

Osage Valley Sentinel   w   1894?
    Conflicting data. Missouri Editor, Mar 1894 says
    Osage Valley Sentinel "has been established at
    Linn Creek." Another source says paper called
    Camden County Sentinel 1889-1892.

People's Tribune   w   1888-
    In Ayer 1888, Rowell 1889.

Reveille   w   1879-1931
    MoHi: 1911-1931; Jan-Apr 17, 1931; May 22,
    1890; Mar 9, 16, 30, Apr 6, May 4, 11, Oct 12,
    Dec 14, 1899; Jun 5, 12, Dec 20, 24, 1902;
    Jly 14, 1905. Film, Sep 1881-Mar 1883; 1892-
    1894; 1896-1910.
    MoSHi: Mar 6, 13, 1890; Feb 11, 25, Mar 3, Apr
    14, 21, 28, Jun 9, 1916. Moved to Camdenton
    as Reveille Apr 1931.
    IaHi: Nov 20, 1902-Oct 3, 1903.

Sentinel   w   1889-1892
    MoHi: Film, Jly 16, 1891-1892.

LINN CREEK (continued)

Stet   w   1873-1875
    Listed in Rowell 1873-1875.

Village Echo   w   1876-1877?
    Mentioned by Hammond.

LINNEUS (Linn County)

Bulletin   w   1871-1951
    MoHi: 1899-1944; Jly 15, 1903; Apr 16, Dec
    10, 1908; Apr 1, May 20, Nov 18, 1896. Film,
    May 30, 1873-May 15, 1879; May 19, 1881-
    1899; 1945-1950. Continued as part of the
    Brookfield Daily News 1951.
    ICHi: Sep 1, 1876.

Democratic Bulletin   w   1859-1861
    Suspended during Civil War, revived as Bulletin,
    according to Organ.

Linn County Centennial   w
    ICHi: Jly 6, 1876. No other data.

Linn County News   w   1881-1946
    MoHi: Jly 25, 1901-1937; Dec 22, 1904. Film,
    Sep 14, 1882-Jun 18, 1885; Jly 17, 1890-
    Jun 8, 1899; Jun 27, 1901-Jun 4, 1903. Moved
    to Brookfield 1946.

Missourian   w   1865-1871
    MoHi: Jun 12, 1869.
    MWA: Dec 27, 1865.

Rambler   w   1954-1956
    MoHi: Film, Jly 8, 1954-Aug 23, 1956. Moved to
    Trenton Aug 30, 1956.

LITHIUM (Perry County)

Enterprise   w   1893
    Listed in Ayer 1894.

LITTLE ROCK (Saline County)

Excelsior Times   w   1888-?
    In Rowell 1893 with 1888 founding date.

LIVONIA (Putnam County)

Beacon   w   1910
    Listed in Ayer 1911.

LOCK SPRINGS (Daviess County)

Herald   w   1896-1917
    In Rowell 1900-1908, Ayer 1898-1918.

News   w   1896
    Noted by Missouri Editor, June 1896.

LOCKWOOD (Dade County)

  Dade County Reflex   w   1939-1940?
    MoHi: Apr 20,1939-Sep 12,1940.

  Globe   w   1882-1884
    Later named Leader, Times, Luminary.

  Independent   w   1882-1892
    In Ayer 1890 with 1882 founding date.

  Leader   w   1883-1888?
    MoHi: Jly 2,1886. In Rowell 1885-1888, Ayer
    1887-1888.

  Luminary   w   1882+
    MoHi: Jly 26,1901-1903; 1908-1910; 1913-
    1919; 1925-1944; Sep 22,1905. Film,
    1904-1907; 1911-Aug 9,1912; 1945+.

  Missourian   w   1901-1915
    MoHi: Nov 1911-Jun 1915; Dec 29,1904. Film,
    May 5,1904-Jun 27,1907.

  Sentinel   w   1894-1898
    Last listed in Rowell 1899.

  Times   w   1882-1907?
    Irregular career. Missouri Editor, Oct 1894, says
    Times had been revived. Not in Rowell 1891 but
    former E&P listed under Independent.

LOCUST MOUND (Miller County)

  Spring Garden Herald   w   1882
    Listed in Ayer-Rowell 1882.

LONE OAK (Bates County)

  Emancipator   w   1890-1892
    Reform paper, short-lived, notes Ashcraft.

LOUISIANA (Pike County)

  American Union   w   1854-1859
    Later named Times, Journal. Some sources use
    1855 as founding date.

  Democratic Banner   w   1833-1852
    MoHi: Film, Apr 18,1846-Jly 9,1851.
    IHi: Film, May 28,1849.

  Democratic Herald   w   1857-1859?
    MoHi: May 21,1857; Oct 6,1859.
    MoSHi: Aug 4,1859.
    MWA: Oct 15, Nov 5,1857.

  Call   d   1887
    Listed in Ayer 1887.

  Gazette   w   1869-1872
    Listed in Rowell 1870-1872.

LOUISIANA (continued)

  Herald   w   1896-1903
    MoHi: Nov 26,1898-1903.

  Journal   w   1854-1893, w,d   1923?
    MoHi: Jan 30,1862; Jun 19,1869. Film, May 19,
    1859-Oct 14,1881; Nov 2,1882-Oct 2,1890.
    Suspended May 27,1893. Ayer 1923-1924 listed
    both evening, weekly.
    NcD: Nov 8,1873.

  Missouri Press   w   1872-1902
    MoHi: May 25,1899-Mar 13,1902. Became Press-
    Journal Mar 20,1902.

  North-East Missourian   w   1853-1856?
    MoHi: Feb 28, Mar 20,27, May 29, Jun 19, Jly 3,
    10,24,1856.
    MoSHi: Jly 1,8,1853.

  Pike County Chronicle   w   1936-1945
    Moved from Frankford 1936. Ended Jun 1945.

  Pike County News   w   1890-1917
    MoHi: Aug 1,1901-Aug 30,1917; Jun 22, Aug 24,
    1905; Feb 5,1914. Film, Oct 4,1890-1898.
    MoSHi: Dec 3,1914.
    WHi: Jan 9-Jun 25,1892.

  Pike County Post   w   1871-?
    Consolidated with Franklin Observer as Post-
    Observer, according to MHR Oct 1920.

  Pike County Record   w   1850-1854?
    Mentioned by Organ.

  Pike County Republican   w   1888-1889?
    In Ayer 1888-1890, Rowell 1889-1890.

  Press   d   1895,1898-1909?   w   1872-1900?
    Confused data. Missouri Editor Sep 1895 tells of
    Press as a new daily; Country Editor May 1898
    also tells of Daily Press as "a bright new candidate
    for public favor." Ayer 1900 lists daily, weekly.

  Press-Journal   w   1855?+
    MoHi: Mar 20,1902-1944; Mar 18,1909; Feb 6,
    1914. Film,1945+. Became Press-Journal Mar
    20,1902. Formerly Missouri Press. 1855 date
    traced to American Union, although other
    sources place 1854 for founding.

  Radical   w   1839?
    Mentioned in county history as continuation of Salt
    River Journal. Also associated with Democratic
    Banner.

  Record   w   1849-1852?
    MoHi: Apr 6,1849; May 3,1850; Sep 29,1851.

  Republican   w   1867-1869, 1882-1887?
    First in Rowell 1869. Latter Ayer-Rowell 1883.
    Some sources associate this with Pike County
    Republican.

LOUISIANA (continued)

Riverside Press   w   1872-1885
    MoHi: Film, Apr 16, 1874-Mar 7, 1878; Mar 20,
    1879-Apr 9, 1885.
    ICHi: Jly 13, Sep 21, 1876.

Salt River Journal   w   1839?
    County history lists paper. See Radical.

Times   w, tw   1898-1927
    MoHi: Jly 26, 1901-Mar 9, 1906. Changed name
    to Twice-A-Week Times, Mar 30, 1906; Mar
    30-Oct 9, 1906; Feb 10, 1914-Oct 28, 1927.
    Sold to Press-Journal Oct 28, 1927.

True Democrat   w   1860?
    MoHi: Dec 11, 1860.

True Flag   w   1864-1866
    Mentioned by Organ. 1864 files noted in MHR,
    Oct 1920.

Union   w   1863-?
    PHi: May 14, 1863, Vol 1, No 1.

LOWNDES (Wayne County)

Leader   w   1906
    Listed in Ayer-Rowell 1907.

LOWRY CITY (St. Clair County)

Herald   w   1899-1901
    In Rowell 1901, Ayer 1901-1902.

Independent   w   1888-1940
    MoHi: Jly 26, 1901-1905; 1908; 1910-Sep 12,
    1940; Jly 10, 1908. Film, 1906-1907. Ceased
    Sep 12, 1940.

Leader   w   1882-1884?
    In Rowell 1885, with 1882 founding date.

News   w   1941
    In MPN, Oct 1941. Formerly mimeographed.

People Voice   w   1899-1900
    In Rowell 1900-1901, Ayer 1900.

Progress   w   1896-1897
    Listed by Rowell-Ayer 1897-1898.

Times   w   1885-1897
    Free Silver, Silver Democrat paper.

LUCERNE (Putnam County)

Bee   w   1887
    Listed in Ayer 1888.

News   w   1923-1924?
    Listed in Ayer 1925.

LUCERNE (continued)

Standard   w   1888-1917
    MoHi: Oct 24, 1890. In Ayer 1890-1918,
    Rowell 1891-1908.

LUDLOW (Livingston County)

Chronicle   w   1936-1941
    Noted in MPN, Apr 1936. Sold 1941 to Chillicothe
    Constitution-Tribune.

Graphic   w   1895-1897?
    In Ayer-Rowell 1896-1898.

Herald   w   1903-1905, 1908, 1910-1935
    MoHi: Jan 6, Apr 14, 1905. Several attempts at
    publishing, according to Ayer.

Journal   w   1898-1901
    Last listed in Ayer 1902.

Leader   w   1902
    Listed in Ayer 1903.

Meteor   w   1906-1911?
    Listed in Ayer 1908-1912.

Mirror   w   1892-1894?
    In Ayer 1892-1894, Rowell 1893-1894.

LUPUS (Moniteau County)

Riverside Gazette   w   1908
    Listed in Ayer 1909.

LURAY (Clark County)

News   w   1889
    Listed in Rowell 1890.

Register   w   1896-1897
    Listed in Ayer 1897-1898.

LUTESVILLE (Bollinger County)

Banner   w   1891-1922
    MoHi: Jly 2, 1903-1904; Jan-May 3, 1923; Aug
    10, 17, 24, Oct 19, Nov 23, Dec 7, 14, 28, 1916;
    Jan 25, Feb 8, Mar 22, 29, Apr 5, 12, May 17,
    24, 31, Jun 7, 21, Jly 12, 19, Aug 2, 30, Sep 27,
    Dec 6, 20, 27, 1917. Film, 1917-Dec 18, 1919.

Herald   w   1872-1875
    Listed in Rowell 1875.

Missouri Herald   w   1872-1874
    NHi: Oct 17, 1872. Under Herald as name used
    for these years.

Times   w   1883
    Listed in Ayer 1883.

Vidette   w   1884
    Listed in Dauchy 1884, Rowell 1885.

McFALL (Gentry County)

Bulletin   w   1882-1883
    In Ayer 1883, Rowell 1883-1884.

Magnet   w   1892-1893
    In Rowell 1893-1894, Ayer 1894-1895.

Mirror   w   1890-1907
    MoHi: Oct 31, 1890. Film, 1903.

New Mirror   w   1912-1920
    Listed in Ayer 1915-1921.

Village News   w   1887
    Listed in Ayer 1888.

Villager   w   1885-1887
    Not to be confused with Village News. Both in
    Ayer 1888.

MACKS CREEK (Camden County)

Central Missouri Leader   w   1903-1934
    MoHi: Apr 20, 1933-Jly 26, 1934. Moved to
    Camdenton 1935.

Camden County Rustic   w   1902-1913?
    MoHi: Film, Dec 31, 1902-1903.

MACON (Macon County)

Argus   w   1864-1870
    MoHi: Jun 19-Aug 28, 1867; Mar 4, 1868-Feb
    23, 1870.
    MWA: Jan 31, 1866.

Beacon   w   1862-1863
    NHi: Jly 23, 1862.

Chronicle   d   1910-1916
    MoHi: Jly 11, 1910-1915. Film, Jan 1-13, 1916.
    Merged with Daily Herald Jan 14, 1916 to
    form Chronicle-Herald.

Chronicle-Herald   d   1910+
    MoHi: 1917; 1919-1950. Film, Jan 14-Dec 1916;
    Jan-Jun 1918; 1951+. See Chronicle.
    MoSHi: Aug 28, 1937.
    Micro-Photo: Film, 1957+.

Citizen   w   1893-1901
    MoHi: Film, Dec 2, 1898-Aug 30, 1901. Sold to
    Republican 1901.

Democrat   w   1883-1901
    MoHi: Nov 25, 1898-Aug 23, 1901. Merged with
    Times Sep 6, 1901.

Democratic Times   w   1871-1875
    Times and Democrat consolidated 1872 as Democratic
    Times. In 1875 Democratic Times, Journal, and
    Daily Pilot bought by stock company which started
    the Examiner.

MACON (continued)

Examiner   w   1865-1879
    MoHi: May 24, 1878; Jan 17, Feb 21, 1879.
    ICHi: Aug 17, 1876.

Express   w   1871
    Listed in Rowell 1871.

Forum   w   1894-1895
    In Rowell 1895. Missouri Editor, Dec 1894, says
    Forum succeeds Populace, defunct.

Gazette   w   1862-1865
    MoHi: Jan 15-Aug 6, 1862; Jan 14, 1863-May 4,
    1865.

Greenback   w   1877-1880
    MoHi: Nov 26, 1879, supplement. In Ayer 1880;
    founding date doubtful.

Greenback Standard   w   1878
    Listed in Rowell 1879.

Herald   d   1913-1916
    MoHi: Nov 15, 1913-Jan 13, 1916. See Chronicle.
    Hammond refers to a Republican as following
    Herald, founded 1860, but no other evidence
    of this.

Independent   w   1877?
    Listed in Pettengill 1877.

Journal   w   1867-1875?
    MoHi: Nov 7, 1876-Oct 29, 1868; Sep 3, 1868.
    Not to be confused with Macon County Journal.

Macon County Dispatch   w   1881
    Listed in Ayer 1882.

Macon County Journal   w   1934-1935
    MoHi: Feb 28, Mar 28, 1935. Mentioned in MPN,
    Apr 1934, Apr 1935.

Macon County News   w   1880?
    Listed in Rowell 1880, no data.

Missouri Granger   w   1874-1876
    MoHi: Jan 7-Jun 26, 1876. Film, Mar 3, 1873-
    1875. Rowell 1876 noted that "Ads will be put
    in three other papers without extra costs."
    ICHi: May 12, 1876.

North Missouri Register   w   1870-1882
    MoHi: Oct 3, 1879-Sep 23, 1881; Jun 27, Sep 19,
    1879; Nov 25, 1881; Sep 1, 15, 22, 1882.

Populace   w   1894
    Listed in Ayer 1895.

Register   w   1861
    Published a few months; equipment seized by
    Third Iowa Regiment which issued Our Whole Union
    (one issue).

MACON (continued)

Register and Leader   w   1914?
    MWA: May 31, 1914.

Republican   w   1871-1929
    MoHi: Apr 22, 1871-1888; 1911-Apr 19, 1929;
    Sep 6, 1883; Aug 14, 1884. Film, 1889-Feb 20,
    1890; Apr-Dec 1890; Apr 17-Aug 27, 1891;
    Jan-Jun 1892; 1893-1910. Hammond refers
    to Republican following Herald in 1860.
    ICHi: Jly 20, 1876.

Times   w   1865-1901
    MoHi: Aug 2-30, 1901; Jan 3, Jly 14, 1880; Aug
    8, 15, 22, Sep 5, Oct 12, Nov 14, 21, 28, 1884;
    Jan 13, 1893. Film, Jan 4, 1889-1896. Merged
    with Democrat Sep 6, 1901.

Times-Democrat   w   1901-1916   d   1916
    MoHi: w, Sep 6, 1901-Dec 28, 1905; Jan 7, 1909-
    Jan 1916; Mar 20, 1902; Jan 18, Mar 1, 1906;
    Aug 27, 1908; Jun 25, 1914. Film, Jan-Aug 23,
    1901; 1906-1908. D, Jan 17-Nov 28, 1916.
    Film, Jly-Dec 7, 1916. Changed to daily Jan
    17, 1916, short-lived.

True Democrat   w   1883
    Listed in Dauchy-Rowell 1884.

True Flag   w   1865-1869?
    Mentioned by Organ.

Union   (Our Whole Union)   1861
    MoSHi: Jun 15, 1861. Single edition. See Register.

Western Messenger   w   1908?
    MoHi: Dec 25, 1908.

MADISON (Monroe County)

Advance   w   1888-1894
    Union List says name used for Times for these years.

Times   w   1888+
    MoHi: Jly 25, 1901-1915; 1917-1944. Film, 1916;
    1945+ Missouri Editor, Nov 1894, reports Advance
    had changed name to Times.

Watchman   w   1885-1887
    Followed by Advance, Times.

MAITLAND (Holt County)

Herald   w   1887-1953
    MoHi: Aug 1901-1905; 1911-1917; Oct 30,
    1890; Sep 14, 1905. Film, 1906-1910. Sus-
    pended May 14, 1953.

Independent   w   1881-1884
    In Rowell 1882-1885, Ayer 1881, 1883.

Monitor   w   1883?-1886
    Listed in Rowell 1886.

MAITLAND (continued)

Newspaper   w   1900
    Listed in Ayer 1900.

Nodaway Valley Herald   w   1887-1889?
    In Rowell 1888-1889, Ayer 1888-1890.

MALDEN (Dunklin County)

Clipper   w   1877-1886?
    Rowell lists through 1886. Hammond says Clipper
    was in Malden in 1879, formerly Dunklin County
    Advocate in Clarkton.

Dunklin County News   w   1886-1912
    MoHi: County News, Oct 24, 1890. News, Jly
    1901-1912. Listed at times as Dunklin News.

Dunklin County Register   w   1895-1896?
    Listed in Ayer 1897.

Merit   w   1904-1955
    MoHi: Film, 1917-1919. Combined with Press
    Aug 11, 1955.

Press   w   1950-1955
    MoHi: Film, Apr 20, 1950-Aug 4, 1955. See Merit.

Press-Merit   w   1904+
    MoHi: Film, Aug 11, 1955+. Merged Aug 11, 1955.

MALTA BEND (Saline County)

Community Weekly   w   1926-1931
    MoHi: Apr 1930-Nov 19, 1931. Named Saline
    County Republican Nov 26, 1931.

Democrat   w   1899
    Listed in Ayer 1900.

Mascot   w   1889
    Listed in Ayer 1889.

News   w   1909-1910
    MoHi: Apr 9-Oct 1909; Dec 1909-1910.

Qui Vive   w   1887-1908
    MoHi: Jly 26, 1901-1902; 1906-1908; Oct 17,
    1890; Feb 10, 1904. Film, 1903-1905.

Record   w   1914-1921?
    Last listed in Ayer 1922.

Saline County Republican   w   1926-1933
    MoHi: Nov 26, 1931-1933. See Community
    Weekly. Transferred to Marshall, name changed
    to Saline County Record Jan 4, 1934.

MANES (Wright County)

Herald   w   1914-1920
    Listed in Ayer 1916-1921.

MANSFIELD (Wright County)

Express   w   1893
  Listed in Ayer 1894.

Mail   w   1894-1908
  MoHi: Dec 2,1898-Oct 28,1899; Jan 22,1904-
  1906. Renamed Republican Oct 28,1899, back
  to Mail before 1904.

Mirror   w   1903+
  MoHi: Dec 26,1912-1944. Film,1945+. (See
  Mirror-Republican) See Hartville Wright
  County Republican.

Mirror-Republican   w   1903+
  Fuller name for Mirror since Ayer 1959.

News   w   1894, 1928-1929
  Two under this title, both brief.

Optic   w   1889
  Listed in Ayer 1889.

Press   w   1908-1912
  MoHi: Oct 9,1908-1909.

Republican   w   1899-1903?
  See Mail.

Wright County News   w   1893
  Listed in Rowell 1894.

MAPLEWOOD (St. Louis County)

Champion   w   1912-1914
  MoHi: Film, Dec 12,1912-1914. Merged with
  News Jan 9,1914 as News-Champion.

Herald   w   1912
  MoSHi: Feb 2,16,23,Mar 1,15,1912.

Journal   w   1911
  MoSHi: Sep 9,1911.

News   w   1914
  See News-Champion. News not in Ayer.

News-Champion   w   1912-1935
  MoHi: 1915-Nov 22,1935. Film,1914.
  MoSHi: Feb 24,Mar 1,22,Jly 5,Sep 27,Oct 12-
  25,Nov 15,Dec 12,27,1912; 1913-1917 inc.
  IU: 1922-1924. Suspended Nov 22,1935.

St. Louis County Observer   w   1934+
  Mostly free distribution.

MARBLE HILL (Bollinger County)

American Palladium   w   1878-1879
  In Ayer 1880.

Banner   w   1943?
  Consolidation story MPN, May 1943.

MARBLE HILL (continued)

Banner-Press   w   1881+
  MoHi: May 10,1923-1944. Film,1945+.

Bollinger County Standard   w   1868-1873
  MoHi: Mar 24,1870. To Fredericktown, according
  to Hammond.

Bollinger County Times   w   1896-1900
  In Rowell 1897-1901, Ayer 1897,1900.

Herald   w   1872-1883
  ICHi: Jly 22,1876. Hammond says moved to
  Ironton, absorbed Palladium, ended 1883.
  Last in Rowell 1884.

Missouri Standard   w   1868-1873
  Name apparently used briefly for Bollinger
  County Standard. In Rowell 1874 as oldest in
  county.

News   ?   1866
  Listed in Madison County Probate files.

People's Press   w   1881-1886
  MoHi: Jly 1901-1903; 1906-1907; 1909-Jan
  11,1923. Film,1904-1905; 1908. Later dates
  under Press.
  MoSHi: Dec 31,1903; Aug 26,1915.

Palladium   w   1878-1880?
  Noted in county history. See Herald.

Press   w   1881-1923
  See People's Press.

Southeast Reflector   w   1881-1884
  In Rowell 1883-1884, Ayer 1883.

True Democrat   w   1872
  Listed in Rowell 1873.

MARCELINE (Linn County)

Herald   w   1913-1929
  MoHi: 1914-Sep 15,1916; Mar 1917-Sep 21,
  1923; Feb 15,1924-May 29,1927; May 23,
  1913. Consolidated with Journal-Mirror Jun
  7,1929,named changed to News.

Journal   w   1888-1912
  MoHi: Dec 30,1898-Jun 1900; 1903; 1905-
  1906; Oct 23,1890; Mar 30,Apr 13,27,May
  4,11,25,1900; Jly 26,1912. Merged with
  Mirror 1912?

Journal-Mirror   w   1888-1929
  See Herald.

Mirror   w   1888-1912
  MoHi: Oct 30,1890; Feb 17,1899; May 6,1898.

MARCELINE (continued)

New Deal   w   1888-1901
    In Rowell 1900-1901, Ayer 1902 with 1888 founding
    date.

News   d   1896   w   1929+
    MoHi: Jun 7, 1929-1944. Film, 1945+. Missouri
    Editor, Oct 1896, says News has been dis-
    continued. See Herald. Present-day paper
    traces history to 1888 through consolidations.
    Apparently 1896 edition was daily with MoHi
    having copies for Apr 16, Jun 15, 20, Aug 8,
    10, 12, 1896.

News and Bucklin Herald   w   1888+
    Name used in full for News since consolidation
    with Bucklin Herald in 1947.

MARIONVILLE (Lawrence County)

Advertiser   w   1887
    In Ayer 1887, Rowell 1888.

Advocate   w   1873
    Listed in Rowell 1874.

Blade   w   1873
    Mentioned by Hammond.

Buzz Saw   w   1886-1889
    Under Free Press as name used briefly.

Commercial   w   1884-1885
    Apparently preceded Buzz Saw. In Rowell 1884-
    1886.

Free Press   w   1883+
    MoHi: Jly 8, 1903-Sep 28, 1904; 1913-1944; Jly
    3, 1952. Film, Sep 1894-Nov 19, 1896; 1897-
    1898 inc. 1899-1912; 1945+. Some use 1882
    as founding date. Missouri Editor, Feb 1894,
    reported the "Free Press is a new publication
    that 'has come to stay.' "

Journal   w   1872
    Published May 5-Aug 24, 1872, according to
    Hammond.

Messenger   w   1876-1877
    Hammond says published Oct 1, 1876-Mar 31,
    1877.

Pioneer Democrat   w   1886
    Listed in Ayer 1886.

Republican   w   1890-1893
    MoHi: Oct 24, 1890. May have been name used
    for Free Press briefly.

Southwest Missourian   w   1877-1880?
    In Rowell 1879-1880, Ayer 1880 with 1877 founding
    date.

MARQUAND (Madison County)

Echo   w   1887-1889?
    In Rowell-Ayer 1888-1889.

Leader   w   1910-1911
    Listed in Ayer 1912.

MARSHALL (Saline County)

Alliance Watchman   w   1891-1892
    Listed as Independent Watchman in Rowell 1893.
    Same other data.

Banner   w   1868-1869
    MoHi: Jun 4, 1869.

Capital   w   1888-1892
    MoHi: Aug 3, 31-Oct 12, 26, Nov 2-Dec 14,
    1888; Jan 11, 25, 1889.
    KHi: Jan 4, 1889.

Courier   d   1884
    Listed in Dauchy 1884.

Democrat   w   1858-1861   d   1878-1879?
    MoHi: d, Sep 7, 1878. J.H. Eakin represented
    Democrat at 1879 press association meeting.
    MoSHi: Jan 15, 1858-Jly 31, 1861.

Democrat-News   w   1873-1931   d   1879+
    MoHi: Jan 19, 1932-1950; May 22, 1903; Dec
    8, 1908; Apr 8, 1909; Oct 7, 1913; Nov 5,
    1953; Jun 20, 1955. Film, 1951+. W, Dec
    24, 1898-1908; 1911-Feb 1917; Jan 2, 1919-
    Oct 22, 1931; Jun 10, Aug 12, 1905; Jan 20,
    27, 31, 1906; Feb 23, 1907; Apr 18, 1908;
    Mar 13, Apr 10, 1909. Film, May 4, 1895-
    Dec 17, 1898; 1909-1910; Mar 1, 1917-Dec
    26, 1918. Weekly suspended Oct 22, 1931,
    sold to Saline County Citizen.
    MoSHi: Sep 1939.
    Murrell Library, Marshall, Dec 1, 1949+.

Gazette   w   1877-1878
    Listed in Rowell 1877-1878.

Independent Missourian   w   1880-1882
    In Rowell 1883 as True Missourian.

Index   d   1900-1905
    See Saline County Index. Apparently Index pub-
    lished daily for brief time.

Meridian   w   1856
    In Newspaper Record 1856.

Messenger   w   1932+
    Shopper publication.

Missouri State Republican   w   1881
    Apparently name used briefly for Saline County
    Republican. In Rowell 1882.

MARSHALL (continued)

News w,d 1879-1888
  MoHi: d, Sep 2, 1885.

People's Record w 1893-1897?
  Populist paper in Ayer 1895-1898.

Progress d 1879, 1889-1917
  Confused. A daily existed in 1879, when R.S.
  Sandidge represented paper at press association
  meeting. Later weekly listed as Saline County
  Progress. Daily Progress in Rowell 1882, with
  founding date of 1879. Later references to
  daily starting in 1889.

Quiz w 1890-1891
  Reform paper listed by Ashcraft.

Record w 1893?-1898?
  In Rowell 1897-1898 with 1893 founding date.

Republican w 1892-1914?
  MoHi: 1903; 1906-May 1914. Film, Dec 23, 1898-
  Feb 28, 1902; 1904-1905. Called Saline Re-
  publican Dec 23, 1898-May 5, 1899.

Saline Citizen w 1895+
  MoHi: 1901-1918; Jan-Mar 28, 1931; Jly 11,
  1903; Aug 12, 1905; Apr 25, May 23, 1908;
  Feb 20, 1909; Apr 4, 1931-1944. Film, Oct
  30, 1895-Nov 3, 1900; 1945. Also known as
  Saline County Citizen, name used since
  Apr 4, 1931.

Saline County Citizen w 1895+
  KHi: Apr 19, 1924. See Saline Citizen.

Saline County Democrat w 1873-1888
  MoHi: Nov 17, 1888.
  ICHi: Aug 23, 1876. In Ayer 1880, 1887,
  Rowell 1873-1889.

Saline County Eagle w 1885
  Listed in Rowell 1886.

Saline County Herald w 1856-1858
  MoHi: Jan 15, 1857. Moved to Arrow Rock, re-
  mained until 1861, and consolidated with
  Marshall Democrat.

Saline County Index w 1880-1905
  MoHi: Mar 1, 1900-1905; Dec 29, 1904.
  MoSHi: Jly 7, 1904.

Saline County Progress w 1865-1917
  MoHi: 1902-1903; 1906-Jly 1917; Jun 25, 1869.
  Film, Jan 3, 1868-Jly 27, 1877; 1878-May 3,
  1895; 1904-1905. Saline County Weekly Progress title used at time. MoHi copies here
  include Jun 16, 23, 30, Jly 28, Aug 11, 1905;
  Feb 16, Mar 16, 1906; May 29, 1908; Feb 26,
  1909; Oct 11, 1912.

MARSHALL (continued)

Saline County Record w 1934-1937
  MoHi: 1934-Jly 17, 1937. Formerly Malta Bend
  Saline County Republican, moved to Marshall
  Jan 4, 1934. For brief time in 1935-1936
  published twice a week.

Saline County Republican w 1870, 1881, 1891
  Rowell 1871 noted 1870 edition; Rowell 1883
  notes start in 1881; Rowell 1895 notes start
  in 1891.

Saline County Standard w 1858
  Party organ for campaign.

Saline Republican w 1892-1899?
  Union Lists say name used for Republican during
  these years.

True Missourian w 1880-1883
  See Independent Missourian.

MARSHFIELD (Webster County)

Advertiser w 1869
  MoHi: Aug 26, 1869.

Chronicle w 1877-1925
  MoHi: Aug 1908-Sep 1920; Apr 7, May 19, 1881;
  Oct 4, 1883; Jly 30, 1908. Film, Oct 26, 1877-
  Oct 12, 1893; Oct 26, 1895-Aug 6, 1908; Oct
  26, Nov 2, 1893.

Citizen w 1870-1872
  MoHi: Sep 7, 1872. In Rowell 1871-1873.

Cyclone w 1921-1922?
  Mentioned in MHR, Apr, Jun 1921.

Democrat w 1869-1879
  MoHi: Dec 25, 1869; Jan 15, 1870; Sep 30, 1876;
  Jly 7, 1877.
  ICHi: Jly 22, 1876.

Farmer's Friend w 1875-1876?
  Listed in Rowell 1875-1876.

Herald w 1930-1942
  MoHi: Nov 10, 1938-Oct 8, 1942. Film, Apr 21,
  1932-Nov 24, 1938.

Mail w 1892+
  MoHi: 1902, 1908-1944; Oct 26, Nov 5, 1893;
  Jun 22, Jly 6, 20, Aug 3-Sep 7, 28, Oct 5, 11,
  Nov-Dec 1905; Jly 23, 1908. Film, Jan 18,
  1893-1901; 1903-1907; 1945+.
  KHi: Mar 25, 1926.

Missouri Yeoman w 1865-1870
  MoHi: Jun 5, 1869. In Rowell 1869-1870.

Radical w 1865
  Hammond says published in 1865.

MARSHFIELD (continued)

Republican Standard w 1884-1892
Also listed as Webster County Republican,
Webster Standard.

Sentinel w 1857-1861
Organ says formerly Buffalo Herald, moved 1857.

Tribune w 1884
May have followed Webster County News,
preceded Standard。

Webster County News w 1870-1883
MoHi: Oct 7, 1880; Dec 22, 1881.

Webster County Record w 1885-1888
Anti-monopoly paper. Moved to Fordland as
Journal.

Webster County Republican w 1884-1894
First listed in Rowell 1893.

Webster Sentinel w 1861
One source says Express sold 1861, renamed
Webster Sentinel. Hammond uses 1859-1861,
Organ 1857-1861 dates.

Webster Standard w 1884-1891?
MoHi: Oct 17, 1890. In Ayer 1887-1892,
Rowell 1885-1891.

Yeoman w 1865-1870
Missouri Yeoman title in Rowell 1870.

MARTHASVILLE (Warren County)

Der Missionar w 1881-1883?
MoWe: 1881-1883.

News w 1896-1898
In Ayer 1898, Rowell 1897-1899.

Record w 1898+
MoHi: 1927-1944. Film, Jly 3-Dec 25, 1903;
1945+. Country Editor, Sep 1898, tells of
start.

MARTINSBURG (Audrain County)

Audrain County Oracle w 1907-1919
Listed in Ayer 1910-1920.

Audrain County Republican w 1900
Listed in Ayer 1900.

Enterprise w 1901-1904
MoHi: Jan 7, 1904. Film, 1903.

Index w 1891
Listed in Ayer 1892。

Message w 1890
MoHi: Oct 24, 1890.

MARTINSBURG (continued)

Monitor w 1900-1952?
First as Monitor in Ayer 1921. Apparently known
earlier as Sunbeam and Audrain County Oracle.

Success w 1898-1899
In Rowell 1898-1899, Ayer 1900.

Sunbeam w 1900-1908
Union List says name used for Monitor for these
years.

MARYVILLE (Nodaway County)

Advocate w 1888-1896? also d, sw
Listed as d, w, sw in Rowell 1891. People's Party
organ.

American Citizen w 1888-1892
In Rowell 1891-1893, Ayer 1890-1892.

Chronicle w 1883-1887
One source says started as Democratic Freeman
1883. In Ayer 1887, Rowell 1888.

Conference Daily d 1876-1878
MoHi: Methodist Episcopal Church publication
marked "First daily in Nodaway County,"
Mar 27-Apr 2, 1878 copies available.

Democrat w 1869-1910 d 1890-1895
MoHi: d, film, Dec 1, 1890-Nov 30, 1894. W
listed as Nodaway Democrat.

Democrat-Forum w 1869-1925 d 1910-1929
MoHi: Aug 2, 1915-May 2, 1925; May 7, 1913.
Film, Jun 4, 1910-1915. Formerly Nodaway
Democrat, Nodaway Forum, and Republican.
Merged with Tribune, became Democrat-
Forum and Maryville Tribune, d, May 3, 1925.
Daily Forum name appeared May 1929.
MoHi: w, Jun 16, 1910-May 7, 1925; Aug 1, 1918.
Weekly took longer title May 7, 1925.

Democrat-Forum and Maryville Tribune d
1925-1929, w 1925-1935
MoHi: d, May 3, 1925-May 21, 1929. W, May
14, 1925-Jun 1935 when it ended.

Democratic Freeman w 1883-1887
See Chronicle.

Duffy's Freeman's Journal w 1888-1889
Anti-monopoly, in Rowell-Ayer 1888-1890.

Forum d 1869+
MoHi: May 23, 1929-1950. Film, 1951+.
Northwest MST: Sep 1939-Jun 1953.
Micro-Photo: Film, 1910+. See Democrat-Forum.

Gazette w 1867
A.C. Votaw of Gazette at press association meeting 1867.

Greenback-Standard   w   1880
    C.H.Thomas press association member 1880.

Item   d   1896-1897
    Brief career. In Ayer 1897. Death in Country
    Editor, Apr 1897.

Journal   w   1866-1870, 1888-1889?
    Two, both short-lived.

Legal Tender News   w   1877-1878
    MoHi: Apr 20, May 18, Jun 1, 1878.

Missourian   w   1897?
    Country Editor, Sep 1897, notes end.

Missouri Standard   w   1890-1891
    Labor and farmers' alliance paper.

Nodaway Democrat   w   1869-1910
    MoHi: Dec 9, 1880; Jly 9, 20, 1903; Jan 7, 1904;
    Feb 2, Jly 20, 27, Aug 10, 17, 24, Sep 21, Dec
    14, 1905; Jan 4-Feb 15, 1906; Apr 16, 1908;
    Oct 21, 28, Nov 4-Dec 30, 1909; Jan 23, 1873.
    Film, Nov 13, 1869-Jun 9, 1910. Merged with
    Republican and Nodaway Forum, w, to form
    Democrat-Forum, w, Jun 9, 1910.

New Tribune   w   1938-1945
    MoHi: Under full title of New Tribune and The
    Conception Courier lists copies Oct 13, 1938-
    1944; Sep 1-Oct 13, 1938. Film, Jan-Aug 30,
    1945. Represents merger of New Tribune and
    Conception Courier Oct 13, 1938. Name
    changed Sep 6, 1945 to Nodaway County
    Tribune.
    Northwest Mo. State College: Sep 1938-1945.

Nodaway County Republican   w   1874-1879
    Union lists says name used for Republican during
    these years.

Nodaway County Tribune   w   1945-1951
    MoHi: Film, Sep 6, 1945-1952.
    Northwest Mo. State College: 1946-1949.

Nodaway County Weekly   w   1957-1960
    Listed as free paper Ayer 1959-1961.

Nodaway Democrat   w   1869-1910
    MoHi: Film, Nov 13, 1869-Jun 9, 1910 See
    Democrat.

Nodaway Forum   w   1900-1910
    MoHi: Oct 24, 1901-Jun 9, 1910; Oct 21, 28, Nov
    4-Dec 30, 1909. See Democrat-Forum.

Northwest Missourian   w   1896
    Listed in Ayer 1897.

Record   d   1898-1899?
    Listed in Ayer 1900.

Register   w   1867-1873?
    Name changed to Republican, later sold to
    Nodaway Democrat. In Rowell 1873.

Reporter   w   1859-1861
    According to Organ was first in county.

Republican   w   1870-1910   d   1906-1910
    MoHi: W, Aug 1870-Sep 6, 1883; Jly 31, 1884-
    Dec 30, 1885; Jly 1894-Dec 1898; Oct 23,
    1890; Nov 29, Dec 13, 20, 1894; Aug 11-
    Dec 29, 1898; Apr 14, Dec 29, 1904; Jun 22,
    Jly 13-Sep 7, 28, Oct 12, Dec 7, 28, 1905;
    Jan 4, 18, Nov 15, 1906. Film, Sep 13, 1883-
    Jly 14, 1884; 1886-Jly 12, 1894; 1899-Jun
    9, 1910. See Democrat-Forum. D, film,
    Oct 24, 1907-Jun 3, 1910.
    NHi: Dec 19, 1872.

Review   d   1895-1898
    Weekly listed as Review and Advocate in Rowell
    1896-1899. Ayer 1899 lists weekly as Griff's
    Review.

Times   w   1877-1884?   1932?-1934
    Rowell-Ayer 1881-1885 lists first Times. Ayer
    1933-1934 lists second. Ayer 1935, 1937 lists
    Nodaway County Times.

Tribune   w   1887-1925   d   1894-1925
    MoHi: w, Jan 1909-Dec 1912; 1915. Film, Nov 7,
    1895-Dec 28, 1905; Jan 1906-Dec 1908. D,
    1904; Dec 1905-May 2, 1925 exc. 1915. Film,
    Oct 2, 1899-Mar 1901; 1902; Dec 1904-Dec
    8, 1905; 1915. See Democrat-Forum. Daily
    Tribune merged with Democrat-Forum to form
    Democrat-Forum and Maryville Tribune May
    3, 1925. Weekly merged May 3, 1925.

Wave   w   1906-1907
    Listed in Ayer-Rowell 1908.

MAYSVILLE (DeKalb County)

Comet   w   1883
    Listed in Ayer 1901.

DeKalb County Democrat   w   1896-1914
    MoHi: Film, Dec 8, 1898-1899; Aug 1901-Oct
    15, 1903.

DeKalb County Herald   w   1886-1956
    MoHi: Apr 23, 1925-1944; Aug 18, 1904. Film,
    Aug 22, 1889-1893, inc. Sep 20, 1894-Jly
    1895; Jan-Aug 13, 1896; 1898; Sep 12, 1901-
    Sep 11, 1902; Oct 1902-Aug 10, 1905; 1945-
    Nov 1, 1956. Consolidated with DeKalb
    County Record-Journal, became Record-
    Herald Nov 2, 1956.

DeKalb County Post   w   1896
    Free Silver paper in Rowell 1898.

MAYSVILLE (continued)

DeKalb County Record-Herald   w   1866+
    MoHi: Film, Nov 8, 1956+

DeKalb County Record-Journal   w   1928-1956
    MoHi: Oct 18, 1928-1944. Film, 1945-Nov 1,
    1956. Formerly Stewartsville Record and
    Clarksdale Journal. Became Record-Journal
    Oct 18, 1928, Record-Herald Nov 2, 1956.

DeKalb County Register   w   1865-1876?
    In Rowell 1876 as Register.

DeKalb County Register and News   w   1867-1877?
    In Rowell 1877-1878. Under Register 1879.

DeKalb County Republican   w   1877-1883
    One source says became Republican Pilot, later
    Pilot. In Rowell 1879-1884, Ayer 1880-1881.

DeKalb County Sun   w   1877?-1924
    Earlier known as DeKalb County Republican,
    Republican Pilot, and Pilot.

Eureka   m   1875?
    MoHi: May 1875, Vol 1, No 1.

Pilot   w   1912-1920?   d   1886?
    MoHi: W, Dec 12, 1912-Sep 16, 1920. Formerly
    Republican Pilot, name changed Dec 12, 1912.
    One copy of daily, Apr 6, 1886, at MoHi.

Record   d   1898
    Listed in Rowell 1898.

Recorder   w   1861
    American Newspaper Directory 1861 lists Recorder
    as weekly at Maysville Courthouse.

Register   w   1867-1889?
    MoHi: 1871-Sep 8, 1875. Western Register to Jan
    5, 1871. Last listed Rowell 1889.

Republican-Pilot   w   1877?-1912
    MoHi: Nov 24, 1898-Aug 3, 1899; Aug 1, 1901-
    Dec 5, 1912, when name changed to Pilot,
    Dec 12, 1912.

Stewartsville Record   w   1928
    MoHi: Jly 5-Oct 11, 1928. Merged with Clarks-
    dale Journal before this date, published at
    Stewartsville until moved to Mayville Jly 5,
    1928. Changed to DeKalb County Record-
    Journal Oct 18, 1928.

Surprise   w   1896
    Mentioned in Missouri Editor, Jun 1896, as a new
    paper.

Western Register   w   1867-1889?
    MoHi: May 28, 1868-Dec 22, 1870. In Rowell
    1869-1889, Ayer 1882-1887.

MAYVIEW (Lafayette County)

Democrat   w   1898
    Country Editor, Jan 1898, Says Dover Democrat
    moved to Mayview.

Era   w   1912-1921
    Last listed in Ayer 1922.

Monitor   w   1892-1894
    In Rowell 1893-1894, Ayer 1894-1895.

Progress   w   1897-1899
    In Rowell 1898-1899, Ayer 1900.

MAYWOOD (Lewis County)

Messenger   w   1904-1912?
    Last listed in Ayer 1913.

Missourian   w   1916-1930
    Last listed in Ayer 1931.

Journal   w   1916-1930?
    In Ayer 1931. Said to have consolidated with
    Lewistown Journal during depression.

Pruning Knife   w   1900-1904?
    In Rowell 1901-1905, Ayer 1902.

MEADVILLE (Linn County)

Messenger   w   1881-1946
    MoHi: Nov 24, 1898-Jly 1900; Apr-Dec 1905;
    Mar 6, 1919-1944; Jun 9, 1905; Jun 29, 1893.
    Film, 1945. Combined with Laclede Blade,
    moved to Brookfield as Blade and Messenger
    Jan 1, 1946.

Missing Link   w   1898-1900
    In Ayer 1900, Rowell 1900-1901.

MELBOURNE (Harrison County)

Herald   w   1902-1906
    In Ayer 1903-1907, Rowell 1907.

Messenger   w   1909-1910
    Listed in Ayer 1910-1911.

News   w   1899-1900
    In Rowell 1900-1901, Ayer 1900.

MEMPHIS (Scotland County)

Chronicle   d   1899-1905?
    MoHi: Feb 2, Oct 27, 1902.

Conservative   w   1866-1881
    MoHi: Feb 26, 1869-Jly 16, 1874; Nov 23, 1876-
    Jly 1, 1880 inc. Mar 12, Jly 2, 1869; Jan 8,
    1874; Dec 26, 1878; Jan 2, 16, 1879; Aug 8,
    1882. Film, Aug 2, 1877-Jly 17, 1879; Sep 9,
    1880-Jly 21, 1881. At one time called Con-
    servator.
    ICHi: Jly 6, 1876.

MEMPHIS (continued)

Democrat   w   1873+
MoHi: 1905-1944; Aug 29, Sep 19, Oct 3, 10,
1883; Oct 24, 1884; Aug 31, 1905; Dec 30,
1916; Apr 30, 1886. Film, Oct 21, 1880-Oct
27, 1881; 1945+. Formerly Scotland County
Democrat. Name changed Jan 1905.

Democratic Standard   w   1897-1899?
Listed in Ayer 1900.

Enquirer   d   1905
Listed in Ayer-Rowell 1906.

Farmers' Union   w   1891-1895
MoHi: Film, Feb 1891-Jan 24, 1895. Changed
name to Herald Jan 31, 1895.

Greenback Tribune   w   1880?
MoHi: Aug 21-Oct 23, 1880.

Herald   w   1895-1896
MoHi: Film, Feb 7, 1895-Jan 1896. See Farmers'
Union.

Herald-Democrat   w   1896
Apparently name used briefly for Herald. Under
this title in Ayer 1897.

Journal   w   1855-1859
MoHi: Dec 5, 1857. To Bethany 1859.

National   w   1882-1888
MoHi: Aug 21, Oct 23, Nov 20, 1884. Film, Nov
16, 1882-1888.

National Democrat   w   1859-1865
MoHi: May 26, Jly 7, Sep 29, 1860. Renamed
Reveille Sep 9, 1865.

Peoples' Messenger   w   1891-1898
MoHi: Film, Mar 19, 1896-Feb 17, 1898.
IaHi: Mar 26, 1896-Jun 17, 1897.

Register   w   1888-1890
MoHi: Film, Dec 20, 1888-Jan 1890.

Reveille   w   1865+
MoHi: 1913-Aug 10, 1916; Mar 5, 1917-1944;
Oct 26, 1871; Aug 13, 1874; Oct 23, 1890.
Film, Sep 9, 1865-Sep 19, 1872; Oct 30, 1873-
Dec 15, 1881; Jan 17, 1884-Jan 14, 1892;
Jan 18, 1894-1912; Aug 17, 1916-Feb 27,
1917; 1945+.
ICHi: Aug 10, 1876.

Scotland County Democrat   w   1873-1905
MoHi: Jly 1901-1904. See Democrat.

Scotland County News   w   1873-1879
MoHi: 1878-Oct 9, 1879; Nov 6, 1879. Film, Sep
10, 1873-Dec 20, 1877.
ICHi: Sep 21, 1876.

MEMPHIS (continued)

Star   sw   1901-1903
MoHi: Film, Nov 6, 1901-Feb 21, 1903.

MENDON (Chariton County)

Citizen   w   1889-1904
MoHi: Film, 1902-1903.

Constitution   w   1904-1951
MoHi: 1920-1941. Film, Jan 10, 1914-1919.
MoSHi: Dec 18, 1908.

MERCER (Mercer County)

Magnet   w   1895-1897
In Rowell 1896-1897, Ayer 1896-1898.

Mercer County Democrat   w   1935-1936
Listed as Mercer County Democrat and Mercer
Signal in Ayer 1937. No listing after 1938.

Searchlight   w   1895-1900
In Rowell-Ayer 1901. Union List refers to
Princeton Post.

Signal   w   1906-1937
See Mercer County Democrat. Under Signal in
Ayer 1907-1921.

MERWIN (Bates County)

Border Telephone   w   1889-1910?
See Hume data. Irregular Ayer-Rowell listings.

Clipper   w   1904-1911
MoHi: Jly 29, 1904. In Rowell 1905-1908, Ayer
1905-1912.

Herald   w   1902-1904
Listed in Rowell 1904-1905.

Mirror   w   1894-1902?
Last listing in Rowell 1903.

Monitor   w   1894-1896
Listed in Ayer 1896-1897.

Sun   w   1916-1919
Listed in Ayer 1917-1920.

META (Osage County)

Headlight   w   1902-1917?
Union List under Herald as name used for these
years. Ayer 1919 list as founded 1891.

Herald   w   1902+
MoHi: Mar 1923-1944; Jly 3, 1952. Film, 1945+.

METZ (Vernon County)

Times   w   1902+
First listed in Ayer 1904.

MEXICO (Audrain County)

Argus w 1894-1895
    In Missouri Editor, Aug 1894, Ayer 1895.

Advertiser w 1896-1899
    Mentioned in Country Editor, Jun 1897. In Ayer
    1898 as Audrain Advertiser.

Audrain County Banner w 1858-1861
    MoHi: Apr 5, 1861.

Audrain County Beacon w 1863-1865
    Consolidated with Ledger 1865, according to Organ.

Audrain County Press w 1879-1882
    MoHi: Jan 14, 1880. In Rowell 1880-1883, Ayer
    1880-1882.

Audrain County Signal w 1856-1858
    Mentioned by Organ.

Audrain Expositor w 1868-1869
    Mentioned by Hammond.

Herald d, w 1879
    Listed in Ayer-Rowell 1880.

Intelligencer w 1855-1942 d 1880-1942
    MoHi: d, May 31-Sep 1897; Jan-Jun 12, 1898;
    Apr-Sep, 1897; Jan-Jun 12, 1898; Apr-Sep
    1902; Jly-Sep 1903; 1904-1905; Jan-Jun 1907;
    1908-Jun 1909; 1910-Feb 14, 1940; Jly 27, 28,
    29, 31, 1903; Dec 19, 1908. Film, Oct-Dec 1897;
    Jun 13, 1898-Mar 1902; Oct-Dec 1902; Jan-
    Jun, Oct-Dec 1903; 1906; Jly-Dec 1907; Jly-
    Dec 1909; Jan-Jun 1925. Became Daily News
    and Intelligencer Feb 14, 1940, suspended Jly
    30, 1942.
    MoHi: w, Sep 3, 1885-1892; 1902-1910; 1913-Jly
    30, 1942; Jly 9, 16, 1903; Aug 10, 17, 1905;
    May 7, 1908. Film, 1893-Mar 1897; Mar 31,
    1898-Apr 5, 1900; Apr-Dec 1901; 1911-1912.
    MoSHi: w, Dec 30, 1909; Apr 21, May 5-Sep 1,
    1910; Jan 4, 11, 18, 1912; Apr 30, 1914; Jan
    27, Feb 12, 1916; Feb 1, 1917.
    KHi: May 17, 1924.
    MnHi: Aug 17, 1939.

Leader w 1872-1875?
    Listed in Rowell 1873-1875.

Ledger w 1855-1956 d 1886+
    MoHi: d, Aug 5-Dec 1901; 1903-1905; 1908-1950;
    May 29, 1894; May 28, 1899; Jly 23, 1903;
    Aug 11, 17, 1905. Film, 1902; 1907; 1951+.
    MoSHi: d, Sep 14, 1887; Apr 21, Jly 3, 1913; Sep
    29, 1927; Sep 30, 1955. W, Dec 23, 1864.
    MoHi: w, Nov 24, 1898-1902; 1903-1918; 1921-
    1922; 1925-1944; Oct 23, 1890; Dec 29, 1892;
    Jly 9, 16, 1903. Film, Sep 21, 1876-Nov 17, 1898;
    1919-1920; 1945-1956. W, discontinued Oct
    11, 1956. Publisher has film 1876+.

MEXICO (continued)

Ledger (continued)
    Micro-Photo: Film, d, 1909+. w, 1876-1909.
    KHi: Jan 26, 1926.
    NcD: w, Mar 3, 1892; Jun 7, 1894; Oct 1, 1896.

Missouri Citizen w 1863
    MoSHi: Jun 16, 1863.

Missouri Ledger w 1855-1956
    Under this title in Rowell 1869-1871 with 1854
    starting date.

Missouri Message w 1899-1918
    MoHi: Jan 15, 1903-1910; 1915-Nov 7, 1918;
    Mar 26, 1908. Film, Nov 8, 1899-Jan 8,
    1903; 1911-1914.

Missouri Messenger w 1865-1876
    ICHi: Jan 20, 1876. Rowell 1875 says only Repub-
    lican journal in 13th Congressional District.

News and Intelligencer d 1940-1942
    MoHi: Feb 15, 1940-Jly 31, 1942. See Intelligencer.

North Missouri Messenger w 1865-1876
    DLC: May 25, 1867. Apparently name used at times
    for Missouri Messenger.

Patriot w 1888
    Listed in Rowell 1889.

Press w 1879-1883
    Apparently same as Audrain County Press.

Regulator w 1887-1888
    In Rowell 1888-1889, Ayer 1888.

Republican w 1882
    Listed in Rowell 1883.

Star Spangled Banner w 1861
    Civil War publication by American Zouaves.

State Leader w 1898-1903
    MoHi: Film, Jly 25, 1901-Sep 25, 1902. Moved to
    Kansas City Jly 2, 1903.

Telegram d 1885

Tribune w, tw 1894-1897?
    In Rowell, Ayer 1896-1898.

Union w 1878-1879
    Later became Audrain County Press, and Press.

MIAMI (Saline County)

Cable w 1870-1871?
    MoHi: May 7, 1870. In Rowell 1871.

Democrat-News w 1921-1922
    MoHi: Mar 3, 1921-Apr 13, 1922.

MIAMI (continued)

Index   w   1874-1880
ICHi: Apr 14, 1876. Moved to Slater 1880,
later Marshall.

News   w   1880-1922
MoHi: 1899-1922; Oct 25, 1890; Feb 16, 1906.

Republican   w   1879
D. M. Puterbaugh represented paper at press association meeting in 1879.

MIDDLETOWN   (Montgomery County)

Chips   w   1882-1951?
MoHi: Aug 27, 1903-1909.

Echo   w   1873
Mentioned in county history.

North Missouri Sentinel   w   1879-1882?
Listed Rowell-Ayer 1880-1881. Press moved to
Laddonia, to start Enterprise.

MILAN   (Sullivan County)

Acorn   w   1872-1873?
NHi: Nov 15, 1872. In Rowell 1873 with
founding date 1867.

Atlas   w   1867?
Listed in Rowell 1872.

Democrat   w   1886
Listed in Ayer 1886.

Farmer   w   1857-1861
Forced to suspend as secession paper.

Free Press   w   1881-1883
Greenback paper. In Ayer 1881-1883, Rowell
1882-1884.

Monitor   w   1898
Listed in Ayer-Rowell 1899.

North Missouri Herald   w   1867-1870
MoHi: Mar 5, 1869-Mar 4, 1870.

Radical   w   1864
Noted in Union List.

Republican   w   1875-1959
MoHi: Mar 5, 1885-Feb 23, 1888; Jly 25, 1901-
1944; Nov 26, 1908. Film, Feb 19, 1875-Feb
26, 1885; Mar 1, 1888-1900; 1945-1958.
Suspended May 21, 1959, sold to Standard.
KHi: Apr 26, 1923.
ICHi: Aug 25, 1876.

Standard   w   1871+   d   1897-1898?
MoHi: w, 1903-1904; 1913-1914. Film, 1945+.
ICHi: w, Sullivan Standard, Apr 21, 1876.

MILAN (continued)

Standard (continued)
Most early data says founding date 1872.
Country Editor, Jan 1898, says Daily Standard,
after about 60 days' experience, had decided
to quit.

Sullivan County Gazette   w   1873
Listed in Rowell 1874.

MILFORD   (Barton County)

Advance   w   1885
Listed in Rowell 1886.

MILLER   (Lawrence County)

Advance   w   1928-1937
MoHi: Dec 6, 1934-Apr 29, 1937. Merged with
Miller News to become News and Advance
May 6, 1937.

Free Press   w   1906-1911
Listed in Ayer 1907-1912.

Herald   w   1900-1917
Listed in Ayer 1901-1918.

News   w   1937-1953
MoHi: Film, Mar 16, 1950-1952. MPN, Apr 1937,
tells of start. Ended May 14, 1953.

News and Advance   w   1937-1950
MoHi: May 6, 1937-1944. Film, 1945-Mar 9, 1950.
Name changed to Miller News Mar 16, 1950,
moved to Mount Vernon, according to MPN,
Mar 1950.

News-Herald   w   1920-1925
MoHi: 1920-Dec 10, 1925. Formerly La Russell
Spring River News. Moved to Miller Jan 1,
1920. Bought by Aurora Advertiser Dec 10, 1925.

Ozark   w   1894-1898
Listed as Ozark Independent in Rowell 1899.

Ozark-Eagle   w   1894-1898
Name used briefly for Ozark.

Press   w   1956+
Listed in Ayer 1963.

MILO   (Vernon County)

Chronicle   w   1911
Listed in Ayer 1912.

MINDON MINES   (Barton County)

Miners' Echo   w   1892
Farm Alliance paper in Ayer 1892.

MINDON MINES (continued)

Minden Itemizer   w   1892
    Listed in Rowell 1893.

Miner   w   1902-1903
    In Rowell 1902-1903, Ayer 1903-1904.

Missouri-Kansas Herald   w   1903-1907?
    In Rowell 1904-1908, Ayer 1905-1906.

MINERAL SPRINGS (Barry County)

Panacea Republican   w   1882
    Listed in Ayer 1882.

MIRABILE (Caldwell County)

Hampton's Mercury   w   1895-1898
    MoHi: Feb 4, 18, Mar 4, 18-Apr 8, 22, 29, May 6,
    Jun 3, 17, 24, 1898.

MISSOURI CITY (Clay County)

Champion   w   1893
    Listed Rowell-Ayer 1894.

Herald   w   1869-1870
    MoHi: Jun 25, 1869.
    MoSHi: Jun 25, 1869-Jly 2, 1870.

Monitor   w   1855-1856
    Hammond says moved to Richfield 1856.

MOBERLY (Randolph County)

American Statesman   w   1896
    Listed in Ayer 1897.

Brother's Optic   w   1887-1893
    Negro. Listed as Western Optic Rowell 1893.

Chronicle   w   1880-1885
    One report says was printed part of this time in
    Missouri City and Salisbury.

Daily   d   1873-1878?
    ICHi: Sep 18, 1876. In Rowell 1874-1879.

Democrat   w   1871-1915   d   1873-1925
    MoHi: d, 1905-1906; Nov 2, 1908-Mar 31, 1925;
    Jun 19, Jly 7, 1905; Oct 15, 1908. Film, Jan
    26-Jun 30, 1896; 1899-1903; Nov 25, 1903-
    1904; Nov 1, 1906-Nov 30, 1908. Copy of
    Sunday edition, Feb 25, 1906; Daily Democrat,
    Oct 28, 1890, w, Oct 16, 1908.
    Micro-Photo: film, w, 1896; 1903-1915. d, 1896,
    1899-1925.

Democrat Leader   w   1926-1932
    Under Union List for name used for Home Press
    during these years.

Enterprise   w   1873-1874
    County history says merged with Monitor 1874.

MOBERLY (continued)

Enterprise & Monitor   w   1869-1878   d   1872-1878
    ICHi: w, Jly 20, 1876. d, Sep 21, 1876. In Rowell
    1874-1878. Under Monitor in 1879. Several
    founding dates used.

Fortschritt   w   1881
    Listed in Ayer 1881.

Headlight   w   1873-1902   d   1873-1895
    MoHi: w, Aug 1, 1901-1902. Missouri Editor, Jly
    1895, tells of end of Daily Headlight. Vol I,
    No 1, Sunday Morning Headlight appeared
    Aug 1, 1886. ICHi: Jly 20, 1876.

Herald   w   1912
    Listed in Ayer 1913.

Herald and Real Estate Index   w   1869
    According to county history brief career.

Home Press   w   1926-1932
    MoHi: Jly 4, 1926-Jun 17, 1932. See Democrat
    Leader.

Index   d   1916-1919
    MoHi: Film, Dec 31, 1918-Jun 1919; Jun 25-28,
    1919. Merged with Monitor Jly 1, 1919.
    Micro-Photo: Film, 1906-1917.

Message   w   1930+
    MoHi: Feb 24, 1933-1944. Film, 1945+.

League Gazette   w   1904-1905?
    MoHi: Dec 1, 1904; Feb 1, 1905.

Middle Man   m   1886-?
    MoHi: Sep 1899. Concerned with "real estate,
    commerce and immigration."

Monitor   w, sw   1868-1932   d   1873-1919
    MoHi: Film, Jan 3-Jun 28, 1876; Jan-Jun 1877;
    1878-1879; 1882-1901; Jly 1902-1916. W,
    1903-Jly 1909; 1917-May 19, 1932; Oct 23,
    1890; Oct 16, 1908. Film, 1880-1904; Aug
    10, 1909-1916.
    MoSHi: d, Jly 3, 1899. Semi-weekly, Mar 10,
    1916-Dec 11, 1917. Stopped May 19, 1932.
    Micro-Photo: Film, w, 1880-1916; 1922-1932.
    D, 1876-1879, 1882-1916.

Monitor-Index   d   1868-1925
    MoHi: Jly-Sep 1919; 1920-1950. Film, Jly 1919-
    Mar 20, 1920; 1951+. Monitor and Index merged
    Jly 1, 1919.

Monitor-Index and Democrat   d   1868+
    MoHi: See Monitor-Index. Full title used for paper
    in today's directories. Monitor-Index acquired
    Evening Democrat Apr 1, 1925.
    Micro-Photo: Film, 1919+.

Morning Chronicle   d   1880-1881
    Listed in Ayer 1881-1882.

MOBERLY (continued)

National Beacon   w   1882
    Listed in Ayer-Rowell 1883.

News   w   1885
    Listed in Rowell 1886.

Once in a While   w   1897
    Listed in Country Editor, Apr 1897, as a "breezy
    advertising sheet."

Randolph County Times   w   1895
    Listed in Ayer 1896.

Randolph Republican   w   1885-1889   d   1888
    Listed at times as Republican.

Saturday Evening Star   w   1909-1911
    Listed in Ayer 1910-1912.

Saturday Sentinel   w   1890
    MoHi: Oct 25, 1890. In Rowell 1891.

Sentinel   d   1891
    Listed in Ayer 1891.

Signal   w   1876
    MoHi: Film, May 13-Jly 1, 1876. In 1875 known
    as LaPlata Home Press.

Silver Star   w   1895
    Missouri Editor, Nov 1895, tells of start.

Star   d   1897-1898?
    In Ayer 1899, founding date 1897.

Times   d   1883, 1885
    Two attempts, both short-lived. Rowell 1884 tells
    of first; Missouri Editor, Apr, Jun 1895, tells of
    start and stop of Times.

Tribune   w   1904-1905
    MoHi: Dec 22, 1904-1905.

Western Optic   w   1887-1896?
    Negro. See Brother's Optic.

MODENA (Mercer County)

Monitor   w   1900-1901
    In Rowell 1901, Ayer 1901-1902.

MOKANE (Callaway County)

Herald   w   1894-1901
    See Herald-Post.

Herald-Post   w   1894 or 1893?   -1909
    MoHi: Jly 26, 1901-1908. In Rowell 1901-1908,
    Ayer 1902-1909.

Missourian   w   1894+
    MoHi: 1910-1920; Jly-Dec 1922; 1923-1925;
    Apr 1926-1944. Film, 1945+.

MOKANE (continued)

Times-Herald   w   1894-1898
    Union List says name used for Missourian for years
    shown.

MONEGAW SPRINGS (St. Clair County)

Spirit   w   1908-1909
    In Ayer 1910.

MONETT (Barry County)

Advertiser   d   1902
    In Ayer 1903.

Barry County Democrat   w   1937
    Ran Apr-Oct, notes MPN, Apr, Oct 1937.

Courier   w   1897-1898
    In Ayer 1898, Rowell 1897-1899.

Eagle   w   1888-1906
    MoHi: Oct 31, 1890. Film, Aug 21, 1903-Jun 1904.

Herald   d   1905-1906
    In Rowell 1906, Ayer 1907.

Journal   w   1919-1921
    MoHi: Mar 2, 1921. In Ayer 1920-1922.

Leader   w   1892-1902?
    Last in Ayer 1902, Rowell 1903.

News   w   1887
    In Ayer 1888, Rowell 1889.

Press   w   1911-1912?
    In Ayer 1913.

Record   d,w   1902-1915
    MoHi: Jly 14, 1914. Film, Jan 22, 1914-Aug 20,
    1915. Formerly Daily Star.
    MoSHi: Jan 14, 1915.

Star   d   1902-1913
    MoHi: Apr 10, 1906-May 8, 1911; Feb 10, Nov 10,
    12, 14, 1908. In Ayer 1903-1914.

Times   w   1899   d   1908+
    MoHi: Oct 30, 1939-1950; May 29, 1908; Dec
    15, 1954. Film, Jly 7, 1908-1910; Jan 11, 1912-
    1920; Aug-Sep 1924; Oct-Dec 1928; 1951+.
    W, Jun 25-Dec 1903; 1913-Oct 1939; May 29,
    1908. Film, Jun 25, 1903-Jun 2, 1907; Jan 1908-
    1910; 1912.
    KHi: Apr 20, 1926; Jly 7, 1928.

MONROE CITY (Monroe County)

Democrat   w   1888-1923
    MoHi: Dec 1, 1898-1914; 1918-1919; Jly 9,
    1902; Aug 10, 1905. Film, 1915-1917.
    MoSHi: Jan 4, 11, 1912.

MONROE CITY (continued)

Monroe County Appeal w 1865-1873
    Moved to Paris 1873.

Journal w 1894-1895
    Start noted in Missouri Editor, Sep 1894. In Ayer
    1895-1896.

News sw,w 1875+
    MoHi: 1914; 1917-1944; Jly 28,1881; Jan 11,
    25, Feb 1-15, Mar 15,29, Apr 5,26, May 17,
    31, Jun 14,21, Jly 19,26, Aug 2-16, Sep 13-
    27, Oct 4, Nov 8-22, Dec 13-27,1882; Oct
    30,1890. Film, Jan 14,1875-Aug 27,1885;
    1887-Jun 1890; 1892-1904; Feb 2,1905-
    1907; 1909; 1912-1913; 1915-1916; 1945+
    Jan 14,1875-1909 w; 1910-Jan 10,1930 sw;
    Jan 16,1930+ w.
    ICHi: Jly 6,1876.

MONTEVALLO (Vernon County)

Spectator w 1898
    In Rowell 1898, Ayer 1899.

Star w 1883
    In Rowell 1884.

MONTGOMERY CITY (Montgomery County)

Farmer w 1892
    In Ayer 1892.

Montgomery County Herald w 1917
    In Ayer 1918.

Montgomery County Independent w 1866-1867
    Mentioned in county history.

Montgomery City Journal w 1857-1861
    Moved to Danville, renamed Chronicle.

Montgomery County News w 1895-1952
    MoHi: Aug 29,1940-1944. Film,1945-1952.
    Formerly Jonesburg Message; to Montgomery
    City Aug 29,1940.

Montgomery County Republican w 1892-1900
    MoHi: Film, Nov 25,1898-Sep 1900.

Montgomery Standard w 1866+
    MoHi: 1880-1883; 1902-1907; 1910-1944; Oct
    24,1890. Film, Sep 1875-Sep 1876; 1884-Mar
    14,1902; 1908-1909; 1945+.
    MoSHi: Jly 31,1908.
    ICHi: Jan 14, Jly 7,1876.
    NHi: Dec 26,1872.

Ray w 1871-1891?
    ICHi: Jly 7,1876. Formerly in Danville.

MONTGOMERY CITY (continued)

Tribune w 1892-1910
    MoHi: 1906-1910; Dec 15,1905. Film,1901-
    Jly 15,1904; Jly 22,1904-1905.
    Montgomery City Library: Misc. copies 1901-1904.

MONTICELLO (Lewis County)

Lewis County Journal w 1878+
    MoHi: 1901-1914; 1916-1944; Apr 12, Jun 29,
    Jly 12,19,1907. Film, Oct 4,1889-1900;
    1915; 1945-1952. Since 1929 at Canton.

North Missourian w 1872-1873
    In Rowell 1873-1874.

Observer w 1877-1908?
    In Rowell 1908. Union List says title for Lewis
    County Journal 1907-1908.

Reporter w 1856
    In Newspaper Record 1856.

MONTROSE (Henry County)

Democrat w 1886,1894-1899?
    Missouri Editor, Feb 1894, tells of change of name
    from Magnet to Democrat. Earlier Democrat
    began Sep 1886.

Herald w 1886
    In Ayer-Rowell 1887.

Herald-Tidings w 1892+
    MoHi: Film, Oct 18,1957+. See Urich.

John Orear's Banner w 1884
    In Rowell-Dauchy 1885.

Magnet w 1886-1893
    See Democrat.

Messenger w 1895-1898?
    Rowell 1883 lists Messenger, printed in Clinton
    Messenger office.

Monitor w 1884-1885
    In Rowell 1885-1886.

News w 1894
    In Ayer 1895.

Recorder w 1899-1918
    MoHi: Jly 26,1901-1903; 1906-1912; 1915-
    Aug 30,1918. Film,1904-1905; 1913-1914.

Signal w 1891-1892?
    MoHi: Nov 12,1891.

Tidings w 1918-1941,1947-1957
    MoHi: Dec 26,1918-Jan 1928; 1929-1941.
    Suspended Dec 9,1941, resumed in 1947.
    Merged with Urich Herald Oct 18,1957.

MONTROSE (continued)

X-Ray w 1898
    In Rowell 1898-1899, Ayer 1899.

MOORESVILLE (Livingston County)

Mention w 1881-1883?
    In Rowell 1882-1884, Ayer 1883.

MOREHOUSE (New Madrid County)

Enterprise w 1925-1926
    Listed in Ayer 1926-1927

Hustler w 1907-1918
    MoHi: Mar 15, 1907-1910. Film, Jan 12, 1917-
    Nov 29, 1918.

Messenger w 1919-1930
    Last listed in Ayer 1931.

Post w 1901
    Listed in Ayer 1902.

Sun w 1904-1906
    In Rowell 1906-1907.

Tri-County Spectator w 1897?-1898?
    Listed in Ayer 1899.

Volunteer w 1899
    Listed in Rowell 1899.

MORLEY (Scott County)

Advance w 1872-1873
    Listed in Ayer 1873-1874.

Headlight w 1894
    Mentioned in Missouri Editor, Jly 1894.

Record w 1891-1892
    Rowell 1891-1893 refer to Benton.

Scott County Banner w 1895-1921
    MoHi: 1920-Aug 1921. Film, 1914-1919.

Scott County Citizen w 1903-1909
    MoHi: Aug 7, 1908. Film, 1909. Formerly Oran
    Scott County Citizen. Moved to Morley Apr
    3, 1908.

Transcript w, sm 1872-1877
    ICHi: SM, May 19, 1876. In Rowell 1875-1878.

MORRISVILLE (Polk County)

Journal w 1910-1918
    MoHi: Film, Jan 12, 1912-1913.

News w 1877-1879?
    Mentioned in county histories.

MORRISVILLE (continued)

Polk County Advocate w 1923-1924
    Mentioned in Union List. No files.

MOSCOW MILLS (Lincoln County)

Booster w 1904
    Listed in Ayer 1905.

Bee w 1907-1908
    In Rowell 1908, Ayer 1908-1909.

Phonograph w 1894-1897?
    Missouri Editor, Sep 1894, tells of Winfield
    Phonograph moving to Moscow.

MOUND CITY (Holt County)

Courier w 1897
    Country Editor, Oct 1897, tells of merger of Times,
    Republican, Democrat and Courier, into the Courier

Globe w 1875-1877
    MoHi: Oct 21, Nov 9, 18, 25, 1875; Jan 20, Feb 17,
    Sep 14, 1876.
    ICHi: Aug 17, 1876.

Holt County Democrat and Craig Leader w 1886-1948
    MoHi: 1933-1944. Film, 1945-Oct 8, 1948. Formerl
    Craig Leader. Moved to Mound City Jan 6, 1933
    Back to Craig 1948.

Holt County Independent w 1927-1929
    MoHi: Sep 22, 1927-Aug 1929. Merged with News-
    Jeffersonian, became News-Independent Sep 5,
    1929.

Jeffersonian w 1891-1914
    MoHi: Nov 24, 1898-May 1900; Jly 1903-1904;
    1907-Jan 29, 1914. Film, 1905-Dec 20, 1906.
    Merged with News, became News-Jeffersonian
    Feb 1914.

Journal w 1915-1925
    MoHi: 1919-Dec 24, 1925; Oct 23, 1924. Suspended
    Dec 24, 1925.
    KHi: Apr 2, 1925.

News w 1879-1914
    MoHi: Jly 19, 1901-Jan 29, 1914; Aug 3, 1900;
    Mar 22, 1901. See Jeffersonian.

News-Independent w 1879+
    MoHi: Sep 5, 1929-1944. Film, 1945+. Formed by
    merger of News-Jeffersonian and Holt County
    Independent Sep 5, 1929.

News-Jeffersonian w 1891-1929
    MoHi: Feb 5, 1914-1928. Formerly News and
    Jeffersonian. Merged Feb 1914. Merged with
    Holt County Independent. Sep 5, 1929.
    KHi: Mar 9, 1928.

MOUND CITY (continued)

Spy   w   1874-1875
    Press moved to Graham 1875.

Times   w   1891-1897?
    Last listed in Rowell 1898.

MOUNDVILLE (Vernon County)

Enquirer   w   1886
    Listed in Ayer 1886.

Monitor   w   1922?
    In Ayer 1925, founding date 1922.

Register   w   1886
    Listed in Ayer 1887.

Times   w   1890-1893
    MoHi: Oct 30, 1890.

MOUNTAIN GROVE (Wright County)

Advance   w   1905-1906
    Listed in Ayer 1906-1907.

Advertiser   w   1897?-1900?
    Also known as Mountain Advertiser, later Journal.

Breeze   w   1885-1886.
    In Rowell-Ayer 1886-1887.

Christain Watchman   w   1884?
    Listed as Republican founded 1884, in Rowell 1892.

Enterprise   w   1903
    MoHi: Film, Nov 26-Dec 31, 1903.

Herald   w   1912-1917
    Listed in Ayer 1913-1918.

Hornet   w   1896
    In Missouri Editor, Feb 1896, as new paper.

Journal   w   1896+
    MoHi: Dec 2, 1898-Oct 1900; Jly 1901-1944.
    Film, 1945+. Founding date 1897 in Ayer 1900-
    1929.

Midget   d   1895
    New daily in Missouri Editor, Aug 1895.

Mountaineer   w   1877
    Mentioned in county history.

Mountain Prospect   w   1882-1894?
    MoHi: Oct 10, 31, 1890. In Rowell-Ayer 1883-1894.

News   d,w   1908-1909
    Listed in Ayer 1909-1910.

Our Country   w   1896
    Listed in Ayer 1897.

MOUNTAIN GROVE (continued)

Republican   w   1892-1893   d   1894
    Directories tell of weekly, Missouri Editor notes
    d start Apr 1894.

Times   w   1883
    Listed in Rowell-Dauchy 1884.

Tribune   w   1894-1895
    In Rowell 1895, Ayer-Dauchy 1896.

Tri-County News   w   1926+
    MoHi: Film, Apr 11, 1957+.

Wright County Clipper   w   1903
    Listed in Ayer 1904.

Wright County Democrat   w   1906
    Listed in Rowell-Ayer 1907.

World's Cresset
    MoHi: 1915-1918. Formerly in Bushyknob. In
    1918 moved to Leachville, Arkansas. Religious
    paper.

MOUNT MORIAH (Harrison County)

Advance   w   1896?
    In Ayer 1900 founding date of 1896.

Success   w   1900
    Listed in Ayer 1901.

MOUNT OLIVE (St. Louis County)

Clayton Democrat   w   1877-1881
    Under Clayton in Rowell 1881-1883.

Mail   w   1877-1878
    Listed in Rowell 1879.

St. Louis County Waechter   w   1878-1882?
    Listed in Ayer 1883.

St. Louis County Watchman   w   1881-1882?
    Under Mount Olive in Ayer 1883.

Star-Republican   w   1878-1882?
    Rowell 1881-1883 refers to Clayton. In Ayer
    1881, 1883.

MOUNT VERNON (Lawrence County)

Advance   w   1949-1951
    MoHi: Film, 1951. Subscription list combined
    with Lawrence Chieftain 1951.

Empire   w   1875-1890?   d   1879-1890?
    County histories tell of the Empire, suspended
    during "early nineties".

Era   d   1905-1907
    MoHi: Film, Nov 13, 1905-Mar 22, 1907.

MOUNT VERNON (continued)

Fountain and Journal   w   1867-1916?
    MoHi: Oct 9,1890; Jun 19,1914. Film,Feb 26,
        1874-1900; 1903.
    MoSp: Jly 13,1876.
    ICHi: Jly 20,1876.

Immigrants Guide   w   1881-1885
    MoSHi: Sep 1882. Founded in Pierce City 1878.
    To Mount Vernon 1881.

Lawrence Chieftain   w   1876+
    MoHi: 1919-1944; Jly 2,1914. Film, Jun 24,
        1880-Nov 24,1892,inc. Sep 1,1892-Jan 20,
        1898,inc; Jan 26,1899-1918; 1945+.
    MoSp: Jly 12,1876.
    ICHi: May 31,1876.
    KHi: Apr 25,1912.

Lawrence County Democrat   w   1871-1872
    Moved to Pierce City, notes Hammond.

Lawrence County Journal   w   1872-1873
    MoHi: Film, Sep 21,1872-Oct 2,1873. Combined
        with Fountain, as Fountain and Journal,1873.

Lawrence County Plain Talk   w   1894
    Populist paper listed in Ayer 1895.

Lawrence County Record   w   1898+
    MoHi: Jly 25,1901-Jun 1902; May 1903-Jly 1904;
        1905-1910; Jly 2,1914; Dec 9,1954. Film,
        1911-Aug 1913; Jan 10-1924; Aug 13-Dec
        1925; Apr-Dec 1926; May 26-Dec 1927; 1934;
        1936-1948; 1950+.

Lawrence County Register   w   1856-1857
    First in county. To Cassville mid-1857, according
    to Organ.

Lawrence County Telegram   w   1891-1893
    In Rowell, Ayer 1892-1894.

Missouri Reporter   w   1857-1861
    Founded by Lewis Lamkin,who started Register.

Progressive Era   w   1914
    MoHi: Jly 3,1914.

Southwest Vindicator   w   1866
    Mentioned by Hammond.

Spring River Fountain   w   1867-1873
    MoHi: Jan 2,Oct 1,Nov 12,1868; Jly 21,28,
        Oct 27,Apr 14,1870; Feb 16,1871; Mar 4,
        11,1869. Film,Feb 28,1867-Jly 20,1871.

Watchman   w   1857?-1861
    In American Newspaper Directory 1861.

MOUNTAIN VIEW (Howell County)

Booster   w   1922
    Listed in Ayer 1923.

MOUNTAIN VIEW (continued)

Ozark Mountain News   w   1930-1941
    Mentioned in MPN, Jun 1941,sold to Standard.

Postman   w   1901-1904
    MoHi: Jly-Dec 1903. Film, Jly 3,1903-Sep 16,
        1904.

Standard   w   1899,1907+
    Ayer 1900 tells of Standard,started in 1899. Next
    listing is Ayer 1908, Standard starting in 1907.

Times   w   1900-1902?
    In Ayer 1901, Rowell 1901-1903.

X-Ray   w   1906-1907?
    In Rowell 1907-1908, Ayer 1907.

MOUNT WASHINGTON (Jackson County)

News   w   1912?-1927?
    Listed in Ayer 1927-1928.

MURPHYSBURG (Jasper County)

Mining News   w   1872-1873
    Listed in Rowell 1872-1873.

NAYLOR (Ripley County)

Advocate   w   1907-1908
    In Rowell 1908, Ayer 1908-1909.

Nail   w   1910-1912
    Listed in Ayer 1912-1913.

Outlook   w   1895
    In Ayer 1896, Missouri Editor 1895.

Recorder   w   1893
    Listed in Rowell 1894.

Transcript   w   1893-1895
    Death in Missouri Editor, Apr 1895.

NECK CITY (Jasper County)

Breezes   w   1901
    Listed in Ayer 1902.

News   w   1900-1907
    In Rowell 1907, Ayer 1901, 1903, 1907-1908.

NELSON (Saline County)

Advance   w   1909-1910
    Listed in Ayer 1910-1911.

Courier   w   1892-1894
    In Rowell 1894, Ayer 1894-1895.

Hummer   w   1894-1897?
    Last in Ayer 1897, Rowell 1898.

ELSON (continued)

Record   w   1911-1914
    Listed in Ayer 1912-1915.

Time Card   w   1889-1906
    In Rowell 1890-1907, Ayer 1889-1900.

NEOSHO (Newton County)

Argus   d   1884
    Published briefly in 1884 before equipment
    moved to Springdale to start Journal Weekly
    Telephone?

Call   d   1881-1882?
    Listed in Rowell 1882.

Chief   w   1854-1858
    Apparently renamed Herald, equipment carried
    away by Confederates 1861 or 1862.

Democrat   d   1905-1952
    MoHi: Jly 17, 1914. Film, Jly 19, 1905-1914;
      Jly 23, 1915-1924; Jly 3, 1925-Jun 29, 1940;
      Jly 1940-1941; Jly-Dec 1944-Nov 1952.
      Name changed to Daily News Dec 1, 1952.
    Micro-Photo: Film, 1905-1952.

District Herald   w   1877
    Mentioned in county history.

Free Press   w   1902-1904
    MoHi: Film, Oct 9, 1903-Sep 30, 1904.

Gazette   w   1868
    Campaign sheet, moved to Granby as Southwest
    Independent. Merged with Investigator Dec 1869.

Herald   w   1858-1861   d   1902-1905
    See Chief for earlier paper. Ayer 1905 lists daily,
    founded 1902. Rowell 1906 lists Herald as semi-
    monthly religious publication.

Investigator   w   1869-1870
    MoHi: Nov 24, 1869; Mar 31, 1870. Later called
    Journal, moved to Granby, soon suspended.

Journal   w   1871-1881
    MWA: Jun 8, 1871.
    ICHi: Jly 6, 1876.
    WHi: Dec 26, 1872. Rowell 1871 says founded 1870,
    other sources 1871.

Mail   d   1888, 1903
    Two brief attempts at publishing.

Miner and Mechanic   w   1873+   d   1879-1880
    MoHi: d, Film, Sep 23, 1879-Mar 25, 1880. w, Jly
      4, 1903-1944; Mar 3, 1909; Aug 19, 1910.
      Film, Oct 25, 1879-1902; 1945+. Formerly
      Granby Miner. Moved to Neosho, changed
      name, 1877.

NEOSHO (continued)

Missouri Army Argus   1861
    MoSHi: Extra published in Nov 1861.

News   d   1905+
    MoHi: Aug 31, 1953. Film, Dec 1, 1952+. See
      Democrat. Started as News 1952.
    Micro-Photo: film, 1953+.

Newton County Democrat   w   1889, 1896
    Rowell 1890 lists as edition of Evening Star.
    Ayer 1897 lists paper, founded 1896.

Newton County Tribune   w   1866-1869
    MoHi: Jun 9, 1869. Merged with Independent 1869.

Populist   w   1894-1895?
    In Ayer, 1895, Dauchy, 1896.

Republican   w   1882-1883?, 1896
    Apparently two, both short-lived.

Rustler   w   1890-1895
    Last listed in Ayer 1896.

Silver Advocate   w   1895
    Listed in Ayer 1896.

Star   d   1889
    Listed in Rowell 1890.

Times   w   1869-1953
    MoHi: 1904-1910; 1913-1944; Nov 6, 1890.
      Film, Jan 7, 1870-Aug 21, 1884; May 20, 1886-
      Oct 30, 1889; 1890-1893; 1911-1912; 1945-
      Jly 23, 1953. Suspended Jly 23, 1953, purchased
      by News.
    ICHi: Mar 30, 1876.
    Micro-Photo: film, 1892-1896; 1901-1910 inc.;
      1913-1944.

Tribune   w   1866   d   1894
    County history notes earlier paper. Missouri Editor,
    Dec 1894, tells of new daily.

Tudor   tw,   d   1902-1903
    Brief career. Various frequency.

NEVADA (Vernon County)

Criterion   w   1879-1881
    Became Southwest Mail. Copy dated March 29,
    1881 (Vol 2, No 29) title Democratic Criterion.
    By Sep called Criterion.

Democrat   w   1868-1893   d   1882-1893
    MoHi: w, Aug 8, 1889; Jly 10, 1890. Directory data
    varied. See Vernon County Democrat. Issue
    of Daily Democrat dated Mar 18, 1885 is Vol V,
    No 158.

Director   w   1892-1899   d   1894-1896?
    MoHi: d, Film, Sep 22-Nov 6, 1894. W, film, Jly
    20-Nov 2, 1894; Apr 15, 1897-Feb 3, 1898.

NEVADA (continued)

Herald w 1888+
    MoHi: Jan-May 1939; 1944. Film, 1945+.
    MoSHi: Jly 3, 1955.
    KHi: Feb 24, 1922; Jly 20, 1923.

Industrial Review w 1890-1891
    MoHi: Oct 31, 1890.

Ledger w 1873-1887?
    ICHi: Jan 13, Jly 6, 1876. In Rowell 1874-1888,
    Ayer 1880.

Living Democrat w 1872-1879
    ICHi: Jan 21, 1876. Under Vernon County
    Democrat Rowell 1880.

Mail d 1883+
    MoHi: Feb 1, 1944-1950. Film, Jly 10, 1883-1888;
    1892-1894; 1896-Mar 1937; Jly 1937-Jan
    1944; 1951+. W edition as Southwest Mail in
    directories. Also listed as Mail and Post during
    some years.
    Micro-Photo: Film, 1883-1888; 1892-1894; 1896+
    KHi: Dec 29, 1924.

New Moon ? 1886-?
    Published "For Boys and Girls."

Noticer w 1886-1894
    MoHi: Nov 6, 1890.

Popular Therapeutics sm 1911-1913?
    MoHi: Jun 3, 1911-May 3, 1913. Not a paper.

Post w 1868-1917 d 1881-1917
    MoHi: w, Jly 1901-Jan 1906; 1909-Oct 1917;
    Aug 18, 1905. Film, Dec 1907-1908. Merged
    with Southwest Mail Oct 1917 to become
    Southwest Mail and the Weekly Post.

Reform Signal w 1884
    Listed in Dauchy 1884.

Silver Slogan w 1895
    Listed in Ayer 1896.

Southwest Mail w 1879-1917
    MoHi: 1906-1915. Film, 1901-1905. See Post.

Southwest Mail and the Weekly Post 1917-1944
    MoHi: 1920-Jan 28, 1944. See Post. Changed to
    Daily Mail Feb 1, 1944.

Times w 1866-1871 d 1881?
    Became Vernon County Democrat 1871, Living
    Democrat 1872, Vernon County Democrat 1880,
    Post 1894. D started 1881, according to
    county history.

Tribune w 1884
    In Dauchy 1884, Rowell 1885.

NEVADA (continued)

Vernon County Democrat w 1872-1887?,
                           1891-1900
    Name used several times. See Times.

Vernon County Republican w 1888-1899?
    At times listed as Republican.

NEW BLOOMFIELD (Callaway County)

News w 1902-1957
    MoHi: Jun 19, 1903-Jun 1905; Jly 1912-1920;
    1924-1944. Film, 1945-1946; 1949-Oct 10,
    1957, when it ceased.

Record w 1905-1906
    In Rowell 1906-1908, Ayer 1906.

NEWBURG (Phelps County)

Democrat w 1939-1952?
    Listed in Ayer 1942-1953.

Independent w 1906-1910?
    Listed in Ayer 1907-1911.

Phelps County News w, d 1894
    Listed in Ayer 1895.

Phelps County Record w 1914-1922
    MoHi: 1920-Oct 1921; Jan-Nov 1922. Film,
    Jan 30, 1914-1919.

Times w 1939-1940
    Listed in Ayer 1941.

NEW CAMBRIA (Macon County)

Advocate w 1891
    Listed in Ayer 1892.

Enterprise w 1874-1876
    ICHi: Jan 12, 1876. Published from office Macon
    Missouri Granger.

Herald w 1881-1885
    In Rowell 1884-1886, Ayer 1883.

Independent w 1894-1912?
    In Rowell 1896-1908, Ayer 1896-1913.

Leader w 1913-1961
    MoHi: Mar 25, 1927-1944. Film, 1945-1961. Ended
    Aug 25, 1961.

Macon County Standard w 1877-1878?
    In Rowell 1878-1879.

Press w 1888-1891?
    MoHi: Oct 25, 1890.

NEW CONCEPTION (Nodaway County)

Herald   w   1900-1905?
In Rowell 1904-1906, Ayer 1901.

NEW FLORENCE (Montgomery County)

Montgomery County Leader   w   1888-1951
MoHi: Dec 2, 1898-1900; 1908-1916; Oct 31,
1890; Apr 13, 1901. Film, 1901-1902; 1906-
1907; 1917-1918; 1945-1951. Ended Oct
19, 1951.

News   w   1893?
In Rowell 1900, with 1893 founding date.

Optic   w   1877-1890
MoHi: Oct 24, 1890.

Plaindealer   w   1870-1871
Moved to Jonesburg as Leader.

NEW FRANKLIN (Howard County)

Echo   w   1893-1895?
See News Echo.

Echo-News   w   1895
Missouri Editor, May 1895, tells of consolidation
Echo, News.

Herald   w   1894
Brief career, "outstanding accounts too heavy."

Howard County News   w   1903-1904
See News.

News   w   1893-1960
MoHi: Jly 1903-Jly 1904; Nov 25, 1898-Mar 23,
1900; 1913-1944. Film, 1945-1954. Named
Howard County News from Jly 1903-Jly 1904.
Last issue Nov 17, 1960.

News-Echo   w   1896-1897
MoSHi: Mar 5, 1897. Rowell 1897 lists News-Echo,
News in 1898.

NEW HAMPTON (Harrison County)

Herald   w   1896-1920
MoHi: Jly 25, 1901-1913; 1916-Jun 1920. Film,
1914-1915.

Tribune   w   1921-1943
Last issue Feb 10, 1943.

NEW HAVEN (Franklin County)

Leader   1895+
MoHi: Jly-Dec 1903; 1913-1944. Film, 1945+.
Missouri Editor, May 1895, tells of founding.

Mail   w   1870?-1883?
Conflict on starting, one source says 1871. May
have become News 1884, Notes 1885.

NEW HAVEN (continued)

News   w   1884-1885   1940-1941
See Mail. Franklin County News title of more
recent paper.

Notes   w   1885-1897?
MoHi: Jan 18, Feb 8, Aug 9, Nov 29, Dec 27, 1889;
Feb 5, 1892; Aug 10, 1894.

NEW LONDON (Ralls County)

Democrat   w   1889
Listed in Ayer 1889.

Herald   w   1867
Thomas R. Dodge attended first editors' meeting
in 1867.

Men Mayhall's News   w   1895-1896
Start noted in Missouri Editor, Nov 1895.

Ralls County Beacon   w   1855-1861
MoHi: Sep 20, 1860.

Ralls County Guide   w   1879-1888
In Rowell 1880-1889, Ayer 1880-1888.

Ralls County Record   w   1865+
MoHi: 1904-1908; 1909-Jan 28, 1944; Dec 27.
1907; Jan-Feb, Mar 13, 1908. Film, Jun 29,
1865-Aug 1876; Nov 1881-Sep 20, 1882;
Oct 1884-Sep 1885; Oct 13, 1886-Oct 12,
1887; Jan-Oct 10, 1888; Oct 25, 1889-Oct
1890; Jly 26, 1901-1903; Feb 15, 1946+.
ICHi: Jun 29, 1876. Closed 1944-Feb 1946,
owner in service.

Ralls County Republican   w   1886-1888?
In Ayer 1886-1889.

Ralls County Times   w   1898-1916
MoHi: Feb 18, 1898-1904; 1908-Jun 2, 1916; Jan-
Feb 7, 1908. Film, 1905-1907.

NEW MADRID (New Madrid County)

Chronicle   w   1872, 1873, 1879-1881
Two noted in county histories.

Commercial Herald   w   1848-1852?
Noted by Kennedy 1852, Organ.

Gazette   w   1846-1854
Renamed Times 1854.

Headlight   w   1894-1908
Union List notes under Portageville Southeast
Missourian about Headlight in New Madrid.

Herald   w   1855?
Listed in Newspaper Record 1856.

Journal of the Times   w   1853?
MoSHi: Jun 25, Jly 1, 1853.

NEW MADRID (continued)

Missourian   w   1894-1895
    Missouri Editor, Feb 1895, notes death.

Record   w   1866+
    MoHi: 1893; 1920-1944; Dec 22,1883; Nov 15,
    1890. Film, Nov 23,1901-1919; 1945+.
    MoSHi: Feb 22-Mar 7,28,1908; Apr 10,17,May
    15,29, Jun 19-Jly 3,31,Aug 28,Sep 18,Oct
    9,23,1909; Apr 27,1912.
    ICHi: Jan 15, Jly 8,1876.

Record-Tribune   w   1876-1879
    Under this title Rowell-Ayer 1880. Data same
    under Tribune.

Southeast Chronicle   w   1879-1882?
    In Rowell 1880-1882, Ayer 1880.

Southeast Missourian   w   1894-1912
    MoHi: Film, Dec 1894-1912. Became Portageville
    Southeast Missourian 1913.

Times   w   1854-1861
    MoHi: Apr 7,1860.

Tribune   w   1876-1879
    Later Record, Record-Tribune.

NEW MARKET (Platte County)

Monitor   w   1891
    In Ayer-Rowell 1892.

NEWBURG (Phelps County)

Democrat   w   1939-1942?
    In MPN, Oct 1942, as celebrating its third
    birthday.

Phelps County News   w   1894
    Noted in Missouri Editor, Jly 1894.

Phelps County Record   w   1914-1922
    Mentioned in Union List.

Times   w   1939-1940
    Ended Jun 28,1940. Subscription list sold to Rolla
    Herald.

NEWTON (Newton County)

Eye   w   1887
    In Rowell 1888. Newtonia?

NEWTONIA (Newton County)

New South   w   1871
    In Rowell 1872.

Gladiator   w   1892
    In Ayer 1892. See Newtown.

NEWTONIA (continued)

Newton County News   w   1890-1906
    MoHi: Oct 30,1890. Film,1903-Jun 27,1907.

News Herald   w   1908
    In Ayer 1909.

Wave   w   1891
    In Ayer 1891.

NEWTOWN (Sullivan County)

Chronicle   w   1895-1926,1936-1937
    Two published under this title.

Gladiator   w   1892-1894
    May be confused with Newtonia. Missouri Editor,
    Feb 1894, says J. A. Graves will revive the
    Newtown Gladiator. Under Newtown in Ayer 189
    1895.

Monitor   w   1887-1890?
    J. A. Graves listed as E&P of Monitor.

Record   w   1890
    Listed in Rowell 1891.

NIANGUA (Webster County)

News   w   1937-1938?
    Only reference in MPN, Feb 1938.

NIXA (Christian County)

Missourian   w   1935-1937
    Listed in Ayer 1938.

News   w   1903-1906
    In Rowell 1904-1907, Ayer 1904-1906.

Reporter   w   1954?-1957
    Listed in Ayer 1957-1958.

NOEL (McDonald County)

Graphic   w   1912-1915,1919-1921
    In Ayer 1915-16,1921-1922.

McDonald County Press   w   1943+
    First listed in Ayer 1955.

News   w   1925-1927
    Listed in Ayer 1926-1928.

Ozark Press   w   1929-1942,1945-1953?
    Paper, also listed as Noel-Ozark Press, suspended
    during World War II.

Owl   w   1924
    Listed in Ayer 1925.

Reporter   w   1899
    Listed in Ayer 1900.

NOEL (continued)

Times   w   1898
    Listed in Ayer 1899.

NORBORNE (Carroll County)

Democrat   w   1900-1923
    MoHi: Apr 28, 1911. See Democrat-Leader.

Democrat-Leader   w   1900+
    MoHi: May 12, 1939-1944. Film, 1945+. Merged
    Democrat and Leader Aug 10, 1923. Under
    Democrat and The Leader MoHi has Aug 10,
    1923-May 5, 1939.

Enterprise   w   1887-1889
    In Rowell 1888-1890, Ayer 1888-1889.

Independent   w   1876-1884
    MoHi: Apr 15, 1881.
    ICHi: Apr 29, 1876. In Rowell 1876-1886, Ayer 1880.

Jeffersonian   w   1888-1901
    MoHi: Dec 2, 1898-Dec 21, 1900.
    MoSHi: Aug 23, 1895-Oct 2, 1896. Merged with
    Leader 1901.

Leader   w   1884-1923
    MoHi: 1905 inc; Jan 11, 1906-Aug 3, 1923; Oct
    24, 31, 1890. See Democrat-Leader.

Leader-Jeffersonian   w   1901-1904
    MoHi: Jly 2, 1903-Aug 25, 1904.

Register   w   1933-1938
    Formerly Tina Interior Journal; to Norborne in 1933.

NORTH KANSAS CITY (Clay County)

Clay County News   w   1920-1923
    Listed as News Ayer 1925.

Co-operative Consumer   w   1935-1944?
    MoHi: 1935-1944.

Gladstone News   w   1957+
    Under North Kansas City Ayer 1960-1961. See
    Gladstone.

Industrial Press   w   1930-1952
    MoHi: Mar 7, 1935-1944. Film, 1945-Jan 14, 1952.
    Ended 1952, became Press-Dispatch Jan 17, 1952.

News   w   1920-1952
    MoHi: Apr 17, 1930-1944. Film, 1945-Jan 10,
    1952. Ended 1952. Became News-Dispatch
    Jan 21, 1952.

News-Dispatch   w   1916+
    MoHi: Film, Jan 21, 1952; Jan 12, 1953-1954+.
    See News.

Press-Dispatch   w   1928+
    MoHi: Film, Jan 22, 1953-1956. See Industrial Press.

NORTH ST. LOUIS (St. Louis County)

Headlight   w   1880?
    NHi: Jly 11, 1880.

Messenger   w   1877
    In Rowell 1878 as Sunday paper.

NORTH SPRINGFIELD (Greene County)

New Era   w, d   1886
    In Rowell 1887; probably continuation of South-
    Wester.

Republican   w   1870
    In Rowell 1871.

Southwest   w   1870-1875?
    In Rowell 1872-1876.

South-Wester   w   1876-1885?
    In Rowell 1877-1886, Ayer 1880-1882.

NORWOOD (Wright County)

Citizen   w, m   1894-1897?
    Rowell 1895 lists as monthly.

Index   w   1927?-1949
    Became Mountain Grove Tri-County News 1949.

Press   w   1915-1916?
    In Ayer 1917.

South Missourian   w   1899-1900
    In Rowell 1900-1901, Ayer 1900.

World's Cresset   w   1902-1910?
    MoHi: Film, 1906-1910. Also Fowler World's
    Cresset. Also published at Trask, Pomona and
    Brushyknob.

NOVELTY (Knox County)

News   w   1919-1920
    In Ayer 1921.

NOVINGER (Adair County)

Free Press   w   1913-1914
    MoHi: Feb 28, 1913-Aug 21, 1914. Formerly Herald
    to 1912. Renamed Herald Sep 2, 1914.

Herald   1904-1946?
    MoHi: 1915-Aug 1916. See Free Press. Also called
    Adair County Herald.

Nugget   w   1902
    In Ayer 1903.

Record   w   1904-1912
    MoHi: Apr 6, 1906-1909; Dec 10, 1909; Jan 7-21,
    1910. Changed to Free Press 1912.

OAK GROVE (Jackson County)

Banner   w   1889+
  MoHi: Jly 27,1901-1905; 1908-1944; Oct 8,
    1898; May 26,1905. Film,1905-Dec 20,1907;
    1945+.
  MoKc: 1907-1932.

Sentinel   w   1866+
  First in Ayer 1960. Formerly Independence Sentinel.

OAK RIDGE (Cape Girardeau County)

Cape County Independent   w   1915-1917
  In Ayer 1916-1918.

Indicator   w   1906-1911
  MoHi: Film,Sep 6,1906-1910.

O'DAY (Barry County)

Globe   w   1887-1888
  In Ayer 1887, Rowell 1888-1889.

ODESSA (Lafayette County)

Adair's Odessa Democrat   w   1883-1942
  See Democrat.

Democrat   w   1883-1942
  MoHi: Nov 2,1901-May 29,1942; Oct 3,1890.
    Merged with Missouri Ledger Jun 5,1942.
    Became Odessan.

Herald   w   1880-1886
  In Rowell 1880-1887, Ayer 1881-1887.

Missouri Ledger   w   1892-1942
  MoHi: 1920-May 29,1942. Film, Jan 9,1914-
    1919. See Democrat. 1892 date doubtful.
    First in Ayer 1900,although Country Editor,
    May 1899,tells of start of paper.

Moon   w   1891-1898
  Allied with Farmers'-Laborers' Union.

News   w   1891
  Same publisher for Moon,Rowell 1893.

Odessan   w   1884+
  MoHi: Jun 5,1942-1944. Film,1945+.

Oracle   w   1901-1903
  MoHi: Film,Feb 27,1902-Mar 19,1903. In Ayer
    1901,1903.

O'FALLON (St. Charles County)

Community News   w   1951+
  Changed to free distribution paper 1961.

Community Record   w   1951+
  Founded 1961,replacing Community News as legal
    paper and using 1951 for founding date. Same
    owners as Community News.

O'FALLON (continued)

Hausfreund   w   1888-1900?
  MoSc: 1899-1900.

Katholischer Hausfreund   w   1883-1910?
  Apparently name used at times for Hausfreund.

Observer   w   1935
  Started 1935 according to MPN,Feb 1935.

OLD ORCHARD (St. Louis County)

Herald   w   1889-1892
  Listed in Rowell 1891-1893.

OLEAN (Miller County)

Independent   w   1904-1912
  In Rowell 1906-1908; Ayer 1905-1913.

News   w   1891-1904?
  In Rowell 1892-1905, Ayer 1892-1900.

ORAN (Scott County)

News   w   1949+
  First listed in Ayer 1950.

Record   w   1890-1892?
  Rowell 1891-1893,reference to Benton.

Scott County Citizen   w   1903-1908
  MoHi: Film,Oct 18,1907-Dec 18,1908. Moved
    to Morley Apr 3,1908.

Tribune   w   1914-1918
  Listed in Ayer 1916-1919.

OREGON (Holt County)

County Paper   w   1881-1883
  MoHi: Jan 7,1881-Jly 27,1883. Formerly Holt
    County Sentinel. Under County Paper for years
    shown. Renamed Holt County Sentinel Aug 17,
    1883.

Holt County Democrat   w   1891-1898?
  Last listed in Rowell 1899.

Holt County News   w   1857-1861
  MoHi: Film, Jly 1,1857-Jly 1,1859. Equipment
    seized by Federal authorities, 1861.

Holt County Press   w   1876-1890
  In Rowell 1877-1890, Ayer 1880-1887.

Holt County Sentinel   w   1865+
  MoHi: Jun 30,1865-1880; Aug 17,1883-1885;
    1911-1944; Sep 11,25,1896; Jun 27,29,1888;
    Oct 31,1890; Jan 9,16,30, Feb 11, Mar 3, Apr
    24,1891. Film, Jan 1886-1910; 1945+. See
    County Paper.

OREGON (continued)

Holt County Sentinel (continued)
MoSHi: Jun 30, 1865- Jun 20, 1869.
ICHi: Sep 22, 1876.
KHi: Mar 9, 1923.

Missouri Valley Times   w   1874-1876
ICHi: Jan 19, May 31, Jun 28, Jly 5, 1876.
Renamed Holt County Press 1876, from Dec 1887-
Sep 1888 named Advocate and Temperance. Then
renamed Press.

People's Advocate   w   1875?
In Rowell-Ayer 1888. Founding date vague.

ORONGO (Jasper County)

Argus   w   1909-1913
Listed in Ayer 1911-1914.

Chief   w   1891
Listed in Ayer 1891.

Eagle   w   1896-1902?
In Rowell 1900-1903, Ayer 1897-1900.

Index   w   1896-1907?
MoHi: Jly 26, 1901-1906.
MoSHi: Jly 26, 1901-1906.

Mineral News   w   1900-1902
In Rowell 1902-1903, Ayer 1902.

Rainbow   w   1892
Listed in Ayer 1892, Rowell 1893.

ORRICK (Ray County)

Advertiser   w   1935-1952?
MoHi: Apr-Dec 1936. In Ayer 1937-1953.

Messenger   w   1914
Listed in Ayer 1915.

Sentinel   w   1958+
First listed in Ayer 1961.

Star   w   1898-1903?
In Rowell 1898-1903, Ayer 1899-1900.

Times   w   1891-1935
MoHi: Jly 9, 1896.

OSBORN (DeKalb County)

Eli   w   1894-1900?
In Rowell 1895-1901, Ayer 1895-1899.

Enterprise   w   1894-1953
MoHi: Aug 8, 1901-1906; 1910-1912; 1917-1936;
1938-1944. Film, 1908-Dec 24, 1909; 1913-
Dec 18, 1914; 1915-1916; 1937; 1945-1953.
Ended Jun 26, 1953.

OSBORN (continued)

Investigator   w   1872-1890?
MoHi: Nov 1, 1890.

News   w   1891
Listed in Rowell-Ayer 1892.

Oracle   w   1883-1885
In Rowell 1885-1886, Dauchy 1884.

OSCEOLA (St. Clair County)

Advance   w   1883-1894
MoHi: Film, Nov 28, 1883-Nov 25, 1886; Dec 2,
1886-Nov 24, 1887. Rowell 1895 lists Democrat-Advance.

Democrat   w   1859-1860, 1871-1875   d   1935-1938
MoHi: Jan 7, Jun 2, 30, Jly 12, 1860. Film, Jly 1,
1871-Jun 20, 1872; Jly 27, 1872-Sep 16, 1875.
See St. Clair County Democrat, Osage Valley.

Democrat-Advance   w   1883-1895
See Advance.

Herald   w   1866-1873?
MoHi: Jun 17, 1869; Jun 22, 1871. Film, Jly 4,
1866-Sep 25, 1873.
Osceola Library: Film, Jly 4, 1866-May 26, 1870.

Independent   w   1849?-1853?
MoHi: Nov 14, 1849.
MoSHi: Jan 18, 1851; Oct 30, Dec 25, 1852; Jan
8, Apr 16, 23, 30, May 7, 21, 28, Jun 11, Jly 9,
23, Aug 13, 27, 1853.

Missouri Army Argus   w   1861-?
MnHi: Nov 30, 1861.

Osage Valley   w   1866-1871
Became Democrat 1871, moved to Appleton City
1875.

Osage Valley Star   w   1859-1861
MoHi: Film, Nov 8, 1860-Feb 28, 1861.

People's Advocate   w   1896-1898
Populist paper.

Platonist   w   1881-1885?
Mentioned by Hammond. Publisher at press associa-
tion meeting 1881. Nameplate, Nov 1885, is Vol II,
No 11.

Prohibition Call   w   1882
Mentioned by Hammond.

St. Clair County Courier   w   1949+
MoHi: Film, Aug 4, 1949+. Formed by merger St.
Clair County Democrat and St. Clair County
Republican Aug 4, 1949. Founding date traced
to 1870 through Democrat.

OSCEOLA (continued)

St. Clair County Democrat   w   1870-1949
 MoHi: Feb 1906-1944. Film, 1945-Jly 1949.
 See Democrat.

St. Clair County Republican   w   1888-1949
 MoHi: 1914-1944; Jly 9, 1908; Jun 25, 1914.
 Film, 1945-Jly 1949.

Sentinel   w   1875-1876
 MoHi: Film, Jan 9, 1875-Jun 3, 1876.

Sentinel-Democrat   w   1876-1878
 ICHi: Jun 29, 1876. Name used briefly?

Sun   w   1876-1892?
 MoHi: Jan 3-Sep 5, 1878; Jly 14, 1881-1882;
 1884. Film, Sep 12, 1878-Jly 7, 1881; 1883;
 1885-1886.

Voice of the People   w   1878-1883?
 MoHi: Film, 1880-Nov 21, 1883. Started as
 Appleton City Voice.

Western Home Seeker   w   1885-1886

Wheel Advocate   w   1888
 Listed in Ayer 1889.

Whig   w   1848-1849
 Apparently renamed Independent 1849, Democrat
 later, according to Organ.

OSGOOD (Sullivan County)

Tribune   w   1909-1913
 Listed in Ayer 1910-1914.

OTTERVILLE (Cooper County)

Argus   w   1890
 Listed in Rowell 1891.

Call   w   1892-1893
 In Rowell 1893-1894, Ayer 1894.

Clarion   w   1860
 Formerly Review, renamed 1860.

First Division Proclamation 1861
 IHi: Film, Dec 13, 1861.

Little Missourian   w   1869
 Listed in Rowell 1870.

Mail   w   1892-1921, 1924
 MoHi: Dec 9, 1898-1902. Apparently closed 1921-
 1924. Resumed 1924, briefly.

News   w   1870
 Listed in Rowell 1871.

OTTERVILLE (continued)

Review   w   1860, 1934-1936
 Earlier paper mentioned in California News Aug
 4, 1860, telling of sale of Otterville Review and
 renaming it Clarion. Second Review listed in Ayer
 1937.

War Eagle and Camp Journal of the Army of the West
1862?
 IHi: Film, Jan 11, 1862.
 ICHi: Jan 1, 1862.

OVERLAND (St. Louis County)

Community News   w   1925+
 MoHi: Apr 1933-Aug 24, 1939.

Gem-Overland-St. John's Record   w   1925-1929
 Listed in Ayer 1926-1930.

News   w   1915-1916
 Listed in Ayer 1917.

Record-News   w   1936-1960?
 First listed in Ayer 1950.

St. Louis County Star   w   1936+
 Free distribution paper.

OWENSVILLE (Gasconade County)

Argus   w   1903-1904
 MoHi: Film, May 8, 1903-1904.

Gasconade County Republican   w   1904?+
 MoHi: 1906-1912; 1915-1944. Film, 1913-1914;
 1945+.

Republican   w   1896
 MoHi: Film, Oct 22, 1896-Jun 3, 1897. Became
 Hermann Republican-Banner, Jun 25, 1897.

Republican Banner   w   1897-1905
 MoHi: Film, 1903-Nov 10, 1905.

OZARK (Christian County)

Advertiser   w   1894-1895
 In Rowell 1895, Ayer 1895-1896.

Christian County Herald   w   1872
 Listed in Rowell 1873.

Christian County Leader   w   1900
 Listed in Rowell-Ayer 1901.
 Ozark Christian Co. Library: Copies 1900.

Christian County Republican   w   1888+
 MoHi: Nov 24, 1898-1907; Feb 18, 1909-1911;
 1913-1944; Jly 16, 1908. Film, 1945+.
 MoSHi: Feb 6, Dec 25, 1889.
 Ozark Christian Co. Library, 1952+.

OZARK (continued)

Christian County Sentinel   w   1897-1898
In Rowell 1897-1899. Ayer 1898.

Democrat   w   1900-1942
MoHi: Jly 17, 1908.
CSmH: Oct 10, 1913.

Free Silver Herald   w   1895-1896
Listed in Ayer 1897.
Ozark Christian Co. Library, copies 1890's.

Herald   w   1895-1899
Ozark Christian Co. Library, copies of 1890's.
Changed to monthly, 1899, devoted to
agriculture, mining, fruit and manufacturing.
CSmH: Jan 15, May 14, 1897; Apr 15, Jun 17,
1898.

Leader   w   1869-1882
Apparently traces history to Monitor. First reference to Leader in Ayer-Rowell 1881.

Mail   w   1890
MoHi: Oct 24, 1890.

Monitor   w   1869-1873?
Listed in Rowell 1870-1873.

Monitor and Leader   w   1869-1880
ICHi: Jun 10, 1876. Apparently part of Leader,
Monitor career. Under full title in Rowell 1875-
1880, then Leader.

News   w   1884?-1890?
Rowell has founding dates of 1871, 1868 although
News does not appear in directory until 1884.

News-Leader   w   1900-1936
Apparently continuation of Democrat, or name used
for some years. First under News-Leader in Ayer
1930, using 1900 founding date.

Republican   w   1876-1881
In Rowell 1877-1882, Ayer 1882.

Republican-Farmer   w   1876-1882
Full title in Rowell 1883. See Republican.

Searchlight   w   1895-1897
Probably succeeded Southwest Rural News and
Stockman.

Southwest Rural News and Stockman   w   1892-1894
In Rowell 1892, Ayer 1894.

Tribune   w   1905-1908
MoHi: Sep 3, 1908. Film, Jun 22, 1905-1908.

PACIFIC (Franklin County)

Democrat   w   1871, 1892
Two, both short-lived.

PACIFIC (continued)

Franklin County Democrat   w   1871-1878
ICHi: Jly 7, 1876.
Washington Museum Society: May 24, 1878.
Probably continuation of Democrat.

Franklin County Progress   w   1865-1870?
Apparently founded in Union as Franklin County
Tribune, later to Pacific.

Herald   w   1880-1891
MoHi: Feb 21, 1889; Jan 2, 30, Apr 3, Sep 11, 18,
Nov 6, Dec 11, 25, 1890; Jan 1, 1891.
DLC: Apr 28, 1881.
KHi: Mar 21, 1889.

Meramec Valley Transcript   w   1891+
MoHi: Oct 6, 1933-1944. Film, 1945+.
MoSHi: Jly 27, 1934. Formerly Pacific Transcript.
Changed Oct 6, 1933.

Our Country Paper   w   1882-1887
Washington Museum Society: Aug 23, 1882-Dec
24, 1884; Jan 14, 1885-Mar 31, 1887; Apr 7-
Jun 9, 1887.

Plowman   w   1931?
United with Transcript 1931.

Plowman-Transcript   w   1931-1932
MoHi: Jan 16, 1931-Nov 11, 1932. See Plowman.
Became Transcript Nov 18, 1932.

Times   w   1907
In Rowell-Ayer 1908.

Transcript   w   1891-1933
MoHi: May 8, 1895-1898; Jly 26, 1901-Jan 9,
1931; Nov 18, 1932-Sep 29, 1933. Became
Meramec Valley Transcript Oct 6, 1933.
KHi: Jan 16, 1925; Sep 17, 1926.

PALMYRA (Marion County)

Courier   w   1832-1848
MoSHi: Oct 18, 1860. See Hannibal Courier.
IHi: Film, Feb 7, 1862.
NN: Aug 15, 1862 (Vol 24, No 23).

Journal   w   1870
Listed in Rowell 1871.

Marion County Democrat   w   1872-1882
MoHi: Dec 12, 1878; Jan 23, 30, Feb 27, Mar 13,
Sep 4, Oct 2, 1879. Listed as Democrat Ayer
1882. Rowell 1883 notes d.
ICHi: Jly 20, 1876.

Marion County Herald   w   1882-1926
MoHi: Nov 24, 1898-Jun 1921; Oct 1922-Jan
1926; Oct 30, 1890.

Marion County News   w   1883?-1925
Listed in Ayer 1924-1926.

PALMYRA (continued)

Marion County Standard   w   1933-1941
    MoHi: Aug 9,1933-Apr 9,1941. Merged with
    Spectator Apr 16,1941. Became Spectator and
    Marion County Standard.

Marion Journal   w   1836-1837
    Mentioned by Organ.

Missouri Baptist Journal   w   1868?
    MoHi: May 9,1868.

Missouri Courier   w   1832-1848
    MoHi: Jly 7,1838; May 16,1844; Feb 5,1848.
    Moved to Hannibal 1848,returned to Palmyra
    1855. Many other name changes.

Missouri Whig   w   1841-1853
    MnHi: Apr 2,1846. See next listing. Name used
    briefly.

Missouri Whig and General Advertiser   w   1839-1841,
                                            1853-1863
    MoHi: Aug 3,1839-Jly 10,1851; Nov 6,1845;
    Dec 9,1847; Oct 13,1853. Film, Jly 17,1851-
    Mar 1859. See Missouri Whig, shorter title
    used for some time. Became Spectator Apr 10,
    1863.
    MoSHi: Oct 24,1840; Oct 15,1846; Jun 17,1852.

New Era   w   1872-1875?
    Listed in Rowell 1873-1875.

Political Examiner   w   1837-1839
    Mentioned by Hammond.

Post   w   1834
    Survived a few months,anti-Jackson.

Southern Sentinel   w   1856-1858
    MoHi: Apr 23,1856-Sep 15,1858.

Spectator   w   1839+
    MoHi: 1899; 1904-Apr 9,1941; Jan 3,Feb 14,
    1879; Sep 28,1883; Jan 2,1885; Feb 28,
    1896; Apr 21,1898; May 10,Dec 20,1900;
    Jan 21,1903; Aug 5,16,1905; Aug 12,1908.
    Film,Apr 10,1863-1898; 1900; 1901-1903.
    See next listing.
    MoSHi: Jan 3,10,17,1912.
    MWA: Apr 11,1873.
    ICHi: Sep 15,1876.

Spectator and Marion County Standard   w   1839+
    MoHi: Apr 16,1941-1944. Film,1945+. Formed by
    merger,Apr 16,1941. Fuller title for Spectator.

PANACEA SPRINGS (Barry County)

Republican   w   1879-1882
    Apparently established in Exeter, moved to
    Panacea Springs 1882,soon suspended.

PANAMA (Vernon County)

Miner   w   1896
    Listed in Ayer 1897.

PARIS (Monroe County)

Appeal and Mercury   w   1868+
    Name used in Ayer, 1943-1952,for Monroe County
    Appeal.

Local Item   w   1894-1895
    Death noted in Missouri Editor, Jly 1895.

Mercury   w   1837-1942
    MoHi: 1873-Jan 9,1942; Aug 24,1844; Dec 27,
    1845; Jun 20,Aug 8,Oct 10,Nov 7,Dec 26,
    1846; Jan 15,Feb 5,Apr 29,May 13,20,Jun
    3,10,17,Sep 9,16,Nov 18,1848; Mar 13,27,
    Apr 3,10,17,24,May 1,29,Jun 12,19,Jly 3,
    1850; Nov 19,1851; Apr 20,Nov 23,1853;
    Mar 7,1855; Apr 23,May 14,1856; Jan 3,
    1862; May 22,Jly 3,1863; Jan 29,1864; Mar
    10,Dec 22,1865. May 11,1866; Apr 17,1867;
    May 12,Aug 4,Dec 1,22,1868; Apr 6,May 18,
    Jun 15,Jly 27,1869; Jan 25,1870; Nov 21,
    1871; Aug 12,1873; Jun 14,1887; Oct 31,
    1890; Oct 19,1900.
    MoSHi: Oct 31,1862.
    MWA: Mar 30,1866.
    KHi: Dec 28,1888.
    Published as Sentinel 1837-1843. Merged with
    Monroe County Appeal, 1942.

Missouri Sentinel   w   1837-1843
    Mentioned by Organ,Union List.

Monroe County Appeal   w   1865?+
    MoHi: 1903; 1907-1944. Film,Feb 27,1874-Nov
    22,1878; Jan 17-Dec 1879; 1881-1902;
    1904-1906; 1945-1950+.
    ICHi: Jan 21,1876.
    KHi: Jly 20-Nov 30,1888 inc.
    Paris, Dulaney Memorial Library, 1941-1947.
    Began in Monroe City,moved to Paris 1873.
    Copy for Feb 27,1874 is Vol 6,No 13.

Plaindealer   w   1894
    People's Party paper,short lived.

PARIS (France)

Stars and Stripes
    MoHi: Feb 8,1918-Jun 13,1919.

PARKVILLE (Platte County)

Courier   w   1857-1862
    Previously known as Southern Democrat, accord-
    ing to Organ.

Independent   w   1885-1899
    MoHi: Film,Dec 16,1897-Jly 6,1899.

PARKVILLE (continued)

Industrial Luminary   w   1853-1855
    MoHi: Jly 26, Aug 9, 16, Nov 22, Dec 6, 1853;
        Jan 17, 31, May 23, 30, Jun 6, 13, Aug 1, 1854.
        See Western Luminary.

Platte County Dispatch   w   1956+
    First in Ayer 1957.

Platte County Gazette   w   1885+
    MoHi: Jly 13, 1899-1900; 1903-1944; Feb 2,
        9, 1950; Jan 4, Feb 8, Nov 1, 1951; Apr 24,
        1952. Film, Sep 26, 1901-1902; 1945+.
    MoSHi: Dec 16, 1938.

Platte County World   w   1896?-1900
    In Rowell-Ayer 1901.

Southern Democrat   w   1855-1857
    KHi: Jun 30, 1885. See Courier.

Western Luminary   w   1853-1855
    Equipment thrown into Missouri River, Organ
    notes. See Industrial Luminary. Apparently same.

PARMA (New Madrid County)

New Madrid County Courier   w   1908-1921
    Listed in Ayer 1915-1922.

Press   w   1921?-1927
    Ayer 1923 says started 1921; Ayer 1927 says 1923.

Tribune   w   1941+
    Also known as Home Tribune.

Victor   w   1908-1913
    MoHi: Jly 2, 1908-Jun 24, 1909. Union List says
    name used for New Madrid County Courier
    briefly.

PARNELL (Nodaway County)

Express   w   1888-1890
    In Rowell 1889-1891, Ayer 1891.

Nodaway County Republican   w   1891, 1900
    Two, both short-lived.

Nodaway County Times   w   1891-1892
    Followed by Ravenwood Gazette.

Review   w   1922-1940?
    Sold to Sheridan Northwest Missourian 1940.

Sentinel   w   1894-1923
    MoHi: Dec 11, 1898-Oct 1909; 1910-1921;
    Mar-Jun 14, 1923.

PATTERSON (Wayne County)

Missouri Weekly   w   1868?
    Mentioned in Union List.

PATTERSON (continued)

Times   w   1873-1875?
    In Rowell 1875. Hammond says it formerly was
    Piedmont Banner, established in 1872, moved to
    Patterson as Times, returned to Piedmont 1876.

PATTONSBURG (Daviess County)

Call   w   1881+
    MoHi: 1902-1944; Mar 4, 1910. Film, 1945+.

Daviess County Republican   w   1901
    Listed in Ayer 1902.

Missouri Trader   w   1899
    Country Editor, Apr 1899 notes start.

Missouri Veteran   w   1884-1885
    In Rowell 1885-1886, Dauchy 1884.

Star   w   1895
    Listed in Ayer 1896.

Star-Press   w   1895-1899
    MoHi: Film, Nov 25, 1898-1899. In Rowell
    1896-1899, Ayer 1897-1900.

Times   w   1894
    Listed in Ayer 1895.

PAX (Lawrence County)

Sunbeam   w   1899-1901
    In Rowell 1900-1903. See Stotts City.

PEDRO (Barton County)

Banner   w   1885-1886?
    Listed in Rowell 1887.

Enterprise   w   1888
    Listed in Ayer 1888.

PERRY (Ralls County)

Bell Telephone   w   1888
    Listed in Ayer 1888.

Enterprise   w   1888+
    MoHi: May 10, 1906-1944; Oct 30, 1890. Film,
    1945+. First in Rowell 1889 with 1888 start-
    ing date.

Gazette   w   1880-1883
    Became Pioneer 1883, Enterprise 1888.

Pioneer   w   1883-1888
    Apparently follows Pioneer.

Star of the West   w   1888?-1898
    In Rowell 1897-1898, Ayer 1898.

PERRYVILLE (Perry County)

Chronicle   w   1885-1889
    KHi: Jan 10,17, Feb 7,1889. In Rowell 1886-
    1889, Ayer 1887, 1889.

Forum   w   1874-1880
    Hammond says succeeded 1880 by Perry County
    Sun, later absorbed by Union.

Monitor   w   1880+
    MoHi: Mar 22, 1956+. Formerly Sun to 1956.

New Era   w   1913-1922
    MoHi: Jly 1,1920-May 4,1922. Formerly New
    Republican Era to Jly 1,1920; suspended
    May 4,1922.

New Republican Era   w   1913-1920
    MoHi: Jun 19,1913-Jun 24,1920. Became New
    Era Jly 1,1920.

People's Forum   w   1874-1878?
    ICHi: Sep 15,1876. Apparently same as Forum.
    In Rowell 1874-1879.

Perry County Democrat   w   1898
    In Rowell 1898-1899, Ayer 1899.

Perry County News   w   1905-1908?
    In Ayer 1906,1909, Rowell 1906,1908.

Perry County Republican   w   1889+
    MoHi: Jly 25,1901-1903; 1905-1944; Feb 9,
    1905. Film,1904; 1945+.

Perry County Sun   w   1880-1956
    MoHi: 1906-1928; Feb 23,1933-1944; Oct 31,
    1890; Dec 22,1904. Film,1945-1954.
    MoSHi: Apr 13,May 4,1933; Aug 30,1934; Jan
    3,10, Feb 7, Mar 28, Apr 18-May 9, Nov 7,
    1935; Jan 9, Feb 6, Apr 2-16, May 21, Jly 2-
    16,1936.
    KHi: Dec 21,1888. Became Monitor Mar 22,1956.

Post Clarion   w   1869-1870
    In Rowell 1870-1871.

Review   w   1897
    "New venture" in Country Editor, May 1897.

Union   w   1862-1882
    MoHi: Jly 2,1869.
    MoSHi: Nov 14,1862.
    ICHi: Jan 28, Jly 14,1876. See Fredericktown
    Conservative.

PHELPS CITY (Atchison County)

Record   w   1868
    In Rowell 1869.

PHILADELPHIA (Marion County)

Bird   w   1906
    In Rowell-Ayer 1907.

Headlight   w   1887-1888
    In Ayer 1887, Rowell 1889.

Journal   w   1911
    In Ayer 1912.

Quivive   w   1880-1886?
    In Rowell 1884-1887.

PHILADELPHIA (Penna.)

Columbian Star   w   1822-1828?
    MoHi: Jun 9,1827-Nov 29,1828.

PICKERING (Nodaway County)

News   w   1900-1904
    In Rowell 1901-1905, Ayer 1901-1904.

Post   w   1927-1928
    In Ayer 1929.

PIEDMONT (Wayne County)

Banner   w   1872,1876,1890-1919
    MoHi: Sep 17,1903. Film,1896-Jun 17,1897;
    Mar 20,1913-Dec 11,1919. Merged with
    Greenville Wayne County Journal Dec 25,
    1919. See Patterson.

Dispatch   w   1889
    In Rowell 1890.

Dollar   w   1877
    Mentioned by Hammond.

Herald   w   1892
    In Rowell 1893.

Journal-Banner   w   1876+
    See Wayne County Journal-Banner.

Leader   w   1880-1887
    In Rowell 1883-1888, Ayer 1883-1887.

People's Vindicator   w   1878
    In Rowell 1879. Pettengill 1878 has Vindicator.

Rambler   w   1884-1888
    See Western Rambler. In histories.

Review   w   1901
    In Ayer 1902.

Sentinel   w   1890-1891
    In Rowell 1891-1892, Ayer 1891.

Times   w   1874-1878?
    In Rowell 1876-1879.

Wayne County Democrat   w   1872-1873
  In Rowell 1873-1874.

Wayne County Journal   w   1873
  In Rowell 1874.

Wayne County Journal-Banner   w   1876+
  MoHi: Mar 5, 1925-1944. Film, 1945+.

Wayne County Journal and the Piedmont Weekly
Banner   w   1876-1925
  MoHi: Dec 25, 1919-Feb 26, 1925. Merged Dec
    25, 1919. Became Wayne County Journal-
    Banner Mar 5, 1925.

Wayne County Republican   w   1904
  In Ayer 1905.

Western Rambler   w   1884
  In Rowell-Dauchy 1885.

PIERCE CITY (Lawrence County)
(Note: Spelling was Peirce City to Jly 20, 1933)

Democrat   w   1872-1882   d   1882
  MoHi: 1903. Film, 1903. Rowell 1874 lists w,
    founded 1872; 1885 notes d, founded 1882,
    w, 1875. Nameplate on d, Apr 8, 1885, is
    Vol I, No 267?

Empire   w   1875-1906?   d   1881-1905?
  MoHi: w, Dec 1898-1900.
  MoSHi: d, Aug 1, 1900.

Empire-Journal   d   1900-1908
  Title noted in A.T. Boothe obituary, MPN, Jly
    1941. Said he edited this d 1900-1908.

Enterprise   w   1881
  Thomas Carolin member of MPA 1881.

Herald   w   1871-1873?
  MoHi: Sep 21, 1872.

Immigrant   m   1878-1881
  Ayer 1881 says this was advertising publication
    called Immigrants Guide. Moved to Mount Vernon
    1881, ended 1885.

Independent   w   1881
  Mentioned in county history.

Jacksonian   w   1870?
  In county history as merging with Star in 1871
    or 1872.

Journal   w   1901-1919
  MoHi: Aug 4, 1916-Jan 10, 1919. Merged with
    Leader as Leader-Journal Jan 17, 1919.

Lawrence County Democrat   w   1875-1899?
  In Ayer 1887-1900. See Mount Vernon.

Leader   w   1905-1919
  MoHi: Jan 3-10, 1919; Jly 10, 1914. Film, Feb
    7, 1913-1918. Merged with Journal Jan
    17, 1919.

Leader-Journal   w   1905+
  MoHi: Jan 17, 1919-Apr 1926; Feb 10, 1927-
    1944; Jly 20, 1933-1944. Film, 1945+.

Record   w   1875-1884
  ICHi: Jly 8, 1876. In Rowell 1876-1884, Ayer
    1880-1881. Hammond said daily appeared
    1882. Became Democrat 1884.

Southwest Commercial   w   1872
  Apparently ran two months.

Southwest Journal   w   1901-1916
  MoHi: Jun 1, 1906-Jly 16, 1916.
  KHi: Oct 12-16, 1901.

Southwestern Populist   w   1894
  Missouri Editor, Dec 1894, tells of merger of
    Neosho Populist and Mount Vernon Plain Talk
    into Southwestern Populist.

Star   w   1869-1871?
  See Jacksonian.

Tri-County Press   w   1921-1922
  Listed in Ayer 1922-1923.

PILOT GROVE (Cooper County)

Bee   w   1882
  In Rowell-Ayer 1883. Hammond says later
    Mirror, Herald, Record.

Chronicle   w   1889
  In Ayer 1889, Rowell 1890.

Cooper County Leader   w   1882-1892
  MoHi: Mar 27, Oct 30, 1890; Nov 27, 1891; Jan
    8, 15, 29, Feb 19, Mar 4, Apr 1, 15, May 13, 27,
    1892. Film, Apr 3-Dec 26, 1890.

Enterprise   w   1899-1907
  MoHi: Jly 25, 1901-1904; 1906; Jan 5, May 25,
    Nov 23-Dec 21, 1905; Jan 3, 31, 1907.

Free Lance   w   1910
  In Ayer 1911.

Herald   w   1882-1900?
  MoHi: Film, Jun 3, 1892-Nov 17, 1893.

Mirror   w   1883-1884
  In Rowell 1884-1885.

Record   w   1880-1937
  MoHi: 1911-Aug 30, 1916; Sep 25, 1931-Sep
    24, 1937; Oct 14, 1921. Film, Dec 24,
    1909-1910. To Boonville 1937 as Cooper
    County Record.

PILOT GROVE (continued)

Sentinel Star   w   1950-1952
   MoHi: Film, Jan 12-Dec 1952. Formed by merger,
      Bosworth Sentinel and Pilot Grove Star Jan 12,
      1950. Ended Feb 28, 1952.

Star   w   1937-1950
   First in Ayer 1941.

PINEVILLE (McDonald County)

Democrat   w   1870+
   MoHi: 1899-1944; Jly 17, 1915. Film, 1945+.
      Paper uses 1876 founding date, but Rowell
      1872 lists first Democrat, founded 1870.
      Possibly News at one time?
   MoSHi: Jun 27, 1913.

Herald   w   1894-1943
   MoHi: 1903-May 1943. In Rowell 1896-1908,
      Ayer 1896-1943.

Hub   w   1899
   In Ayer 1900.

Independent   w   1890-1891
   MoHi: Oct 25, 1890. In Rowell 1891-1892,
      Ayer 1891.

McDonald County Advocate   w   1873
   Mentioned in county history.

McDonald County Republican   w   1894-1896
   In Rowell-Ayer 1895-1897.

News   w   1874-1893
   ICHi: Jly 13, 1876. Hammond claims News
      forerunner to Democrat.

Pilot   w   1879-1880
   Greenback paper. Press to Arkansas.

Press   w   1870
   In Rowell 1871. Short-lived.

Record   w   1884-1885
   Listed in Rowell 1885-1886.

Republican   w   1896-1905
   Continuation of McDonald County Republican.

PLATTE CITY (Platte County)

Advocate   w   1874-1880
   Consolidated with Landmark 1880. Listed at times
   as Platte County Advocate. In Rowell 1876.

Argus   w   1844-1862
   MoSHi: Jan 14, 1848-Feb 16, 1849. Named Platte
      County Conservator 1862. See Platte County
      Argus.
   IHi: Film, Feb 26, 1847.
   DLC has Vol 2, No 14, Sep 26, 1845, known as Argus.
      Also, Sep 24, 1847.

PLATTE CITY (continued)

Atlas   w   1857-1864
   MoHi: Sep 5, Oct 3, 10, 31, Dec 19, 1863; Jan
      30, 1864.

Border Times   w   1869?
   In Rowell 1869, but only name.

Eagle   w   1842
   Brief career before being moved same year to
   Weston. Apparently back to Platte City 1844 as
   Argus. Later to Weston again.

Platte County Advocate   w   1874-1880?
   ICHi: Apr 21, 1876. See Advocate. Listed in
      Rowell 1876.

Platte County Argus   w   1884-1925?
   MoHi: 1898-1925.
   KHi: Mar 6, 1924.

Platte County Conservator   w   1862-1864
   MoHi: Jan 10, Feb 21, Mar 7, 21, Apr 4, 1863.
   MoSHi: Jly 19-Dec 6, 1862.

Platte County Democrat   w   1871-1873?
   In Rowell 1874, Patrons of Husbandry.

Platte County Gazette   w
   KHi: Sep 28, 1922, which is Vol 38, No 34.

Platte County Landmark   w   1865+
   MoHi: Jun 9, 1871-Sep 11, 1874; Mar 1898-
      1944. Film, Sep 18, 1874-Feb 4, 1881; Oct
      10, 1890-Aug 12, 1898; 1945+ Jly 17, 1959.
      Established in Weston 1865.
   MoKc: Jun 9, 1871-Sep 6, 1878.
   KHi: Nov 23, 1877; Aug 16, 1878; Dec 13, 1918.
   ICHi: Sep 8, 1876.

Platte County Republican   w   1888-1889
   In Rowell 1889-1890.

Platte County Reveille   w   1866-1871
   MoHi: Jly 6, 1866-Jly 2, 1869; Jly 12, 1867.
      Film, Jly 9, 1869-Jun 2, 1871.
   MoKc: Jly 6, 1866-Jun 2, 1871.

Platte County Sentinel   w   1864
   MoHi: Mar 24, Apr 7, Jun 23, 1864. Began in
      Weston 1862? Kansas troops destroyed plant
      1864.

Reporter   w   1856
   In Newspaper Record 1856.

Tenth Legion   1861
   MWA: Mar 30, 1861. Secession paper.

PLATTSBURG (Clinton County)

Clinton County Democrat   d,w   1866-1944?
   MoHi: w, Dec 28, 1906-Jan 1943. Formerly
      Democrat-Lever to Dec 28, 1906.
   KHi: d, Sep 25, 1925; Sep 15, 1928.

Clinton County News   w   1859-1860
   Changed to Northwest Reporter 1860, destroyed
   by fire 1862, Organ notes.

Clinton County Register   w   1866-1883
   MoSHi: Apr 7, 1866-Mar 30, 1867; Dec 6, 1878.
   Univ. of Kansas City: Dec 7, 1867.
   ICHi: Apr 14, 1876. Under Register-Lever in
      Rowell 1885.

Clintonite   w   1897-1898
   MoSHi: Jly 15, 1897. In Rowell 1897-1899,
      Ayer 1898-1899.

Critic   w   1892
   People's Party paper, Rowell 1893.

Defender   w   1878
   Greenback Party campaign paper.

Democrat   w   1882-1895?
   MoHi: Film, May 10, 1883-Nov 27, 1884. Mis-
      souri Editor, Mar 1895, tells of merger of
      Democrat and Register-Lever.

Democrat-Lever   w   1866-1906
   MoHi: Dec 2, 1898-1900; Nov 23-Dec 21, 1906.
      Renamed Clinton County Democrat 1906.
   MoSHi: Jly 14-Aug 11, 1825, Sep 1-15, 1899;
      Feb 6, 1900. Founding data confused, first
      under this title in Rowell 1895 with 1894
      starting date.

Jeffersonian   w   1885-1894
   Missouri Editor, Mar 1895, tells of sale of
   Jeffersonian and its new name Democrat.

Leader   w   1895+
   MoHi: Jly 26, 1901-1912; 1916-1939; 1943-
      1944. Film, Oct 11, 1895-Jly 19, 1901; 1913-
      1915; 1945+.

Lever   w   1873-1883
   ICHi: Aug 18, 1876. Rowell 1885 lists Register-
      Lever.

New Constitution   w   1865
   Hammond says published in 1865.

Northwest Reporter   w   1860
   See Clinton County News.

Purifier   w   1880-1881
   In Rowell 1880-1882, Ayer 1880.

Reflector   w   1870
   Mentioned in county history.

PLATTSBURG (continued)

Register-Lever   w   1866-1895
   Apparently part of Clinton County Democrat
   history. In Rowell 1885-1894, Ayer 1888-1895.

Republican   w   1881-1882
   Publisher in press association 1882.

PLEASANT HILL (Cass County)

Cass County News   w   1901-1935
   MoHi: Nov 17, 1927-Apr 25, 1935, when ended.

Cass County Republican   w   1893, 1920-1925
   MoHi: Oct 1920-Sep 18, 1925. First in Ayer
      1895.

Cass County Times   w   1874-1876
   In Rowell 1875-1876.

Dispatch   w   1872-1883
   See Pleasant Hill Times Dec 29, 1960.

Gazette   w   1890-1900?
   MoHi: Oct 30, 1890. Renamed Post.

Herald & Progress   w   1876-1877
   In Rowell 1877-1878.

Journal   w   1869
   MoSHi: Apr 29, 1869.

Leader   w   1869-1872, 1893
   MoHi: Jun 11, 1869. Second in Ayer 1894.
   MoSHi: May 14, 1869-Oct 11, 1872.

Local   w   1872-1915
   MoHi: 1903-Sep 24, 1915. Jun 7, 1889; Oct 24,
      1890; Aug 19, 1892; Jly 6, Nov 30, 1894.
      Film, Oct 14, 1886-1902. Name changed to
      Register Oct 8, 1915.
   KHi: Dec 29, 1899; Jan 5, 1900.

Local Dispatch   w   1886
   MoHi: Film, Apr 28-Oct 7, 1886.

Local-Missourian   w   ?
   MoHi: Film, 1894; 1896.

Mid-Week   w   1904-1906
   In Ayer 1905-1906, Rowell 1905-1907.

News   d   1927
   Lasted one week in Sep 1927.

Post   w   1899-1901   w   1920's
   Listed in Ayer 1902. Pleasant Hill Times Dec 12,
      1960, said "The Post, was established and operated
      for a few weeks in the 1920's." Earlier Post
      followed Gazette.

Progress   w   1896-1897
   Listed in Ayer 1897-1898.

PLEASANT HILL (continued)

Register w 1872-1919?
  MoHi: Oct 8, 1915-1916. Film, Jan 5-Oct 5,
  1917. Formerly Local. Changed name Oct
  8, 1915. Last in Ayer 1920.

Review w 1865-1900?
  Formerly Union.

Times w 1887+
  MoHi: 1904-1944. Film, 1945+. Starting inde-
  finite. Copy for Jan 1, 1904 is Vol 16, No 2.

Union w 1866-1870
  MoHi: Sep 17, 1869. Name changed to Review,
  according to Hammond.

Western Beacon w 1858-1861
  MoHi: Jly 17, 1858. First in county, according
  to Organ.

Western Dispatch w 1872-1886
  MoHi: Film, Apr 21, 1886.
  ICHi: Jly 19, 1876. Last listing Rowell 1886.
  In Rowell 1887 have Local Dispatch, monthly.

PLEASANT HOPE (Polk County)

Eclipse w 1904-1906
  In Ayer 1905-1906, Rowell 1905-1908.

X-Ray w 1897-1898
  Listed in Rowell 1898-1899.

PLEASANTVILLE (Sullivan County)

News w 1878
  Listed in Pettengill 1878.

POINT PLEASANT (New Madrid County)

Tribune w 1876-1877
  In Rowell 1877-1878, Pettengill 1877.

POLLOCK (Sullivan County)

Tribune w 1901
  Listed in Ayer 1902.

POLO (Caldwell County)

Champion w 1891
  Listed in Rowell 1892.

Herald w 1915
  Apparently merged with News mid-1915.

News w 1903-1915
  Last listed in Ayer 1916.

News-Herald w 1903-1953
  First under this title in Ayer 1917. Suspended in
  Aug 1953.

POLO (continued)

Post w 1866-1902?
  Last listed in Rowell 1903.

Vindicator w 1901-1907
  In Rowell 1904-1908, Ayer 1902-1907.

POMONA (Howell County)

Post 1896-1900
  Siloam Optic became Pomona Post, according to
  Missouri Editor, Apr 1896.

Republican w 1898
  Republican "has come to stay" said Country
  Editor, Jan 1898.

Sentinel w, sm 1905
  Originally weekly, later semi-monthly.

World's Cresset w 1906-1907?
  MoHi: Nov 22, 1906-Jly 25, 1907. Also in Trask,
  Brushy Knob and Fowler.

POPLAR BLUFF (Butler County)

American d 1895-1923
  MoHi: Sep 7, 1917-Jly 28, 1923. Name changed
  to Interstate American Jly 30, 1923.
  Poplar Bluff Library: Apr 1919-Sep 1923.

American Republic d 1916+
  MoHi: Mar 12, 1928-1950. Film, 1951+.
  Poplar Bluff Library: Oct 1, 1927-Mar 1941.
  Formed by merger Interstate American and
  Daily Republican Mar 12, 1928.
  Micro-Photo: film, 1893-1914; 1923+.

Black River County w 1875
  Mentioned in country history.

Black River News w 1869-1873
  MoHi: Sep 10, 1869. Became Headlight, Citizen.

Butler County Advocate w 1886-1893?
  Also known as Advocate.

Butler County Democrat d, w 1904-1908
  MoHi: Jan 7, 8, 11, 12, 16, 18-23, 25, 26, 29, 30,
  1904. Film, Sep 18, 1906-Sep 19, 1908 inc.
  W, Jan 14, 28, 1904. Listed as daily for brief
  time. See Citizen.

Butler County Journal w 1901?-1903
  Listed in Ayer 1904.

Butler County Leader w 1935
  Bernie Newsboy moved to Poplar Bluff, given
  this title. From MPN, Jan 1935.

Butler County News sw 1938-1941?
  Several mentions in MPN 1938-1942.

POPLAR BLUFF (continued)

Citizen   w   1869-1908   d   1897-1908
    MoHi: D,Nov 6,1890; Aug 31,1899. Film,Jly
        10,1905-Jly 13,1907 inc. W,film,Aug 1878-
        Aug 1879; Aug 1882-Feb 1883; Feb-Aug
        1889; Aug-Dec 1890; Jan-Jly 1891; Jan
        1895-Mar 1896; Dec 15,1898-Sep 24,1908.
        Combined with Butler County Democrat Oct
        8,1908.

Citizen-Democrat   d   1893-1915?   w   1869+
                                        tw   1909
    MoHi: D,Apr 16,1913-1914. Film,Jan 1,1915-
        Dec 24,1915. W,1911-1938. Film,Oct 8-
        Dec 31,1908. Dec 31,1909-1910; Jan 12,
        1939-Nov 4,1942; Jan 1947-Dec 1950;
        1952-1955. TW,film,Jan 5-Dec 10,1909.
    Micro-Photo: Film,w,1933-1942; 1947-1950;
        1952+.

Democrat   w   1894   d   1907-1908
    Weekly in Rowell-Ayer 1895; d in Rowell 1908,
        Ayer 1908-1909.

Enquirer   w   1886
    Listed in Ayer 1886.

Enterprise   w   1896-1897
    Populist paper. In Rowell 1897,Ayer 1897-1898.

Herald   d   1897-1898
    In Rowell 1897-1899,Ayer 1898-1899.

Interstate American   w   1923-1928
    MoHi: Jly 30,1923-Mar 11,1928.
    Poplar Bluff Public Library: Oct 1,1923-Sep
        30,1927. See American Republic.

Journal   d,w   1901-1903
    In Rowell 1903-1905,Ayer 1904.

New Era   w   1875
    Listed in Rowell 1876.

Renovator   w   1884-1887
    Became Republican 1888 says Hammond.

Republic   w   1888
    In Rowell 1889,Ayer 1888.

Republican   w   1891+   d   1902-1915
    MoHi: d,May 3-Nov 1913. Film,Nov 1913-
        Dec 1915. Changed to w Dec 30,1915. W,
        Dec 30,1915-1944. Film,Apr 2,1891-Mar
        29,1917; 1945-1954. Formerly Renovator.
        First in Rowell 1892,Ayer 1891.
    KHi: d,Jun 14,1926.
    Micro-Photo: Film,w,1891-1929; 1933+.

Sentinel   d,w   1901
    Listed in Rowell-Ayer 1902.

POPLAR BLUFF (continued)

Southeast Enterprise   w   1890
    Farm Alliance paper in Ayer 1891.

Southeast Missourian   w   1879
    In Rowell-Ayer 1880. Absorbed by Citizen.

PORTAGEVILLE (New Madrid County)

Critic   w   1899?-1911
    Founding date in Ayer 1908,first listing.

Review   w   1935+
    First in Ayer 1937.

Southeast Missourian   w   1892+
    MoHi: 1919-1944; Sep 26,1919. Film,Jan 3,
        1913-1918; 1945+. See New Madrid.

PORTLAND (Callaway County)

Ledger   w   1900-1901
    Listed in Rowell-Ayer 1902.

Moon   w   1894
    Start noted in Missouri Editor,Apr 1894.

Times   w   1894-1895,1898-1900
    First Times merged with Mokane Herald 1895.

POTOSI (Washington County)

Eagle   w   1889-1890
    MoHi: Oct 30,1890.

Independent   w   1872-1934
    MoHi: 1902-Jan 24,1929; Oct 15,1896; Jly
        15,1897. Film,Mar 20-Dec 25,1873; Jan
        1894-Mar 1895; 1896-1897; 1899-1901.
        Merged with Journal 1934.
    ICHi: Jly 6,1876.

Independent-Journal   w   1872+
    MoHi: Jan 31,1929-Jan 18,1934 under Weekly
        Independent and Potosi Journal. Jan 25,
        1934-1944. Film,1945+. Independent-Journal
        purchased Washington County News Jly 13,
        1942.

Journal   w   1894-1928
    MoHi: Jly-Dec 1903; Dec 1915-1928. Film,Aug
        1894-Aug 16,1916. Suspended Dec 26,1928.
        Purchased by Independent Jan 28,1929.

Miner's Prospect   w   1846-1849
    MoSHi: Sep 20,1849. Mentioned by Organ.

Southeast Democrat   w   1889-1891
    In Ayer 1891-1892,Rowell 1892.

Republican   w   1885?-1887
    Listed in Rowell 1888.

POTOSI (continued)

Washington County Journal w 1867-1875
   MoHi: Film, Apr 25, 1867-Dec 22, 1870.

Washington County Miner w 1856-1861
   Mentioned by Organ.

Washington County News w 1935-1942
   MoHi: Oct 9, 1936-Jly 9, 1942. Suspended Jly
   9, 1942, sold to Independent-Journal Jly
   13, 1942.

POWERSVILLE (Putnam County)

Helper w 1901?-1918
   Listed in Ayer 1918-1919.

Pioneer w 1900
   Listed in Ayer 1901.

Putnam County Democrat w 1935-1937
   Listed in Ayer 1937-1938.

Record w 1901-1916 1935-1937
   MoHi: Film, Jan 2-Dec 25, 1903; Jan 7-Sep 7,
   1916. Second Record suspended Oct 1937.

PRAIRIE HILL (Chariton County)

Booster w 1923
   Listed in Ayer 1924.

Herald w 1923
   Mentioned in E&P, Jun 9, 1923, as starting.

Swastika w 1908-1913
   Listed in Ayer 1909-1914.

PRINCETON (Mercer County)

Advance w 1866-1879

Mercer County Advocate w 1866-1881
   According to county history named People's
   Press 1881.

New Era w 1891
   People's Party paper in Rowell-Ayer 1892.

People's Press w 1881-1902
   MoHi: Nov 6, 1901-Aug 20, 1902. Film, May 9,
   1894-Jan 30, 1895; 1899; 1900-Jan 30, 1901.
   Changed to Press Aug 27, 1902.

Post w 1896-1944
   MoHi: Jly 17, 1903-Nov 16, 1944. Film, Mar 23,
   1901-Feb 14, 1903; Nov 20, 1903-Nov 4,
   1904. Merged with Telegraph to form Post-
   Telegraph Nov 23, 1944.

Post-Telegraph w 1873+
   MoHi: Nov 23-Dec 1944. Film, 1945+. See Post.
   Princeton Mercer Co. Library: 1956-1959.

PRINCETON (continued)

Press w 1881-1907
   MoHi: Aug 27, 1902-1907. Formerly People's
   Press.

Progress w 1885-1886
   Listed in Ayer 1887-1888.

Reporter w 1859-1861
   Name changed to Unionist 1861, Organ notes.

Telegraph w 1873-1944
   MoHi: Aug 1901-Nov 16, 1944; Oct 29, 1890;
   Jly 5, 1905; Mar 17, 1897. Film, May 4,
   1892-Apr 26, 1893; May 1, 1895-Apr 1896;
   Apr 1897-Apr 1902. See Post.
   ICHi: Jly 6, Sep 7, 1876.

Unionist w 1861
   See Reporter.

PURCELL (Jasper County)

Press w 1907-1910
   In Ayer 1909 as Press and Flag of Purdy.

PURDIN (Linn County)

Champion w 1898-1902
   In Rowell 1898-1903, Ayer 1899-1903.

Enterprise w 1911-1945
   Listed in Ayer 1913-1945.

PRINCIPIA COMMUNITY (St. Louis County)

Communist 1881-1883
   MoSHi: Oct 1881, printed in Buffalo; Mar 1883
   printed in St. Louis.

PURDY (Barry County)

Barry County Beacon w 1881-1884
   Greenback paper, short-lived.

Barry County Gazette w 1913-1914
   Listed in Ayer 1915.

Community Leader w 1934
   Mentioned in MPN, Oct 1934.

Courier w 1893
   Listed in Rowell-Ayer 1894.

Flag w 1887
   Listed in Rowell 1887.

Flag of Purdy w 1896-1907
   Rowell 1907 lists News; 1908, Flag of Purdy and
   Purdy News.

Herald w 1883
   Listed in Rowell 1884.

PURDY (continued)

News   w   1896-1907
See Flag of Purdy.

Review   w   1921?-1924
Listed in Ayer 1922-1924.

Rural Notes   w   1883
Listed in Rowell 1884.

Star   w   1895-1896?
In Rowell 1895-1896, Ayer 1896.

Sun   w   1891
Listed in Ayer 1891.

Transcript   w   1891-1893?
In Rowell 1892-1894, Ayer 1892.

PUXICO (Stoddard County)

Express   w   1887?-1889
In Rowell 1888-1890, Ayer 1888-1889.

Herald   w   1925-1930
MoHi: Film, Mar 27, Oct 2, 1930.

Index   w   1895-1925?
Union List says name used for Herald.

Press   w   1930?-1953?
First in Ayer 1937, founding date 1919. MPN,
Jun 1942, says Press observed 8th anniversary
May 13, 1942. Last Ayer 1954.

Record   w   1894
Noted in Missouri Editor, Jun 1894.

Tri-County News   w   ?-1931
MoHi: Film, Aug 14, 1930-Sep 4, 1931. In Ayer
1932, founded in 1895.

QUEEN CITY (Schuyler County)

Globe   w   1876-1877
In Rowell 1876-1878

Herald   w   1877-1878
NHi: Dec 28, 1877. In Pettengill 1878.

Leader   w   1897-1924
MoHi: Jly 26, 1917-1919. Merged with Transcript Apr 6, 1917. See Monitor-Leader.

Leader-Transcript   w   1897-1924?
MoHi: Apr 6, 1917-1919. Apparently title used
1917-1919.

Monitor   w   1924
In Ayer 1925. Apparently merged with Leader.

Monitor-Leader   w   1888+
Traces founding date to Transcript? First under
this title in Ayer 1926 with 1896 founding date.

QUEEN CITY (continued)

Transcript   w   1887?-1917
MoHi: Jly 26, 1901-Dec 22, 1916. See Leader.
Rowell 1888 and early Ayer's, give 1887
as founding date for Transcript.

QUITMAN (Nodaway County)

Herald   w   1904-1907?
In Rowell 1905-1907, Ayer 1905.

Record   w   1887-1903
In Ayer 1888-1904, Rowell 1888-1905.

RAVENNA, Ohio

Western Courier   w   1827-1837?
MoHi: May 12, 1827-May 3, 1828; May 5, 1836;
Apr 27, 1837.

RAVENNA (Mercer County)

Advance   w   1888-1889?
In Ayer 1888-1889, Rowell 1889.

News   w   1900
Listed in Ayer 1901.

Searchlight   w   1895-1900?
In 1897-1900 printed in Mercer as Searchlight.

RAVENWOOD (Nodaway County)

Gazette   w   1893-1952
MoHi: Aug-Dec 1901, inc.; 1902-Oct 1909;
1910-1912; 1915-1944; Oct 15-Dec 24,
1909. Film, 1913-1914; 1945-1952.
Suspended Apr 10, 1952.

RAYMORE (Cass County)

Tribune   w   1895-1896?
In Rowell-1896-1899, Ayer 1896-1897. See
Freeman Tribune.

RAYTOWN (Jackson County)

News   w   1926+
First listed in Ayer 1929.

Weekly Shopper   w   1948+
Free distribution paper.

RAYVILLE (Ray County)

Enterprise   w   1904-1919
In Rowell 1906-1908, Ayer 1905-1920.

REA (Andrew County)

Andrew County Times   w   1888-1891
MoHi: Oct 25, 1890. In Rowell 1889-1892,
Ayer 1889-1891.

REA (continued)

Times w 1897-1899
Listed in Ayer 1899-1900.

REEDS (Jasper County)

Times w 1909-1910
In Ayer 1911.

REEDS SPRING (Stone County)

Advertiser w 1907
In Rowell 1908.

Stone County Democrat w 1910
Short-lived. Not in Ayer.

RENICK (Randolph County)

Enterprise w 1912-1917
In Ayer 1913-1918.

Reporter w 1885-1886?
In Rowell 1886-1887, Dauchy 1885.

REPUBLIC (Greene County)

Banner w 1892
In Ayer 1892.

Greene County Democrat w 1899
In Ayer 1900.

Greene County Republic w 1888-1894?
Last in Ayer 1895.

Imperialist w 1892-1893?
In Rowell 1893-1894, Ayer 1894.

Monitor w 1894+
MoHi: Nov 21, 1907-1910; 1913-1944; Oct 15-
Dec 24, 1909. Film, 1911-1912; 1945+.
KHi: Aug 30, 1906.

Record w 1933-1958
MoHi: Jan 20, 1938-1944. Film, 1945-1958.
Suspended May 1, 1958.

Republic w 1888-1894?
MoHi: Oct 23, 1890. Last in Rowell 1895.

Venture w 1887
In Rowell 1887.

REVERE (Clark County)

Current w 1898-1902?
MoHi: Film, Mar 24, 1898-Jly 18, 1901.

Register w 1902
In Ayer 1903.

RHINELAND (Montgomery County)

Record w 1902-1952
MoSHi: Nov 15, 1918.

Sunbeam w 1896-1900
In Rowell 1896-1901, Ayer 1897-1900.

RICHARDS (Vernon County)

Chronicle w 1890-1892
MoHi: Oct 16, 1890.

Progress w 1895-1933
In Rowell 1897-1908, Ayer 1896-1934.

RICHFIELD (Clay County)

Border Ruffian w 1855-1856
Apparently first was Enterprise, then this, later
Monitor.

Enterprise w 1854-1855
MoSHi: Nov 25, 1854-Sep 14, 1855.

Flag w 1861
Suspended quickly.

Monitor w 1856-1861
MoSHi: Dec 8, 1855-Jun 23, 1856; Feb 2, 1856.

RICH HILL (Bates County)

Appeal w 1896
Noted in Missouri Editor, Feb 1896.

Bates County Appeal w 1894-1897
Name used 1897 for Bates County Populist
founded 1894.

Bates County Critic w 1898-1900
In Rowell 1898-1901, Ayer 1900.

Bates County Populist w 1894-1897
See Bates County Appeal.

Bates County Republican w 1881-1960?
MoHi: 1920-1944. Film, 1945-1954.

Bazoo w 1883
In Dauchy 1883.

Chronicle w 1880-1883
In Rowell 1884.

Coming Nation w 1892-1903
MoHi: May 24, 1902. Film, Jun 7, 1902-1903.
Socialist paper.

Critic w 1898-1900
Apparently shorter name for Bates County Critic
as listed in Ayer 1901.

Daily d 1883
In Rowell 1884.

RICH HILL (continued)

Fireside   m   1895
    KHi: Apr 1895.

Gazette   w   1880-1884   d   1882?
    Became National Gazette. D in Rowell 1883,
    founded 1882.

Herald   w   1884-1887
    In Rowell 1885-1888, Ayer 1887.

Miner World   w   1896-1897?
    In Ayer 1898.

Mining Review   w   1880+
    MoHi: Nov 24, 1898-1944; Aug 10, 1905; Nov
    28, 1907; Apr 9, 1908; Mar 4, 1909. Film,
    1945+.

Morning Sun   d   1883
    In Dauchy 1884.

News   d   1884?-1956
    D stopped May 31, 1956. Weekly Mining Review
    continued. News not in Ayer.

Review   d   1886-1955?
    MoHi: Feb 7, 1888. D edition of Mining Review.
    Apparently became Daily News 1955.

Star   w   1884-1889?
    In Rowell 1889-1890.

Sun   d   1883
    In Rowell 1884.

Tribune   w   1890-1911
    MoHi: Aug 1, 1901-1910; Jan 25, 1900.

Western Enterprise   w   1881-1919
    MoHi: Jly 1902-Sep 1904; 1905-1919; May 23,
    1902; Mar 5, 1909; May 20, 1904; May 20,
    1910.
    Bates County Library: Sep 1881-1892.

Western Observer   w   1881?
    In Dauchy 1898, founding date 1881. Hammond
    says published 1881-1885.

RICHLAND (Pulaski County)

Cyclone   w   1885-1909
    MoHi: Film, Jan-Sep 10, 1903. In Rowell 1886-
    1908, Ayer 1887-1910.

Leader   w   1910-1911
    In Ayer 1911-1912.

Mirror   w   1906+
    MoHi: 1919-1944. Film, 1913-1918; 1945+.

Pulaski County Democrat   w   1870's?
    Mentioned by Organ.

RICHLAND (continued)

Pulaski County Tribune   w   1879-1884
    In Rowell 1884.

Register   w   1895
    Missouri Editor, Jly 1895, tells of start.

Review   w   1937
    After three issues, combined with Mirror.

Sentinel   w   1872-1880
    MoHi: Jan 10, 17, 24, 1873.
    ICHi: Jly 7, 1876.

Sun   w   1870
    Listed in Rowell 1871

Times   w   1838-1939?
    Sale to Mirror noted in MPN, Jan 1939. See
    Newburg Times.

Western Observer   w   1881-1886?
    In Rowell 1884-1887, Ayer 1881.

RICHMOND (Ray County)

Alliance Defender   w   1891
    Listed in Ayer 1891.

Argus   d   1896?
    MoHi: Jun 14, 1896.

Bulletin   w   1859-1860
    Merged with Mirror 1860.

Conservator   w   1852-1945
    MoHi: Apr 5-Sep 13, 1861, inc.; Jly 10, 1862-
    Jly 7, 1864, inc.; May 14, 1865-1866, inc.;
    1867-1901; 1911-Jan 11, 1945; Sep 13, 1861;
    Apr 23, Jly 16, Nov 5, 1863; Jan 7, Mar 24,
    31, Apr 7, 1864; Sep 30, Oct 14, Dec 23, 1886;
    Jly 30, 1903; Apr 14, 1904; Jan 11, 18, 25, Jun
    1, 22, Jly 13, 20, 27, Aug 20, 1908. Film, 1902-
    1910. Formerly Herald, Mirror. Known as
    North-West Conservator Apr 1861-Apr 1863;
    May 1865-Feb 1866. Suspended Sep 1861-Jly
    1862; Jly 1864-May 1865. Ceased Jan 18,
    1945.
    MWA: Nov 18, 1865.
    ICHi: Jun 30, 1876.
    IU: 1937-1944.

Critic   w   1889
    Listed in Ayer 1889.

Democrat   w,d   1873-1906   w   1935
    MoHi: May 22, 1879-Dec 20, 1888; Oct 30,
    1884. Daily listed 1893-1895.
    NN: Feb 2, 1888.
    KHi: Sep 27, 1888.

RICHMOND (continued)

Farmers' and Laborers' Advocate w 1882
    Also known as Laborers' Advocate. Under brief
    title in Rowell 1882, fuller title 1883.

Herald w 1852-1853
    MoHi: Mar 17-Oct 1,1852.
    MoSHi: Oct 15,Nov 26,Dec 3,1852.
        First in county, according to Organ. Became
        Mirror 1853, later Conservator.

Item d 1896
    Only mentioned is Missouri Editor, Sep 1896,
    which tells of "revival" of the Daily Item.

Mirror w 1853-1861?
    MoHi: Feb 18-Sep 2,1853; 1854-Apr 21,1855;
        Sep 11-Dec 25,1857; Jan 1-Oct 16,1858,
        all inc.; Sep 18,1858.

Missouri Freeman w 1865-1866?
    Mentioned by Hammond.

Missouri Odd-Fellow w 1894
    Start noted in Missouri Editor, Mar 1894.

Missourian w,sw 1898-1946
    MoHi: Jly 25,1901-1944; Nov 9,1905. Film,
        1945-Apr 24,1946.
    MoSHi: Dec 21,1905; 1906 ex. Apr 26,Sep 6;
        Jan 3-Jun 27,1907; sw 1942-1943. Purchased
        by News Apr 25,1946.
    KHi: Aug 30,1917.

News w,sw,tw d 1914+
    MoHi: 1919-1944. Film, Jly 8,1915-Sep 21,
        1916; 1945+. Publication varied, sw Jly-
        Sep 1915; tw, Jan 27,1919; d listed 1898-1913.

Northwest Conservator w 1852-1945
    MoHi: Sep 13,1861; Apr 23,1863. See
        Conservator.

Plain Dealer sm 1901
    Semi-monthly listed in Ayer 1902.

Ray County Conservator w 1952+
    MoHi: Film, Oct 19,1953+. First in Ayer 1955.

Ray County Chronicle w 1872-1878?
    MoHi: Jun 7,1878. In Rowell 1873-1879.
    ICHi: Jly 1,8,1876.

Ray County Herald w 1945+
    MoHi: Film, Oct 15,1953+. See Hardin News.

Ray County Republican w 1890-1908
    MoHi: Nov 8-Dec 27,1906; Jan 3-Feb 28,Mar
        14-Apr 25,May 16,Jun 7,20,27,Jly 11-Oct
        17,Oct 30-Dec 12,1907.

RICHMOND (continued)

Rayite w 1873?
    In Rowell 1890 with founding date 1873. May
    have been name for Democrat for year,same
    publisher.

Register d 1895
    Start of evening Register noted in Missouri Editor,
    Oct 1895.

Republican w 1866-1872
    MoHi: Jun 23,Dec 1,1869. Hammond says paper
        known as Ray County Chronicle 1872-1879,
        later as Democrat.

Review d 1895
    Missouri Editor, Mar 1895,tells of start; Missouri
    Editor, Apr 1895,tells of death.

RIDGEWAY (Harrison County)

Blade w 1882
    Listed in Rowell-Dauchy 1883.

Free Press w 1884
    Listed in Rowell-Dauchy 1884.

Journal w 1891-1941
    MoHi: 1911-Dec 18,1941. Film,Apr 3,1891-
        May 1894; Dec 15,1898-1910. Suspended
        Dec 18,1941.
    KHi: Jan 20,1921.

RITCHEY (Newton County)

Reflector w 1894
    Start noted by Missouri Editor, Oct 1894.

Telephone w 1887
    Listed in Ayer 1887.

ROCHEPORT (Boone County)

Boone County Democrat w 1876?
    MoHi: Oct 16,1876.

Commercial w 1878-1900, 1901-1909?
    MoHi: Feb 15,Mar 22,May 17,Jun 28,Aug 23,
        30,Sep 20,27,Oct 4,25,Nov 1,Dec 20,1895;
        Jan 3,10,17,Mar 27,Apr 17,May 8,15,29,
        Jun 5,19,26,Jly 3,10,24,31,Aug 7,21,Sep
        4,Oct 9,30,Nov 6,27,Dec 25,1896; Jan 8,
        15,Feb 12,Sep 17,Nov 12,Dec 10,1897; Jan
        21,Apr 29,Nov 4,1898. Film,May 13,1887-
        Dec 21,1894 inc. Apparently two. No
        directory listings between 1901-1907.

Democrat w 1901-1906
    MoHi: Apr 19,May 3,Jun 21,Aug 9,Sep 6,Oct
        4,18,1901; Mar 21,Nov 7,1902; Jan 2,9,
        1903; Aug 26,Nov 18,1904; Feb 10,1905.
        Film,Apr 12,1901-Mar 16,1906.

ROCHEPORT (continued)

Enterprise   w   1869-1872
    MoSHi: Sep 13, 1872. In Rowell 1871-1872.

Progress   w   1906-1917
    MoHi: Nov 13, 1908. Film, 1908-Dec 18, 1914;
    Jan 1915, inc.-Aug 3, 1917.

Times   w   1869
    MoSHi: Mar 11, 1869. In Rowell 1870.

ROCKPORT (Atchison County)

Atchison County Democrat   w   1897-1900
    Rowell 1900 noted edition printed for Watson.
    Don't confuse with Atchison Democrat.

Atchison County Independent   w   1937-1952
    In Ayer 1952 with 1937 founding date. See MPN,
    May 1952, on sale.

Atchison County Journal   w   1863-1927
    MoHi: Aug 30, 1879-1884; 1911-Apr 1927; Nov
    5, 1909. Film, 1885-Aug 18, 1892; 1893-1910.
    Sold to Mail Apr 26, 1927.
    ICHi: Jly 8, Sep 9, 1876.

Atchison County Mail   w   1878+
    MoHi: 1919-1944; Jan 19, 1906; Nov 12, 1909.
    Film, Jly 15, 1880-Aug 3, 1882; Oct 18, 1883-
    1889; 1890-Sep 2, 1898; Dec 1898-Nov
    1899; Mar 2-Dec 14, 1900 inc; Jan-Jun 1901
    inc; Jly 1901-1918; 1945+. Formerly Demo-
    crat Mail. Changed name Jly 15, 1880.
    KHi: Apr 20, 1923.

Atchison Democrat   w   1876-1881
    MoHi: Film, Aug 14, 1879-Jly 14, 1881.

Banner   w   1857-1859
    Pioneer paper in county, notes Organ.

Commercial   w   1906
    Listed in Ayer 1907.

Democrat   w   1884-1889?
    MoHi: Film, Aug 2, 1888-Jun 1889. Formerly
    Missouri Agitator.

Democratic Mail   w   1878-1880
    MoHi: Film, Aug 29, 1878-Jly 8, 1880. Named
    Atchison County Mail Jly 15, 1880.

Grangers' Advocate   w   1873
    Listed in Rowell 1874.

Herald   w   1859-1861
    Data from Organ.

Missouri Agitator   w   1884-1888
    MoHi: Film, Dec 24, 1884-Jly 26, 1888. Named
    Democrat Aug 2, 1888.

ROCKPORT (continued)

Missouri Express   1871-1872
    Listed in Rowell 1873.

Sentinel   w   1871?
    In Rowell 1871-1872. Hammond says name
    changed to Express, later News, Granger
    Advocate. (No listing on News.)

Sun   w   1876-1882
    MoHi: Film, Jan 12-Dec 27, 1882.

ROCKVILLE (Bates County)

Booster   w   1908-1916
    MoHi: Jan 14, 28, Feb 4, 25, Mar 3-24, Apr 7, 1916.

Gimlet   w   1897
    Listed in Ayer 1898.

Globe   w   1883-1885
    In Rowell 1885-1886, Dauchy 1885. Followed by
    Star.

Leader   w   1923+   w   1897-1898?
    Ayer 1899 lists Leader, apparently brief career.
    Moved to Appleton City.

Post   w   1890
    Listed in Ayer-Rowell 1891.

Reflex   w   1893-1902?
    In Rowell 1894-1903, Ayer 1894-1900.

Review   w   1918
    Listed in Ayer 1919.

Star   w   1886-1904
    In Ayer 1902 with 1901 starting date.

ROCKY COMFORT (McDonald County)

Independent   w   1896-1917?
    Last listed in Ayer 1918.

McDonald County Guide   w   1902-1904
    In Rowell 1902-1905, Ayer 1903-1904.

Ozark Times   w   1919-1922
    Listed in Ayer 1920-1923.

Richwood Telegram   w   1904-1909?
    Listed as Telegram in Rowell 1907.

Rock o' Comfort   w   1891-1895?
    In Rowell 1892-1894, Ayer 1892-1896.

Rocky News   w   1891-1898
    Rowell 1895 has same data for News as for Rock o'
    Comfort.

Tri-County Standard   w   1898
    In Rowell 1898-1899, Ayer 1899.

ROGERSVILLE (Webster County)

Record   w   1912-1939
    Consolidated with Seymour Citizen Feb 1939.

Reporter   w   1891?
    Listed in Ayer 1891.

Star   w   1896
    Listed in Ayer 1897.

ROLLA (Phelps County)

Advertiser   w   1934-1959
    Consolidated with New Era 1959.

Central Missouri Herald   w   1866-1960
    MoHi: Film, Apr 7-Jun 23, 1960; Jan 4-Feb 23,
    1962. Formerly Daily Herald. Suspended Jun
    23, 1960, resuming as Daily Herald.

Camp Sweeny Spy   w   1861
    MoSHi: Jly 4, 1861.
    IHi: Film, Jly 4, 1861.

Eagle   w   1875-1876
    ICHi: Jun 22, 1876. In Rowell's 1876 Centennial
    Newspaper Exhibition Book and directory.
    Hammond says an Eagle was started 1870,
    short-lived.

Express   w   1859-1875   d   1861?
    MoHi: W, film, Jly 30, 1860-May 9, 1863. D,
    Dec 27, 1861. Rural Express, Jan 6, 1866.
    Express, weekly, film, Jly 17, 1865; Jun 17,
    1867; Jun 27, 1868; Nov 2, 1872-Dec 27,
    1873; Feb 25, 1875. Apparently published
    under different titles. Last in Rowell 1875.
    MWA: w, Jan 20, 1866.

Fort Wood Sentinel   w   1941+
    In Ayer 1961 with 1941 founding date.

Herald   w,   tw,   d   1866-1962
    MoHi: D, Film, May 17-Sep 1950; Jly 6, 1953-
    Dec 31, 1960. Became daily May 17, 1950,
    weekly Sep 7, 1950; D again Jly 6, 1953;
    ceased publication Apr 1, 1960, resumed Jun
    27, 1960. TW: film, Mar 21, 1949-May 15,
    1950, when it became daily. W: Dec 1,
    1898-Feb 15, 1900; Jly 22, 1909-1944; Mar
    4, 1875; Jun 5, 1879; Jan 22, 1880; Sep 29,
    1887. Film, Mar 18, 1869-Dec 22, 1898;
    1945-Mar 14, 1950; Sep 7, 1952-Jly, 1953.
    MoSHi: Jly 17, 1913; Jan 2-Mar 6, Mar 20-
    Apr 17, May 1-Nov 20, Dec 4-23, 1941.
    Merged with Phelps County Democrat to
    become Herald-Democrat Feb 22, 1900.
    Renamed Herald Jly 22, 1909. Ceased com-
    pletely Feb 23, 1962. Daily ceased Dec 29,
    1961. From Apr 1 to Jun 27, 1960 known as
    Central Missouri Herald, weekly.
    ICHi: Aug 17, 1876.
    KHi: Apr 15, 1886; Jly 12, 1888.

ROLLA (continued)

Herald-Democrat   w   1866-1909
    MoHi: Feb 22, 1900-Jly 15, 1909. Formed by
    merger of Phelps County Democrat and Herald
    Feb 22, 1900. Became Herald Jly 22, 1909.

Irrespressible Vedette   w   1892-1893
    Populist paper, possibly less than year.

Journal   w   1870
    Noted in county history.

New Era   w   1875-1939   d   1939-1946
    MoHi: d, Sep 25, 1939-Mar 18, 1946. W be-
    came d Sep 25, 1939, renamed Daily News
    Mar 19, 1946. W, 1903; 1914-Sep 15, 1939;
    May 16, 1896. Film, 1889-Mar 22, 1890.
    KHi: w, Dec 12, 1924; Feb 24, 1928.

News   d   1875+
    MoHi: Mar 19, 1946-1950. Film, 1951+.

New Era-Advertiser   w   ?-1961
    Merged with Daily News 1961 at age of 82,
    according to MPN, Oct 1961.

Our Regiment   ?
    IHi: Film, Jly 22, 1861.

Phelps County Democrat   w   1898-1902?
    In Rowell 1900-1902.

Rural Express   w   1859-1869?
    See Express. Fuller name for some time.

Phelps County New Era   w   1875-1877?
    MoHi: Film, Jun 24, 1876; Oct 27, 1877.
    ICHi: Aug 19, 1876. See New Era.

Sharp Shooter   w   1899-1911?
    Also referred to as Missouri Sharp Shooter,
    Rowell 1904, 1908, Ayer 1901.

Standard   w   1898-1899
    In Rowell 1898-1899, Ayer 1899-1900.

Times   w   1907-1929
    MoHi: Mar 10, 1910-1928; Jan-Aug 22, 1929.
    In Ayer 1908-1930.

ROSCOE (St. Clair County)

Eagle   w   1897
    Country Editor, Aug 1897, says Eagle "has ceased
    to soar." No directory data. May be Osage
    Valley Eagle, Free Silver paper in Ayer 1898.

Osage Valley Eagle   w   1897
    See Eagle.

St. Clair County Gazette   w   1870-1871
    In Rowell 1870-1871.

OSEBUD (Gasconade County)

Advertiser w 1911
Listed in Ayer 1912.

OSENDALE (Andrew County)

Journal w 1891
Listed in Ayer 1892

Signal w 1891-1935?
In Rowell 1892-1908, Ayer 1894-1936.

OTHVILLE (Chariton County)

Bee w 1907-1917
In Rowell 1908, Ayer 1908-1918.

USH HILL (Audrain County)

Sentinel w 1895
Start noted in Missouri Editor, Oct 1895.

Union Banner w 1891
Listed in Ayer 1892.

USHVILLE (Buchanan County)

American w 1919
Listed in Ayer 1920.

Advocate w 1900
Listed in Ayer 1901.

Buchanan County Democrat w 1894?
In Ayer 1925, founding date 1894.

News w 1894-1898?, 1903-1924?
In Rowell 1895-1899, 1905-1908, Ayer 1904,
1911-1924.

Times w 1915-1917
Listed in Ayer 1916-1918.

RUSSELLVILLE (Cole County)

Central Missourian w 1930-1944
MoHi: Film, Sep 20, 1934. Suspended Oct 26,
1944, "not enough patronage."

Central Missouri Leader w 1904?-1927
In Ayer 1909, founding date 1904.

Rustler w 1896-1929?
MoHi: Mar 20-27, Apr 10-17, 1908; Jan 21-
Dec 29, 1916. Film, Jan 21, 1916-Mar 23,
1933.
MoSHi: Jun 27, 1913. Last in Ayer 1930. Union
List says part of Cole County Rustler
(Jefferson City)

RUTLEDGE (Scotland County)

Record w 1893-1907
In Rowell 1897-1908, Ayer 1896-1908.

Reporter w 1915-1916
In Ayer 1917.

ST. CHARLES (St. Charles County)

Advertiser w 1845-1846
MoSHi: Apr 15, 1843; May 4, 1844. Formerly
Free Press, later Missouri Patriot.
IHi: Film, Jan 1, 1846.

Banner w,d 1889-1897?
MoHi: Jly 11, 1895. See Banner-News.
KHi: d, Mar 16, 1925. (Banner-News)

Banner-News w 1864-1956 d 1889+
MoHi: w, Jly 25, 1901-1902; Apr 30, 1908-
1909; 1911-1944; Jly 9, 1903; Apr 23, 1908.
Film, 1945-1956. Ended w, Nov 8, 1956. D,
1903-May 1905; May 1908-Jan 12, 1911;
Oct 12, 1897; Jly 10, 11, 13-16, 1903; Apr
23, 1908; May 21, 1959; Oct 24, 1904-May
1905; Film, 1904-1932-1943; 1945+.
Former by merger News, Banner. Became
Daily Banner-News Oct 24, 1904.
MoSHi: Apr 16, 1904; Sep, Oct 26, 31, 1912;
Nov 7, 24, 1913; Dec 21, 22, 1916.
Microfilm Cen: Film, 1950-Jun 30, 1961.

Chronotype w 1849-1853
MoSHi: Nov 24, 1849; Nov 9, 1850; Jly 2, 1853.
Univ. of KC: Jly 9, 1853.
NcD: Jly 24, 31, 1853. Formerly Western Star,
later Reveille.

Clarion w 1835-1839
DLC: Feb 23, 1839. Later Free Press, Advertiser,
Missouri Patriot, according to Organ.

Cosmos w 1835-1902
MoHi: Feb 8, 1899-Feb 5, 1902; Dec 9, 1869;
Nov 25, 1874; Dec 22, 1897; Feb 16, Mar
30, 1881. Film, Jan-Dec 20, 1882; Jan-Sep
10, 1884; Jan-Dec 21, 1887; 1889-Nov 25,
1896 inc; 1897-Dec 7, 1898; 1901. Merged
with Monitor to become Cosmos-Monitor Feb
12, 1902.
ICHi: Aug 9, 1876.

Cosmos-Monitor w 1836-1957 d 1894-1959
MoHi: W, 1902; 1904-1905; 1907; Sep-Dec 1909;
1913-1918; 1920-1923; 1928-1944. Film,
1903; 1906; 1910-1912; 1918; 1921; 1923-
1927; 1945-Jan 30, 1957. Discontinued Jan
30, 1957. D, film, Jan 11-Jun 28, 1909; 1916-
1917; 1921-Jun 30, 1926; Jan-Jun 1927;
1928; Jan-Jun 1930; Feb 1957-May 18, 1959.
Discontinued May 18, 1959.
MoSHi: Mar 6, 1873; Aug 23, 1915; Dec 21, 1916.
MWA: W, Jly 1, 1863; Mar 22-29, 1876.
Microfilm Cen: Film, w, 1909-1959 inc.

ST. CHARLES (continued)

Cosmos-Sentinel w
    MoHi: Jun 17,1869. Result of consolidation.
    Shortened to Cosmos 1868.

Demokrat w 1852-1916
    MoHi: Oct 30,1890; Feb 4,1909.
    MoSHi: Complete set.
    MWA: Oct 19,1865.
    ICHi: Jun 15,1876.

Free Press w 1840-1844
    Formerly Clarion, later Advertiser.

Jeffersonian w 1825-1844?
    Known as Jeffersonian Republican 1827, moved
    with capital to Jefferson City.

Journal w 1881-1882
    In Rowell 1881-1882, Ayer 1882.

Kaleidoscope w 1861?
    In American Newspaper Directory 1861.

Missourian w 1820-1822
    MoHi: Jun 24,1820-Oct 1822.
    MoSHi: Film, Jun 24,1820-Oct 24,1822.
    MWA: Jun 27,1821.
    AzTP: Film, Jun 24,1820-Oct 24,1822.
    DLC: Jun 24,1820-Oct 24,1822.
    KHi: Film, Jun 24,1820-Oct 24,1822.

Missouri Advocate w 1824-1825
    Mentioned by Organ, Union List. Later became
    Enquirer in St. Louis.

Missouri Gazette 1823-1824
    DLC has Vol 1, No 18, Apr 1,1824. Sold to
    Missourian, moved to Jefferson City.
    MoSHi: May 6,1824.
    MWA: Jun 10,1824.

Missouri Patriot w 1846-1847
    MoSHi: Aug 20,1846; May 6-Jun 11, Jly 23-
    Aug 13, Sep 3-Nov 5, Nov 19-Dec 17,1846;
    Jan 7-Apr 15, Apr 29, May 6-20, Jun 3, 17-
    Jly 8, Aug 12-Sep 23, Oct 21,1847. Formerly
    Advertiser, later Western Star.
    IHi: Film, Jly 15,1847.

Monitor w,d 1894-1902
    MoHi: D, Film, Aug 10,1894-Apr 30,1898, inc.
    Merged with Cosmos Feb 12,1902.

News w,sw 1867-1897 d 1889-1897?
    MoHi: D, Mar 22,1897. W, film, Oct 13,1870-
    Feb 15,1872. Merged with Banner.
    MoSHi: Mar 17,1896.
    NHi: Mar 19,1881.
    ICHi: Mar 23, Jly 8,1876.

ST. CHARLES (continued)

Republikaner w 1880?-1903?
    MoHi: Aug 23, Dec 13,27,1901.

Reveille w 1854-1865?
    MoSHi: Jun 3,1854, Apr 20,1860. Formerly
    Chronotype, later consolidated with Sentinel.

Sentinel w 1866
    See Reveille. After 1867 called Cosmos-Sentinel.

Sonntagsblatt w 1872-1879?
    Noted in G-AN&P.

Union (Die) w 1876?-1877?
    Noted in Rowell 1877.

Western Star w 1847-1848
    Formerly Missouri Patriot, later Chronotype,
    according to Organ.

Zeitung w 1872-1879?
    Noted in Rowell 1875-1879.

ST. CLAIR (Franklin County)

Chronicle w 1924+
    MoHi: Mar 17,1927-1944; Oct 10,1946. Film,
    1945+.

Gazette w 1896
    In Ayer 1897. Silver Democrat paper.

Howard County Echo w 1899?-1904
    In Ayer-Rowell 1905.

Ozark News w 1940-1952
    MoHi: Aug 22,1940-1944. Film,1945-1952.
    Merged with Chronicle Oct 1952.

Times w 1913-1917?
    In Ayer 1915-1918.

STE. GENEVIEVE (Ste. Genevieve County)

Beocachter w 1880-1881?
    In Ayer 1881, Rowell 1882. German.

Correspondent and Ste. Genevieve Record
    w 1821-1823
    First in county, short-lived according to Organ
    who claims a French paper was there after 1780.

Creole w 1850-1851
    Press to St. Louis. See Record. Formerly Missouri
    Democrat.

Democrat w 1850?, 1916-1919?
    MoHi: Jan 7-May 19,1916.
    MoSHi: Jun 8,1850.

Fair Play   w   1872-1943, 1945+
    MoHi: Aug 30,1902-Jan 16,1943; Jun 17,1875;
        Jun 15,1876; Mar 23,1901. Film, Jun 14,
        1872-1877; Jan 10,1880-Nov 27,1886; 1888-
        Aug 30,1902; 1946+.
    MoSHi: Apr 23,1874; Jun 17,Oct 15,Dec 2,
        1875; Apr 27,May 4,Jun 15,1876; Jun 16,
        Sep 29,Nov 3,1883; Feb 21,May 9,Jun 6,
        Nov 14,Dec 5,12,1885; Nov 13,1886;
        Oct 13,1888; Jun 20,27,Aug 3-17,1929;
        Mar 22,Sep 20,1930; Jan 3,10,Feb 7,1931;
        Jun 10-Jly 8,Nov 11,Dec 1933; Jan 13-Feb
        3,16,Mar 17,Apr 14-Sep 22,Oct 22,Nov 17-
        Dec 1934; 1935-1942; Jan 2-16,1943; Dec
        8-29,1945; Jan-Sep 28,1946.
    ICHi: Jly 6,Aug 10,1876. Did not publish
        between Jan 16,1943-Dec 21,1945.

Freie Blatter   w   1876-1881?
    In Rowell 1877-1882. Ayer 1880 says 1874 found-
    ing date. German.

Free Press, Freie Presse   w   1874-1876
    ICHi: Jly 22,1876. In Rowell 1875-1876,
    English-German editions.

Freisasse   w   1875
    Listed in Rowell 1875.

Herald   w   1882+
    MoHi: Jly 27,1907-1944; Mar 20,1897. Film,
        May 6,1882-Apr 11,1908; 1945+.
    MoSHi: Jan 5,1924; Aug 31,1929; Aug 30,Sep
        20,1930; Jly 30,1932; Apr 22,May 6,Oct 7-
        Nov 18,Dec 30,1933; 1934-Sep 28,1946 with
        only a few missing issues.
    KHi: Sep 15,22,1888.

Herold   w   1882-1918?
    MoHi: Jan 10,1903-Jan 14,Sep 1905-1906;
        1909. Film,May 6,1882-Apr 16,1908; Jly
        27,1909-1918.

Independent   w   1852-1861
    MoSHi: May 16,Jly 18,Aug 15,Nov 12,26,
        Dec 10,1857.

Little Giant   w   1880-1881
    Listed in Rowell-Ayer 1881.

Missouri Citizen   w   1859?
    MoSHi: May 13,1859. No other data.

Missouri Democrat   w   1833-1850
    Apparently continuation of State Gazette
    and Southern Gazette. Press moved to St. Louis,
    according to Organ.

Missouri Gazette   w   1859
    Mentioned in county histories.

Missouri Magnet   w   1913-1914?
    English, German paper in Ayer 1914-1915.

News   w   1899-1904?
    Also referred to as County News.

News and Advertiser   w   1868-1872
    MoHi: Mar 11,1869. In English and German.

Pioneer   w   1850
    MoSHi: Feb 16,1850. May have appeared briefly
    in 1849.

Plaindealer   w   1851?-1862
    MoHi: 1853; Feb 22,Mar 1,8,15,22,1861.
    MoSHi: Oct 23, Dec 11,25,1852; May 7,
        Jly 9,23,Aug 6,1853; Jun 9,1855; Feb
        24,Mar 9,30,Apr 13,20,Jun 29,Jly 13,
        27,Sep 7,28,Oct 7,Nov 9,30,Dec 28,
        1860; Jan 8,Mar 29,Aug 30,Nov 15,22,
        29,Dec 27,1861; Feb 28,Apr 11,1862.

Rail Road Extra   1872
    MoSHi: Feb 24,1872. No directory data.

Post-Bote   w   1880
    In Rowell-Ayer 1881. German.

Record   w   1821
    MoHi: May 29,1821. One page only. See
    Correspondent and Ste. Genevieve Record.

Representative   w   1865-1866
    MoHi: Mar 3,Apr 21,1866.
    MoSHi: Mar 31,1866.
    WHi: Apr 7,1866.

Southern Gazette   w   1833
    Followed State Gazette, soon renamed Missouri
    Democrat, according to Organ.

State Gazette   w   1831-1833
    Discussed by Organ. See Southern Gazette.

ST. JAMES (Phelps County)

Home News   w   1896-1900?
    Missouri Editor, Nov 1896, tells of start. In Ayer
    1901.

Journal   w   1896-1959
    MoHi: Jly 26,1901-Mar 1923. Sold to Rolla
        News 1959. See Leader-Journal.
    KHi: Nov 19,1926.

Leader   w   1928-1959
    MoHi: Apr 15,1937-1944. Film,1945.

Leader-Journal   w   1896+
    MoHi: Nov 1959+.
    MoSHi: Sep 8,1960. See Journal, Leader.

ST. JAMES (continued)

News w 1893-1900?
In Rowell 1894-1901, Ayer 1895-1897.

Progressive News w 1912-1914?
Progressive Party paper. In Ayer 1914-1915.

Republican w 1910-1916
MoHi: Jan 6-Mar 9, 1916. Listed in Ayer 1911-1916.

Tribune w 1871
Listed in Rowell 1871.

Vindicator w 1896
Listed in Ayer 1897.

ST. JOSEPH (Buchanan County)

Advance w 1882-1887?
Apparently Sunday paper for a time. In Rowell 1885-1887.

Adventurer w 1848-1853
MoKc: May 3, 1850-Apr 1851. Became Cycle 1853, later the Journal. Suspended 1862. Also listed as Adventure.

Advocate d 1881
Listed in Rowell 1882.

American w 1892
Listed in Ayer 1892.

American Eagle w 1907?
In Rowell 1907, no founding date.

Appeal w 1913-1920?
Negro publication, in Ayer 1915-1921.

Ballot dw 1890?
MoHi: d, Nov 8, 1890. Rowell 1891 also said weekly edition published.

Catholic Tribune w 1878-1942
MoHi: Jly 27, 1901-1942; Oct 25, 1890. Film, Mar 1889-Feb 8, 1903.

Chronicle d,w 1876-1878?
Listed in Rowell 1877-1878.

Commercial w,d 1872-1875?
W in Rowell 1872, d, w in Rowell 1875.

Commercial Advertiser d,w 1872-1874
Listed in Rowell 1873-1874.

Commercial Cycle w 1848-1856?
MoHi: Film, Jan 5, 1855-Dec 5, 1856. See Adventurer.
MWA: Dec 16, 1853.
ICN: Film, Jan 5, 1855-Dec 5, 1856.
DLC: Film, Jan 5, 1855-Dec 5, 1856.
KHi: Film, Jan 5, 1855-Dec 5, 1856.

ST. JOSEPH (continued)

Courier w,d 1899+
Legal publication, although not listed as such in some early directories.

Deutsche Zeitung w 1868-1869?
Listed in Rowell 1869.

Democrat w 1930-1933, 1935
Ayer 1933-1934 listed Democrat founded in 1930. MPN, Jan 1935, noted a new paper, the Democrat.

Dollar Herald w 1862?
Listed in Ayer 1880 as "Weekly edition of Herald. Said to be established in 1862; not in Rowell.

Eye w 1905-1917
MoHi: Dec 5, 19, 1908; Jan 9, 1909. Film, Dec 24, 1909-1914.
KHi: Mar 26, 1915.

Foster's Forecasts w 1891
Listed in Rowell 1892.

Free Democrat w 1859-1861
MoHi: Film, Aug 6, 1859-Apr 13, 1861.
MoSHi: Jun 9, 1855.
MWA: Oct 13-27, Nov 17, 1860.
KHi: Film, Aug 6, 1859-Apr 13, 1861.

Free Press w 1859-1861
Mentioned in county history.

Gazette w 1845-1903? d 1855+
MoHi: d, 1911-1950; Jan 11, 1870; Oct 27, 1890. Film, Jun 28, 1868-Jun 26, 1870; 1872-Jun 1874; Dec 1, 1874-1894; 1896-1910; 1951+. W, Apr 25, 1855. Film, Apr 25, 1845-Oct 4, 1854; Jly 9, 1868-1873; 1885-1886; May 10, 1888-Jun 1889; Apr-Dec 1890; Jan-Mar 1892; Nov 1898-Aug 3, 1900.
MoSHi: d, film, Apr 25, 1845-Aug 28, 1846; May 11, 1859; May 16, 1860; Nov 14, 1885; Dec 20, 1903. W, film, Jly 9, 1868; Jun 27, 1872; Jly 4-Dec 25, 1873.
MoKc: d, film, Jly 1, 1868-Jun 26, 1870; 1872-Jun 30, 1874. W, film, Jly 9, 1868-1873; 1887-Nov 24, 1892. Suspended during Civil War. Consolidated with Herald 1900; renamed Gazette 1902.
MWA: w, Nov 30-Dec 7, 1853.
DLC: w, film, Apr-Dec 1845; Apr-Dec 1846; 1847-Oct 4, 1854; Sep 7, 1876.
IaHi: w, Apr 19-Dec 27, 1883; Jan 3-Sep 4, 1884.
KHi: w, Sep 13, 1877-Aug 3, 1900; Dec 26, 1893; Apr 4, 1913. Film, Apr 25, 1845-Oct 4, 1854. D, Mar 1, 1874. Trade editions, Jan 1887, 1888, 1889; Sep 9, 1888.
NbHi: Film, Apr 25, 1845-Oct 4, 1854.
NHi: Apr 17, May 1, 1873.
NjR: w, Nov 22, 1854.
Micro-Photo: Film, d, 1868+ W, 1868-1900 inc.

Gazette-Herald   w 1845-1903? d 1900-1902
   MoHi: d,film,Aug 1,1900-Mar 29,1902. W,
      Jan-Nov 1901. Film,Aug 9-Dec 27,1900.

Good Way   w 1879-1881
   Religious. Ayer 1880-1881,Rowell 1882.

Grip   w 1882-1883
   In Dauchy-Rowell 1883.

Herald   d,w 1862-1900
   MoHi: d,Oct 9,1876-1881; Nov 1882-Jun
      1885; 1886-1888. Film,May 8,1874-Jun
      24,1876; Jun 14,1885-May 21,1886; 1889-
      Jly 1900. Morning Herald to Oct 10,1876:
      Sep 1865-Feb 11,1875; Jan-Oct 9,1876.
      Film,Feb 12,1862-Mar 3,1866; May 8,
      1874-Jun 24,1876. W,Feb 4,1869-1870;
      Jly 30,1896. Film,Mar 20,1862-Oct 27,
      1864; 1883-1890; Jly 1891-1899.
   MoSHi: Jan 1,1875; Aug 23-Dec 21,1881;
      Jan 3-Jun 30,1883; Jan 1-Jun 30,1889;
      Jly 1-Dec 31,1891; 1892-1893; Jan 2-
      Jun 30,1900.
   MWA: w,Oct 30,1862; Jan 11,1866.
   DLC: d,Dec 12-31,1865; Jan-Oct 1866;
      1867-Nov 11,1868.
   KHi: d,Mar 14-Apr 1,1877; Jan 1-Jun 29,
      1882; Trade Editions,Jan 1886-1889; Jan
      1886-1888 inc. Film,Feb 13,1862-Feb 11,
      1865. W,Apr 5,1877-Nov 15,1902.
   NbHi: d,Jun 5,1892 inc.
   NHi: Dec 12,1869; Jun 17,1863.
   WHi: d,Sep 19,23,1863; Jly 21,Aug 1,1864.
   Micro-Photo: Film,d 1865-1900. W,1890;
      1894-1899。

Intelligencer   w 1879
   M.P.Chapman represented paper at MPA meet-
      ing in 1879.

Journal of Commerce   w 1885-1899
   In Ayer 1894-1900.

Journal   w 1847-1861?,1915-1916   d 1885-1887?
   DLC: Jan 6,1860. (Vol 13,No 36).
   KHi: d,Aug 23,1892; Jly 12-15,1911.
   MWA: w,Nov 15,1861. Rowell 1886-1887 lists
      d. Ayer 1917 lists third Journal.

Leader   w 1884-1889
   MoHi: Aug 7,1886. In Rowell-Ayer 1889.

Mirror   w 1886-1904?
   In Rowell 1905. Negro.

Missouri Valley Independent   w 1922-1927
   MoHi: 1923-Nov 1927. Became Fraternalist
      Nov 1927.

Missouri Vindicator   w 1868?
   MoSHi: May 23,1868. No other data.

Modern Farmer   w,m 1899?
   MoHi: Nov 15,1899.
   KHi: m,1907-Jly 1910 of Modern Farmer & Busy
      Bee.

Monday Leader   w 1884-1887?
   Also Leader, Monday Morning Leader.

Monday Morning News   w 1877-1878
   Rowell 1878-1879 lists as commercial. Hammond
      says suspended few months, in 1879 became
      Western News. Rowell 1885 lists as w edition of
      Evening News.

National Protest   w 1895-1897,1910?-1928?
   Two listings。First ends with Ayer-Rowell 1898,
      second Ayer 1911-1929。

New Era   w 1862-1863
   KHi: Apr 14,1862. Noted in county history.

News   d 1879-1904?   w 1890-1911?
   MoHi: d,Aug 27-29,31,Sep 19,1903; Oct
      25,1890. Film,Oct 25,1885-Sep 15,1903.
      As Evening News, Mar 1,1881. Film,May 3,
      1879-Oct 19,1885. Formerly Western News
      to May 3,1879; became Daily News Oct
      21,1885. Merged with Evening Press to be-
      come News and Press Sep 21,1903.
   Micro-Photo: Film,d,1885-1904. Evening
      News, 1879-1885.
   KHi: w,Sep 21,1894-Feb 19,1901,inc.

News and Press, News-Press   d 1879+
   MoHi: Sep 21,1903-Feb 28,1905; Jan 2,1905;
      Mar 1,1905-1950. Film,1951+. Became News-
      Press Mar 1,1905.
   MWA: Jan 1,1888.
   NbHi: Dec 3,1901; Feb 3,6,Apr 4,Jun 23,1902;
      Apr 9,Jun 3,Aug 21,1903; Nov 29,1907.
   WHi: Jan 1,1917-1919。
   Micro-Photo: Film,1904+.
   KHi: Apr 25,1905-Oct 17,1921; Apr 3,1913.
   DLC: Feb 1,1904.

Observer   w 1906-1933
   MoHi: Sep 1,1906-1914; 1916-1932. Film,1915.
      Merged with Union Jan 6,1933.

Post   w 1902?-1909?
   German paper in Ayer 1907-1910.

Press   d 1902-1903
   MoHi: Film,Aug 26,1902-Sep 19,1903. See
      News-Press. Became News and Press Sep 21,
      1903.

Radical   w 1887-1890,1895-1909?
   Apparently two Radicals. Negro.

Record   d 1898-1899
   In Ayer 1900,daily,Sunday morning paper.

Red Ribbon Advocate   w   1878-1879?
  MoHi: Jun 28, 1879. Devoted to "temperance
    and advertising." Free distribution.

Reflector   w   1871-1872
  Listed in Rowell 1872.

Reporter   d,w   1875-1878
  County history says weekly founded 1875, daily
    1878, both short-lived.

Republican   w   1894-1895
  Short-lived, no patronage said Missouri Editor,
    Feb 1895.

Saturday Argus   w   1893
  KHi: Jan 28, 1893. In Rowell 1893-1894, Ayer
    1894.

Saturday Chronicle   w   1875-1876
  MoHi: Feb 19, 1876.

Saturday Democrat   w   1879-1883?
  In Rowell 1880-1884, Ayer 1880-1881.

Saturday Globe   w   1896-1897
  Silver Democrat, in Ayer 1897-1898.

Saturday Record   w   1898
  Start in Country Editor, Apr 1898.

Saturday Review   w   1875-1878
  Listed in Rowell 1877-1879.

Sparks   w   1884
  In Rowell 1885 as Sunday paper.

Spectator   w   1902-1909
  In Rowell 1904-1907, Ayer 1903-1909.

Standard   w   1871-1873
  MoHi: Aug 28, 1873. Film, Sep 7, 1871-Aug 28,
    1873.
  KHi: Sep 29, 1873.

Star   w   1887-1893?   d   1905-1908
  MoHi: Oct 24, 1890. Film, Nov 27, 1905-Feb
    28, 1906; Oct 30-Dec 31, 1908.
  KHi: d, May 5, 1908.

Stock Yards Daily Journal   d   ?
  MoHi: Dec 29, 1904; Sep 25, Oct 3, 4, 1905;
    Feb 16, 21, 1906.

Statesman   w   1903
  Listed in Ayer 1904.

Sun   d   1881
  Noted in county history.

Sunday Visitor   w   1885-1886
  Listed in Rowell 1886-1887.

Telephone   tw   1878
  Listed in county history.

Times   w   1888   d   1897-1898
  MoHi: d, Film, Sep 13, 1897-Mar 16, 1898.
    In Ayer 1888, 1898, Rowell 1897-1898.

Tribune   w   1863   d   1863-1864   d   1870
  MoHi: Oct 24, 1870 copy of Evening Tribune.
    County history says daily absorbed by
    Morning Herald 1864.
  WHi: d, Mar 10, Apr 19, Jun 10, 24, Jly 19, 27,
    Aug 24, 1864.

Union   w   1864-1871?   w   1899-1929?
  MoHi: d, Sep 3, 1870. w, Jan 8, 1909-1921; Jan
    6, 1870. Two under this title. Rowell 1869-
    1870 lists both d, w. Second was union pub-
    lication. See Observer.
  WHi: Sep 27, 1866; May 22, 1867.

Union Advocate   w   1898-1899
  Listed in Rowell 1898-1899.

Union-Observer   w   1898+
  MoHi: w, 1933-1944. Film, 1945+. Mentioned
    in MPN, Jan 1936, Jun 1940.

Vindicator   w   1865
  Noted in county history.

Volksblatt   d   1865-1911   w   1858-1924
  MoHi: w, Feb 3, 1906. Also known as Wochent-
    liches Volksblatt and Das Westliche Volks-
    blatt. Sunday edition printed briefly. Since
    1924 printed as part of Kansas City Presse?
    German.
  MWA: d, Aug 26, 1876. w, Feb 10, 1866.
  KHi: tw, Oct 19-Dec 21, 1924.

Wasp   d,w   1886-1894?
  In Rowell 1891-1894, Ayer 1894-1895.

Wathena Gazette   w   1889-1892?
  KHi: Apr 11, Aug 8, 1891. In Rowell 1893 as
    Times and Wathena Gazette.

West   w   1858-1860   d   1859-1860
  MoHi: Film, May 8, 1859-Apr 28, 1860. California
    News, May 26, 1860, notes Daily West had
    suspended, lost $1,500 in past 12 months.
  KHi: w, May 8, 1859-Apr 28, 1860.

Westliche Volksblatt   d   1860-?   w   1859-?
  In Rowell 1879-1883. See Volksblatt.

Western Industrial Advocate   w   1873
  Noted in Rowell 1874.

Western News   w   1878-1883
  MoHi: Aug 12, 1881-Nov 12, 1882; Jan-Aug
    1883. Became Evening News Aug 1883.

Winners of the West   m   1923-1944?
   MnHi: Dec 30,1926-1944. In Ayer 1944 as
     organ for Independent War Veterans.

ST. LOUIS (St. Louis County)

Abend-Anzeiger   d   1835-1912
   MoS: Oct 1898; Sep 1901-Dec 1907; Apr-Jun
     1908; 1909-Apr 1912.
   MoSHi: Dec 8,1848; Jly 13,1850-1851; Apr
     21,Dec 22-23,1857; Jan 16,18,20,1863.
   MWA: Apr 12,1863. See Anzeiger des Westens,
     Mississippi Blaetter.

Abend Post und Tageblatt   d   1888-1898
   MoHi: Oct 28,1890.
   MoS: Apr 1888-Jun 1897. G-AN&P notes
     Abendpost, w, 1872.

Abend Schule   w,sm   1854-1940
   MoS: Complete set.
   MoSCHi: Complete set.
   KHi: Feb 12,1903-Mar 24,1904. G-AN&P says
     was sm 1854-1874; w,1874-1905,fortnightly
     1905-1940. Pettengill 1877 lists Abend Schule
     w, Beiblatt, m, same publisher.

Abendstunde   w   1946?
   Noted in G-AN&P.

Abendzeitung   d   1867-1868
   Merged with Die Neue Welt.

Advance   w   1881?-1908?
   MoHi: Jun 13,1908. Negro. Rowell 1893
     lists Afro-American News, founded 1873.

Advertiser   d   1861
   In American Newspaper Directory 1861.

Ad Writer
   MoHi: Jun 1899.

Age   w   1847
   MoSHi: Feb 20,1847.

Airport News
   MoSHi: Sep 7,1929.

Altenheim Nachrichten   1906?
   Noted in G-AN&P.

Altruist   m   1877-?
   MoHi: Jun 1901.
   KHi: Apr 1885-May 1917 inc.

American   w   1844-1846?,1928+ d,1845,1924,
     1950-1952
   MoHi: w,film,Dec 14,1949+.
   MoS: Dec 7,1844; Dec 6,1846. D,1950-1952.
   MoSHi: d,Dec 17,1936.

American (continued)
   IHi: Film, Jan 6,Mar 14,1846.
   Microfilm Cen: Film, 1950-1952. D 1924
     lasted 43 issues.

American Baptist   w   1875-1893?
   MoHi: Aug 31,Sep 14,28,Oct 5-19,Nov 2,1893.
   KHi: Jly 12,Aug 23,1888.
   MnHi: Dec 21,1887; Feb 5,1891.

American Baptist Flag   w
   MoSHi: May 5, Jun 23, Jly 28,1886; Apr 13,
     May 11,18, Jun 1,15,22, Jly 20,1887;
     Jun 6,1895.

American Bulletin
   MoSHi: Nov 15,1842.

American Celt   w   1883-1893
   MoHi: Feb 7,1891.

American Eagle   w   1894-1905?
   MoHi: Dec 17,1905. Negro.
   KHi: Dec 17,1905.

American Hotel Reporter
   NHi: Jly 11,18-19,1878.

American Journalist   w   1883-?

American Legion News
   MoSHi: May 28,1936.

American Nationalist   w   1882
   Listed in Dauchy 1883.

American Tribune   w   1874-1875,1883-?
   MoSHi: Mar 8,14,Apr 12,1883; May 26,Oct
     23,1884; Mar 18,1886; Jly 14,1887.
   DLC: Oct 16,1874. Vol 1,No 1.
   IHi: Film,Mar 8,1883.

American Wheelman   m   1885-?

American Working Girl
   MoSHi: Mar 25,1899.

Amerika   d   1872-1924
   MoHi: Film, Jun 1-Nov 30,1874; Sep 1,1875-
     Aug 31,1876; Jly 1,1914-Apr 1915; Jly
     1915-Dec 1920. Sunday,film,Sep 3,1876-
     Oct 13,1878. W,film,Oct 23,1872-Oct 9,
     1878; Oct 22,1884-Oct 13,1886; 1901-1902.
   MoS: 1903-Jun 1914; 1921-Nov 1924.
   McCon: 1921-1923.
   MoSC: 1872-Apr 1921; Oct 23,1872-1924 inc.
   MoSHi: Oct 17,1873; Jun 6,1877; Jan 18,1880;
     Dec 20,1886; Aug 10,1888; Apr 10,1899;
     Apr 2,1902; Jly 8,22,1904; Sep 8,15,1912;
     Jun 4,1916; Oct 12,26,1919; May 16,1920;
     Jan 4,7,11,14,1921; Apr 16,1922; 1922-1923.
   ICHi: Aug 23,Sep 27,Oct 11,1876.

Amerika und Herold des Glaubens w,sw 1872-1924
  MoCon: 1921-1923.
  MoS: Not all catalogued.
  MoSc: Oct 23, 1872; Oct 23, 1921-Jun 1924.
  MoSC: Complete.
  MoSHi: Some on file. See Amerika. This full
    title used at times. Amerika absorbed Herold
    des Glaubens.

Amerika Allgemine Zeitung fur Wahreit und Recht
d,w 1876
  Listed in Pettengill 1877.

Amerika Worchentliche Ausg. w 1873-1874?
  MoS: Oct 22, 1873-Oct 14, 1874.

Antipfaff (Der) w ?
  MoSHi: Apr 19, Jly 6, 1842; Mar 1843; May 1,
    1844.

Anzeiger des Westens d,w 1835-1912?
  MoHi: Jly 15, 1843; Sep 8, 15, 1861.
  MoS: w, 1835-1844 inc; 1844-Oct 17, 1846;
    1868-Jun 5, 1898. SW, Oct 30, 1841-Oct 6,
    1842 inc. Weekend, Jly 24, 1864-Jun 5, 1898
    inc.
  MoSHi: w, Oct 31, 1835-Oct 31, 1837; Oct 21,
    1843-1851 inc. D, Nov 26, Dec 10, 1836; Feb
    18, Apr 11, 1843; Jly 3, 10, 1847; Aug 13, Dec
    8, 9, 1848; Sep 2, 1849; Jan 16, 18, 20, Aug
    28, 1852; Oct 6, 14, 25, Nov 10, 1853; Jan 24,
    Feb 4, 1854; Apr 21, Dec 22-23, 1857; Feb 20,
    1859; Dec 6, 1860; Oct 17, 1876; Mar 6,
    1883; Oct 4, 1891; Sep 20, 1901; Apr 2, 1902;
    Oct 7, 1904.
  MWA: Oct 21, 1860; Apr 13, 1862.
  ICHi: Sep 3, Oct 24, 1876.
  IHi: Film, Dec 28, 1839-Jan 31, 1863 inc. Neue
    Anzeiger des Westens, Jly 28, 1863-Jly 15,
    1869 inc.
  KHi: d, Sep 4, 1888.
  WHi: Oct 25, 1860.

Appell w 1890?
  Noted in G-AN&P.

Arbeiter-Zeitung w 1898-1931?
  MoHi: Apr 18, 1908.
  MoSHi: Mar 22, 1902; Jly 1, 8, Aug 25, Sep 30,
    1905; Aug 25, 1906; 1912-1916; 1918-1928;
    Sep 14, Dec 21, 28, 1929; Jan 4-18, 1930;
    Jan 30, Feb 13, Mar 13, 27, Apr 10, 1931.
  MoS: Aug 27, 1898-Aug 20, 1910; 1912-Nov 8,
    1930.
  MWA: Aug 1, 1914.

Argus w 1912+
  MoHi: 1921-1944. Film, 1915-Dec 13, 1918;
    Feb 21, 1919-1920; 1945+.
  MoS: Film, 1943-1954; Nov-Dec 1955; Apr 13,
    1956-1957.

Argus (continued)
  MoJcL: 1952; Oct 4, 1954-1955; 1957; 1959.
    Present Argus is Negro paper.
  Micro-Photo: Film, 1954+.
  Microfilm Cen: Film, 1943-1954.

Ariel w 1842-1843?
  MoSHi: May 25, 1843.
  MnHi: Dec 22, 1843.

Attack ?
  MoSHi: Nov 1, 1950.

As You Like It w 1890
  In Ayer-Rowell 1891. Slogan, "A paper with
    modern ideas and no fads."

Aurora Socialis
  MoSHi: Jan 5, 1919.

Baden News-Press w 1948+
  Free distribution paper.

Bank Note Reporter and Counterfeit Detector
  MoSHi: Dec 1, 1857.

Barnburner w 1849-1850?
  Union List says followed by Signal.

Beacon w 1829-1832
  MoHi: Apr 13-Nov 14, 1829; 1830-1832.
  MoS: 1829-1831 inc; Film, Apr 13, 1829-1832.
  MoSHi: Feb 6, 1830; Sep 22, Oct 6, 13, 1831.
    Film, 1829-1831; Feb-Dec 1832.
  MoKc: Film, 1829-1832.
  MoSM: Jly 21, 1831.
  MWA: Mar 1-8, Jly 26, 1832.
  AzTP: Film, Feb 2-Dec 6, 1832; Jun 27, 1829-
    Jun 26, 1832.
  Ct: Mar 30, 1829; Jly 29, Sep 9, Oct 7, 21, Nov
    4, 11, 1830; Apr 7, May 12, Jun 9, Jly 7, 14,
    Aug 18, 25, Oct 6, 13, Nov 24, Dec 22, 1831.
  CSmH: Aug 29, 1829.
  DLC: Apr 13, 1829; 1830-Dec 6, 1832. (Country)
    Aug 29, Sep 13, Oct 3, 1829.
  KHi: Film, Apr 13, 1829-Dec 6, 1832.
  IaHi: Film, 1829-1832.
  Micro-Photo: Film, 1829-1832.

Brauer Zeitung w 1894-1902
  Noted in G-AN&P.

Bread and Votes 1917?
  MoSHi: Mar 18, 1917. Socialist.

Breeze w 1884
  CtY: May 3, 1884.

Brentwood Scope w 1950+
  First in Ayer 1960. Free.

Bulletin   w   1838,1860   d   1859-1861
  MoS: Apr 19-Oct 13,1860.
  MoSW: Oct 18,1859-Oct 13,1860.
  MoSM: Oct 18,1859-Apr 18,1860.
  MoSHi: Aug 8,1861.
  MoSj: 1859-Mar 1860.
  DLC: w, Jly 17,1860. D, Jly 12,13,Aug 7,1861.
  MWA: d, Jly 19,1859.

Bulletin of Commerce   w   ?
  MoSHi: Aug 22,1908.

Buyer's Guide
  MoSHi: Various spring,fall issues for 1905,1908-
    1928. Became Market Guide 1930.

Call   d   1884,1890
  MoHi: Jun 5,1884.
  MoS: Jun-Jly 1884. Rowell 1891 lists d,founded
    1890.

Carondelet Advertiser   w   1880
  In Ayer 1880.

Carondelet New Era   w   1859-1860
  MoSHi: Feb 5,1859; Jan 28,Oct 27,1860.

Carondelet News   w   1900-1935?
  MoHi: Jan 31,1903-1935.
  MoS: Sep 8,1900-1906; 1908-1935 inc.

Carondelet Progress   w   1891-1899
  MoHi: Film,Nov 26,1898-Apr 29,1899; May
    6,1899-May 19,1900. Became South St.
    Louis Progress May 6,1899.

Carondelet Review   w   1869-1876?
  ICHi: Jly 9,Sep 10,1876. In Rowell 1874.

Cavalier   w   1867
  MoSHi: Jan 20,1867.

Catholic News Letter   w   1845-1848
  MoSHi: May 2,1846.

Censor   w   1896-1904?
  MoHi: Jly 25,1901. Commentary on political,
    social life.

Central Afro-American   w   1909-1914?
  Negro.

Central Baptist   w
  MoHi: Feb 22-Mar 7,Jun 20,Aug 15,Sep 19,
    1872; Jly 20,Aug 10,31,1893.
  MoSHi: Jun 2,1870; Aug 22,1878; Feb 28,1889.
  ICHi: Oct 5,1876.
  KHi: Jly 19-Sep 13,1888; Jun 30,1910-Nov 28,
    1912.
  MnHi: Aug 10,1905.

ST. LOUIS (continued)

Central Christian Advocate   w,d
  MoHi: Jun 16,1869; Feb 11,1885.
  MoSHi: Dec 22,1853.
  ICHi: d,Apr 7,1864. W,Sep 13,1876.
  IHi: Film,Dec 4,1861; Nov 7,1866; Dec 17,1873.
  KHi: Nov 19,1873; 1880-1934 inc.
  McD: Scattered copies 1855-1860,1862,1868,
    1869,1871,1873,1874,1887,1889,1898.

Central Post   w   1870
  MoSHi: Oct 22,1870.

Christian Advocate   w   1851-?
  MoHi: Jun 3,1858; Nov 3,1859; Dec 6,1860;
    Apr 26,1866; Jly 10,1872; Jan 30,1878;
    May 20,1896; Oct 29,1890.
  ICHi: Sep 20,1876.
  MoS: Aug 28,1851-1922,1924+ exc. Apr 1862-
    Sep 21,1865,when suspended briefly.
  MoSHi: 1861; Jan 2,9,23,Apr 17,1862; Jan-
    Feb 12,26,Apr 9-May 7,28,Jun 4-Aug 20,
    Sep 3-Dec 31,1913. Some for 1914-1916,
    1918-1931; Oct 12,1934; May 20,1938;
    Oct 4,1945.
  KHi: Apr 4,1861-Apr 17,1862; Oct 31,1888-
    Feb 6,1889.
  NcU: Jan 15,1879.

Chronicle   d   1880-1905   w   1878?
  MoHi: Aug 1,1873; Oct 28,1890; Aug 22,1891;
    Feb 11,1892; Feb 18,Mar 16,1893; Sep 20,
    1898; Aug 7,Dec 4,1895; Jun 15,1896.
    Film, Jly 24-Aug 31,1901. Under Evening
    Chronicle,Sep 10,1887; Dec 2,1889.
  MoS: Jly 1880-1890; 1891-Sep 1892; Jan-Jun
    1893.
  MoSHi: Aug18,1891; Jly 9,1893; May 27,28,
    1896; Jly 9,1898; Oct 30,Nov 6,7,1900;
    Jan 1,Apr 2,1901; Jun 13,1903. Evening,
    Jun 30,Oct 27,1882; Feb 23,24,Mar 1,3,
    19,24,Apr 20,Jun 23,1883; Apr 30,1889.
  NHi: w,Sep 7,1878.
  NHi: d,Nov 9,1881; Jan 23,31,Mar 29,Apr
    20,Jun 20,30,Dec 26,1882; Feb 22,26,
    Mar 24,Apr 19-21,Sep 29,Dec 4,8,31,
    1883; Jan 9,Apr 30,May 1,7,1884.
  KHi: d,Jly 31,1888.
  NcU: Aug 31,1878.
  T: May 11,1898.
  Microfilm Cen: Film,Jan 1892-Dec 1902 inc.
    Under Evening, Jly 1880-Sep 6,1890.
  MnHi: Feb 24,1892; Jly 22-25,1896.

Chronik   d,w   1861
  German. In American Newspaper Directory 1861.

Church Progress   w
  MoHi: 1903-Apr 1907; Apr 1908-May 23,1929;
    Nov 8,1890; Apr 16,1908.
  MoSHi: Scattered issues for 1916-1929.

Cimeter   w   1884-1886?
   IHi: Film, Jan 3, 1884-Feb 5, 1885 inc. In
       Rowell 1885, Ayer 1887, one time as temperance.

Citizens' Informant
   MoSHi: Jly 6, 1895.

City   w   1834?
   MoHi: Jan 25, 1834 inc.

Clarion   w   1914-1919
   Negro. Last in Ayer 1920.

Coleman's Rural World   w   1848-1916
   MoHi: 1867-1869; Dec 26, 1868; Nov 6, 1869;
       Apr 2, 9, 23, Aug 13, 1870; Oct 23, 1890;
       Apr 2, Dec 10, 1896; Jan 15, 1908. Film,
       1870; Feb-Aug 1879; Jan 27-Dec 1881; Jan
       25-Dec 1883; Jan 14, 1886-Dec 1888; 1890;
       Jan 22-May 14, 1891; Dec 15, 1865-Jun 29,
       1893 inc.
   MoSHi: 1850-1877; 1879-1880; Feb-Nov 1881;
       Mar-Dec 1882; Feb 1883; Mar-Dec 1884;
       Jan-Nov 1885; Mar-Jly 1886; Jan 20, Apr 7,
       May 5, 12, 1887; Jun-Nov 1888; 1889; Feb-
       Jly 1890; 1891-1895 inc; Oct 8, 1896; Aug-
       Dec 1905; Jun 1, 8, 1910.
   CoD: Jun 7, 1873.
   ICHi: Oct 4, Nov 22, 1876.
   IHi: film, Dec 21, 1882; Jan 4, 1894-Dec 26,
       1895 inc.
   KHi: Jan 5, 1899-Dec 20, 1915.
       Merged with Journal of Agriculture and Star
       and Farmer to become Journal of Agriculture
       June 1916.

Commercial   w
   MoHi: Feb 9, 1876 inc. Volume number missing.
   ICHi: Jly 21, 1876.

Commercial Advertiser   w   1826-1827?
   Ct: May 23, 1827.

Comercio del Valle   w   1875-1885?

Commercial Bulletin   d, tw, w   1835-1841?
1866-1869?
   MoHi: Aug 10, 1839; Nov 24, 1840. Under
       Commercial Bulletin and Missouri Literary
       Register, tw, Jun 17, 26, 1835; Mar 24, 1841.
       MoSHi has Dec 2, 1840; Nov 10, 1841; May
       18, 1835-Dec 31, 1836 under this longer title.
   MoSHi: d, Sep 3, 1838; Nov 19, 25, Aug 25, 1840;
       Feb 4, 1841.
   MoSM: 1840 inc.
   MWA: Oct 4, 1841. Fuller title, Nov 4, 1840.
   WHi: May 18, 1835-Dec 31, 1838.

Commercial Gazette   w   1867-1883?
   MoHi: Aug 1872-Jly 1877; Jan 1878-Dec 1883.
       Formerly Home Journal and Commercial
       Gazette and under this title MoSHi has Aug
       21, 1872-Jly 23, 1874. Became Commercial
       Gazette Nov 1, 1873. In Rowell 1876, Ayer
       1881.
   MoSHi: 1874-1877; 1879-1883.
   DLC: Sep-Dec 1881; Jan-Oct 26, 1882.
   ICHi: Aug 31, 1876.
   NN: Jly 6, 1876.

Commercial News and Labor Gazette   w, sm
1908?-1915?
   MoHi: Jan 16, 1915.
   MoSHi: Jan 28, 1911.

Commercial Record   m   1878
   MoHi: Nov 1878. Advertising organ.

Commercial Review and Manufacturer's Record   w
1876?
   Listed in Pettengill 1877.

Communist   w   1845?-1846?   1883?   m   1871-1872?
   KHi: Mar 1879-Feb 1885.
   NcD: Feb, Mar, Sep, Oct 1871; Apr, Aug 1872.
       Noted in G-AN&P. Published in Principia
       Community. Apparently later publication
       appeared in St. Louis 1883.

Conservative
   MoSHi: Extra, Apr 15, 1865.

Contributor   w   1883
   In Dauchy 1884 as Negro paper.

Countersign   d   1864-?
   CSmH: May 17, 1864.
   MHi: Scattered copies for 1864.

Countian
   MoS: Jan 6, 1953-1960.
   Microfilm Cen: Film, 1961-Jun 30, 1962.

County Legal Record & Advertiser
   MoSHi: Apr 4, 1861; Oct 28, 1862; Oct 31,
       1863; Feb 13, 1866.

County Watchman
   See Clayton Watchman-Advocate.

Courier   w   1892-1895   d   1873-1875
   MoS: 1892-1894 inc. Rowell 1874 lists evening
       edition, also weekly called Missouri Blaetter.
       Ayer 1894 lists Courier as a Single Tax paper,
       as does Rowell 1893-1894. Rowell 1874 lists
       Wochentlicher Courier, w.
   KHi: w, Mar 19, 1892.

Critic w 1876-1900?
     MoHi: Nov 1, 1890.
     MWA: Jly 19, Aug 9, 1884.
     KHi: Sep 16, 1888.
          Conflicts in founding date. Directories use
          1875, 1876, 1882. DLC issue, Oct 31, 1896,
          is Vol 8, No 20. Paper briefly was a Sunday
          society publication, independent at other
          times.

Democrat d 1842-1875 tw, w
     MoHi: d, Feb 20-Sep 2, 1844; Aug 15, Sep 24,
          1873.
     MoS: 1866-Jly 1874; May 1855-Jun 1857;
          1858-1859; Jan 14-Mar 1861; 1862-1875.
     MoSG: 1854-1875.
     MoSHi: Mar 20, 1866; Oct 22, 1868.
     MoSM: Jly 1857-1858; 1861-Jun 1864 inc;
          Jan-Jun 1865; 1867-1875 inc.
     MWA: Feb 14, Jun 5, Aug 27, 1857; Mar 19, 31,
          Apr 5, Jly 22, 1859; May 12, 1860-Jun 30,
          1864; Feb 8, May 12, Aug 29, Sep 2, Dec 7,
          27, 1865; Jan 3, Apr 26, Jly 6, Aug 13, Nov
          19, 29, Dec 25, 1866; Sep 17, 1867; Feb 10,
          16, Mar 13, May 11, 1868; May 2, Nov 18,
          1870; Apr 9, 1872; Jan 1, Sep 1, 1874; Jan
          1, May 14, 1875.
     CSmH: d, Feb 3, 1868.
     DLC: Feb 20-Sep 2, 1844; Mar 5, May 30, Jly-
          Dec 1874; Jan-May 19, 1875.
     IHi: film, Jan 6, May 21, Aug 11, 20, Sep 23,
          Oct 27-28, Dec 31, 1874; Jan 1, Feb 27,
          Mar 6, 12, 17, Apr 14, 22, 1875.
     KHi: Feb 20-Sep 2, 1844.
     NHi: Jun 1-2, 1873; Apr 5, 20, 1875.
     Micro-Photo: film, d, 1843-1844.
     Microfilm Cen: film, 1873-Jun 4, 1875.

          Founded 1842 as Native American Bulletin;
          1843-1844 as Old School Democrat and Weekly
          Herald; 1844-1851? St. Louis Democrat; 1852
          Missouri Democrat. Rowell 1873 lists Democrat
          as morning, tw editions, Missouri Democrat w.
          Combined with Globe.

Democratic Bulletin w 1898-1899?
     Rowell 1898 lists English, German editions. In
     Rowell 1899 lists Democrat Bulletin, same data.

Democratic Free Press w 1864
     MoHi: Jly 2, 1864, Vol 1, No 10. Apparently
     called Free Press at times.

Demokrat w 1903?-1908?
     Noted in Ayer 1905-1908.

Demokratische Presse w 1852-1854
     Noted in G-AN&P. Continued as Missouri
     Zeitung.

Demokratische Tribune w 1850?-1852
     Noted in G-AN&P. Absorbed Deutsch Amerikaner.

Detector w 1856?
     Listed in Newspaper Record 1856.

Deutsch Amerikaner w 1851
     Published briefly, English and German.

Deutsch Amerikanische Krieger Zeitung w 1885?
     In Dauchy with 1885 founding date.

Deutsch-Blatter w 1853
     Survived for only one month.

Deutsch Tribune w 1847-1848, sw 1847,
tw 1848, d 1844-1852?
     MoSHi: Jun 5, 1845; Aug 31, 1847; Jun 28, Dec
          26, 1849; Jly 15, 1844-Mar 1852; Sep 20, 27,
          Oct 4, 18-Nov 29, Dec 27, 1848; Jan 3-Feb
          28, 1849.

Deutsche Wochenschrift w 1939+
     MoS: Oct 24, 1940-Feb 27, Apr 3-10, May 22-29,
          1941; Oct 16-Nov 13, 1941-Mar 26, Apr 9-
          May 28, Jun 18-Aug 20, 1942.

Deutsche Zeitung w 1861?
     In American Newspaper Directory 1861.

Dispatch d 1864-1878 w, tw
     MoHi: d, Feb 24, Apr 2, 10, 17, May 2, 26, 29, 31,
          1865; May 17, 1866; Nov 25, 1869; Aug 20,
          1870; Jun 21, 28, Jly 5, 12, 1874; Feb 7, Mar
          27, Dec 21, 1876; Jan 2, 1877; Jan 2, 21, 31,
          Feb 13, 1878. Film, Dec 12, 1865-Nov 1, 1866;
          1874-1877. W, Sep 18, 1869.
     MoSHi: Nov 28, 1864-Dec 14, 1866; Apr 6-Dec
          1869. Sunday, Jly 5, 1874.
     MoSW: Nov 21, 1864-1866.
     MoSM: Nov 21, 1864-Jun 1866; Jly 1867-1870;
          1873.
     MoSPo: 1874-1878.
     MWA: d, Jun 13, 1866; Oct 20, 1869. W, Jun 9,
          1866. TW, Jun 13, 1866.
     CSmH: Sep 16, 1867; Jan 4, Apr 2, Jun 17, 1868.
     ICHi: d, Oct 11, 1871. W, Aug 3, Sep 1876.
     IHi: Film, May 2, 1865.
     NbHi: Mar 4, 1865.
     NHi: Jun 17, 1869; Mar 1, Apr 4, Jun 25, 1873;
          Apr 2, 13-14, 1875; Feb 2, Apr 5, Jun 29,
          1877; Jun 13, 25, 1878.
     WHi: d, Feb 18, 21, Mar 27, Apr 12, 17, 1865; Dec
          21, 1866; May 13, 1869. Film, Jan 1874-1877.

Dyer's News Letter w 1896-1898?
     Follows Censor.

Enquirer sw, w 1815-1829
     MoHi: w, Dec 23, 1818-1819; May 17, 1820-
          Sep 2, 1822; 1823-1824; Dec 23, 30, 1818;
          Jan 6-20, Feb 3, 10, 24, Mar 3, 10, 24, Oct
          16, 20, Nov 20, 24, 1819; Jan 13-Feb 17,
          Mar 3-24, 1821. SW, Sep 4, 1819-Aug 20,
          1820.
     MoSM: Feb 28, 1825-1826; 1819-1820 inc.

Enquirer (continued)
MoSHi: Sep 1,1819-Aug 30,1820; May 10,1820-
1821; Jan 12,1822-May 17,1825; Jan 8,12,
Mar 24,31,Apr 7-28,May 5,26,Jun 9-30,
Jly 14-Aug 25,1819; Jan 8,12,1820; Dec 29,
1821; May 20,1822; Dec 27,1823; Jly 12,
1824; Dec 10,1825; Apr 8,1826·
AzTP: film,w,1819-1824.
Ct: Jun 14,1827.
DLC: w,Dec 29,1819; May 10-Dec 1820; Nov 12,
1821; 1822-1823; Jan-Jun,Nov 20,Dec 11,18,
1824; Jan 10-31,May 7,1825. (Country edition)
Sep-Dec 1819; Jan-Aug 1820; Nov 12,1821;
Jly 19,26,Aug 30,Oct 18,Nov 8,1824.
KHi: film,Mar 17,1819-Dec 18,1824.
WHi: film,Mar 17,1819-Dec 18,1824.
Micro-Photo: film,1819-1824.

Emigrant   w   1817-1818
Discontinued Aug 1818,succeeded by Enquirer.

Ephemeron, or Fair Gazette
MoSHi: Oct 31,1855.

Equality   w   1905
MoSHi: Apr 3,1905. Vol 1,No 1.

Es Videke   w   1913-1918?
MoS: Dec 27,1918. Hungarian.

Evangelist   w,m   1874?-?
MoHi: Oct 23,30,1884.
MoSHi: 1875-1877.
ICHi: Apr 1876.
KHi: Jly 29,1886.

Express   d   1860-1866?   1881?
MoSW: Film,Dec 17,1864-Aug 19,1866.
MoSM: Mar-Oct 1860 inc.
T: Jly 28,1881.

Farmers' Advertiser   m   1866-1867?
MoSHi: Jan 1866-Dec 16,1867.

Farm Progress
T: Sep 15,1908; Nov 1,1909; Sep 1,1910.

Farmers' and Mechanics' Advocate   w   1833-1835?
MoHi: Jan 2,1834-Apr 18,1835.
MoSHi: Oct 16,1834.
DLC: 1834; Jan-Apr 18,1835.
ICHi: Dec 19,1833.

Farm Progress
MoSHi: Jly 1908-Jun 15,1910; Jan 1-Dec 15,
1912.
Fiery Cross   w
MoHi: Jly 1923-Dec 1924.

Flag of Our Union   w   1845-1852?
MoHi: Oct 12,1850.
MoSHi: Feb 12,1852."Literary and miscellaneous
family journal."

Fountain   w
MoSHi: May 12,1849.

Franklin Avenue Weekly Bulletin   w   1875-?
MoHi: Oct 23,1875.
ICHi: Feb 5,1876.

Freedman's Journal   w   1878-1880
In Ayer 1881 as Freeman's Journal.

Free Press   w   1832-1833   w   1864
MoHi: Jan 3-Oct 24,1833.
MoKc: Film, Jan 3-Oct 24,1833.
MoS: Jan 3-Oct 24,1833.
MoCaT: Sep 26,1833.
MoSHi: May 23,1833. Film,Jan-Oct 1833.
AzTP: Film,Jan 3-Oct 24,1833.
CSmH: May 30,1833.
DLC: Jan-Oct 24,1833.
ICHi: Sep 27,1832.
IaHi: Film, 1833.
KHi: Film, Jan 3-Oct 24,1833.
WHi: Jan 3-Oct 24,1833.
MnHi: Sep 20,1832.
Missouri Democrat, May 20,1864,tells of start
of Free Press,new Democratic organ.

Freie Blaetter   w   1851-1853
MoHi: Vols 2,4-52.
MoS: Mar 18,1851-Mar 6,1852; Apr 24,1852-
May 5,1853.

Freisinnige   w   1846?
Noted in G-AN&P.

Freiheitsbote fur Illinois
MoSHi: Jun 24,1840.

Friedunsvate   w   1896
Start noted in Missouri Editor,Feb 1896.

Funsten's Reporter
T: Jan 13,1892.

Gazette   d,w   1868-1870?   d   1838-1845?
w   1840,1861
MoHi: d, Jun 4,1870.
MoSM: d, Jly 1839-1844.
MWA: d, Sep 3,18,1838; Aug 12,1841.
CSmH: d,Mar 11,1845.
DLC: d,Feb 13,1839; Oct 3,1840; Sep 22,1842;
Dec 11,1845. (Country,tw) Feb 8,12,14,Dec
2,1839.
IHi: Dec 13-20,1845; Jan 13,1846.
ICHi: w,Mar 22,1845.
MHi: Jun 18,1846.
Micro-Photo: Film, 1845-1846.

Gazette (continued)
Early paper also called Evening Gazette. DLC
copy, Aug 31, 1838, Vol 1, No 49.

Gazette Extraordinary   Jly 10, 1812
MoSM: Broadside declaration of war between
U.S.-England.

Gem-Overland St. John Record   w   1925-1932?
Noted in Ayer 1929-1933.

Globe   d 1872-1875   w, sw 1872-1875
MoHi: d, Jan 4-Dec 1873. Film, Jly 20, 1874-
May 19, 1875. Under Daily Globe, Jan 7, 30,
Feb 4, 8, 10, 15-18, 20, 26, 27, Apr 3, 19, May
16, 25, Jun 1, 3, 11, 14, 17, Jly 30, Aug 13, 14,
17, 28, 31, Sep 6, 7, 25, Oct 12, Nov 7, 8, 13,
14, 17, 19, 23, 24, Dec 3, 8, 21, 28, 1873; Jan
8, 11, 29, Feb 18-21, 26, Mar 8, 18, 19, 22, 26,
30, Apr 12, May 2, 10, 11, 14, 16, 18, 21, 25, 30,
Jun 4, 7, 9, 14, 17, Aug 26, Sep 7, 18, 21, 22, 25,
Oct 18, 28, Nov 6, 8, 14, 22, 25, 29, 30, Dec 8,
14, 19, 20, 21, 26, 28, 1874; Jan 2, 17, 24, 27,
Feb 1, 8, 10, 11, 14, 15, 17, 24, 27, 28, Mar 13,
Apr 2, 3, 4, 6, 7, May 3, 10, 16, 1875. W, May
30, Jun 6, 13, Jly 11, Aug 1, 29, 1873; Jun 27,
1878; Apr 8, 15, Aug 12, Sep 16, 23, Oct 21,
28, Nov 18, Dec 2, 23, 30, 1880; Mar 10, Jun
9, Jly 7, 1881; Feb 14, 1884; Jly 4, 8, 11, 15,
18, 22, 25, 29, Aug 1, Nov 18, 1902.
MoS: Aug 1872-Jun 1874.
MoSHi: d, Jun 23, 1874; Apr 6, 8, 1875.
MoSM: d, complete.
MoSG: d, 1874-1875.
DLC: d, Jly 19-Dec 1872; 1873-May 19, 1875.
NHi: Jun 3, 1873; Apr 6, 1875.
NN: d, Apr 11, 18, Oct 11, 12, 1873; Mar 25,
27, Oct 6-9, 1874.
IHi: Aug 10, 22, Sep 20, Nov 9, 1872; Dec 25,
1873; Aug 22, Sep 14, 16, 1874; Feb 25, 1875.
KHi: w, May 8, 1874.
Microfilm Cen: Film, Jly 1872-Dec 1875.
Merged with Democrat May 20, 1875.

Globe-Democrat   w   1875-1926?   d 1875+
MoHi: Daily Globe-Democrat, Jan 26, 1876-
Feb 1878; Jun-Aug 1879; 1920-1950;
Sep 23, 1896; Jun 25, 1911; Mar 11, 1912;
Sep 1-6, 1945. Film, Jun 1, 1875-Apr 7,
1876; 1880+. Weekly Globe-Democrat,
1892-1894; 1896-Mar 1898; Jan-May 1902;
May 30, Jun 6, 13, Jly 11, Aug 1, 29, 1873;
Sep 25, 1874; Jun 27, 1878; Apr 8, 15, Aug
12, Sep 16, 23, Oct 21, 28, Nov 18, Dec 2, 23,
30, 1880; Mar 10, Jun 9, Jly 17, 1881; Feb
14, 1884; Jly 4, 8, 11, 15, 18, 22, 25, 29, Aug
1, Nov 18, 1902. Film, Aug 2-Dec 27, 1877;
Apr 4, 1878-Dec 23, 1880; Sep 22, 1881; Feb
18, 1886-Feb 17, 1887. St. Louis Globe-
Democrat, Sep 23, 1896; Jun 25, 1911; Mar 11,
1912; Sep 1-6, 1945; May 23, Jun 16, 17, Jly
12, 31, Aug 12, 14, 16, Sep 12, 14, 17, 26, Oct

Globe-Democrat (continued)
2, 5, Nov 13, 15, 20, 21, 22, 27, Dec 1, 2, 8, 9,
13, 16, 1875; Jan 2, 3, 5, 10, 25, 1876; Feb 10,
Mar 4, Apr 10, 11, 16, May 13, 14, 24, 25, Jun
9, 10, 15, 18, 20, 30, Jly 23, Aug 11, 20, Sep
13, 22, 28, Oct 5, 22, Nov 4, 8, 17, 20, 23, 27,
28, 30, Dec 1, 4, 8, 14, 21, 22, 30, 31, 1878;
Jan 3-5, 19, 20, 25, 27, 29, 31, Feb 1, 2, 4-9,
15, 16, 22, Mar 2, 8, 9, 16, 20, Apr 5, 15, May
4, 17, 31, Sep 1-9, 14, Oct 9, 13, 21-26, Nov
1-3, 8, 10, 21, 27, 29, Dec 7, 13, 15, 21, 22,
1879; Jan 8, 10, 11, 16, 17, 19, 22, 25-27,
31, Feb 1, 2, 7, 8, 13-15, 17, Mar 13, 14, 20,
Apr 1, 3, 10, 23, 26, 28, 30, May 2, 8, 10-12,
18, 22, 24, 26, 1880; Apr 1-5, 8, 17, 21, 30,
May 8, 9, 20, Jun 5, 15, 25-30, Sep 1, 2, 17,
21, 26, Oct 2, 22, 23, 24, Nov 5, 8, Dec 11,
24, 1881; Jan 4, 8, 17, 19, 20, 22, 24, 27, 28,
Feb 10, 11, 22, Mar 8, 9, 11, Apr 26, 30, May
13, 31, Jun 14, 16, 18, 21, 29, 30, Jly 1, 4, 6,
9, 10, 17, 20-23, 26-30, Sep 9, 16, 22, 1882;
Jan 1-6, 9, 10, 13, 27, Feb 5, 11-13, 23, 27,
Mar 10, 16, Apr 11, 20, May 6, Jun 12, Jly
13, 17, 18, 22, Aug 9, 12, 16, 26, 29, 30,
Oct 9, 11, 12, 13, 18, Nov
7, 10, Dec 17, 25, 1883; Feb 11, 17, Mar 4,
16, 23, Apr 1, 26, Jun 10, 13, 16, 17, 19, Jly
23, Aug 31, Sep 1, 6, 9, Nov 22, May 3,
1884; May 2, 10, 17, 24, 30, Jun 30, Jly 5,
6, 30, Aug 7, 13, 14, 16, 20, Sep 5, 6, Oct
5, 10, 22, 18, 22, 24, 25, 28-31, Nov 22, 29, 30,
Dec 4, 6, 12, 13, 20, 29, 1885; Jan 10,
13, 24, 31, Feb 3, 7, 13, 20, 27, Mar 3-5, 10,
11, 13, 20, 29, Apr 1, 2, 9, 13, 17, 18, May
2, 16, 17, Jun 2, 13, 17, 20, Jly 16, 18, 29,
Aug 8, 14, 23, 28, Sep 5, 9, 12, 21, 26, Oct
3, 7, 10, 17, Nov 16, 19, 20, 23, 27, 28, Dec
4, 12, 20, 1886; Jan 24, Feb 20, Mar 5, 12,
17, 23, 24, Apr 16, 24-26, May 8, 12, 22,
24, 29, Jun 1, 2, 5, 17, 18, 21, Jly 17, 31,
Aug 3, 4, 15, 25, 28, Sep 10, 20, 25, Oct 30,
Nov 11, 23, 1887.
MoS: May 20, 1875+. Film, Apr 22, Oct 22, 1875;
1880+.
MoSW: May 1885-Aug 1886; Sep 1887-Jun
1889; Jan 1894-Dec 1897; Mar 1898-Apr
1903; Mar 1904-Feb 1909; May 15-Jun 20,
Jly-Aug 1909; Mar 1910-Dec 1918. Film,
1960+.
MoSHi: Jun 5-26, Oct 1876-Apr 1894; 1900-
Oct 1918.
MoJ: 1901+.
MoSM: Jun 1875+. Some missing in early files.
MoWeW: Sep 1932+.
MoJcL: 1880-1948 inc.
MWA: d, 1875-Jun 1879; Jun 24, 1880; Oct
19-21, Nov 5, 1881; Apr 20, 1883; Aug 8,
1892. TW, 1875-1892; Apr 11-18, May 30,
1899.
CoU: TW, Mar 31, 1921. Film, Apr 3, 1853-1879.
DLC: May 20-Dec 1875; 1876-1884; Apr-Dec
1885; 1886-1887; Jly-Dec 1888; 1889-1900;

Globe-Democrat (continued)
Jan-May, Jly-Dec 1901; 1902-1917; Jan-Jly,
Oct-Dec 1918; 1919+.
ICHi: w, Aug 25, Nov 25, 1876. D, Sep 19, Nov 1,
1876; Jly 24, 1885.
IU: 1893-1951.
IHi: w, Jun 30, Dec 15, 29, 1876; Jan 25, Feb 2,
1877; Dec 4, 25, 1879; Jan 22, Mar 4, Jun 3,
Nov 18, 1880; Apr 26, May 10-17, 31, 1883;
Oct 23, 1890; Apr 20, 1893; Oct 2, 1894;
Jan 14, 1896. D, Jun 16, Aug 27, 1875; Jly 25,
27, Aug 18, Sep 30, 1876; Aug 11, Sep 18, Dec
4, 24, 1877; Sep 21, Oct 23, Nov 11, Dec 6,
9, 12, 14, 20, 25-27, 30, 1878; Jan 14, 18, 22,
25, Feb 7, 12-15, 1879; Jun 27, 1886; Sep 26,
29, Oct 5, 18, 23-24, 1888; Dec 7, 1889; Mar
8, Sep 20, 1890; May 6, 1891; Apr 8, 1893;
Jan 15-19, 1897; Nov 6, 1940; Jan 27, 1943;
Apr 13, Aug 15, 1945; Nov 3, 1948.
Film, Nov 16, 1899-Dec 31, 1934.
IaHi: w, Nov 10, 1881-Nov 23, 1882.
NcU: Aug 24-25, 27, 30, 1878; Dec 28, 1882;
Jly 9, 1893.
KHi: d, Nov 25, 1876; Feb 13, 1885; May-Dec
1896; Oct 29, 1899; Aug 1, 1918; Apr 8,
1923. W, May 6, 1886; Jun 23, 1892.
LNT-MA: Sep 23, 1904.
LU: Sep 22, 1881.
MnHi: d, Oct 30, 1880; Jly 17, 1883; Jly 18, 20-
21, 29-31, Aug 2-6, 8, 11-12, Sep 8-9, 11, 13,
Oct 16, 22-26, 28, 30-31, Nov 2, 4, 8-13, 15-
16, 18, 20-24, 27, 1887; Jly 22, 26, 1896; Oct
7, 1898; May 3, 1903; Apr 2, 4, 1908; Sep 29,
1940. W, May 30, 1878.
NHi: May 9, Dec 23, 1877; Feb 3, Aug 18, 20,
Sep 8, Nov 8, 17, 1878; Jan 18, Feb 2, Mar
2, Aug 27, Oct 3, Nov 5, 7, 20, 22, 24, 1881;
Jan 5, 24, Mar 5, 12, May 2, Jly 8, Sep 17,
1879; Jun 24, Jly 10, Dec 12, 28, 1880; Jan
20, 22, Apr 1, 4, 18, Aug 27, Sep 26, 28, Oct
2, 11, Dec 3, 1882; Jan 13-14, Feb 11-13,
23-27, Mar 7, Apr 20, May 5, 6, 29, Dec 10,
22, 29, 1883.
T: Nov 24, 1885; Dec 31, 1887; Jan 3, 14, 21,
24, Feb 6, 1888; May 6, 1903. TW, May 26,
Aug 29, 1921; Jun 23, 1924. W, Nov 20,
1890; Jan 8, Apr 9, 30, 1891; Jun 10, 1926.
Microfilm Cen: Film, Jan 1876-Dec 1879.

Golden Era   w   1851?-1854?
MoSHi: May 6, 1854. Also dated in Alton, Ill.

Golden Era Life   w, sm   1882-1886
Ayer 1886 lists weekly, Ayer 1887 semi-monthly.
Prohibition publication.

Gospel Banner   w
MoHi: Mar 29, 1855.

Gottes Freund der Pfaffen Feind
MoSHi: Jly 1863; Feb 1864.

Guardian   w   1865-?
MoSHi: Dec 30, 1865; Jan 6, 13, Aug 18, Nov
17, 1866; Aug 17, 1867; Mar 28, 1868 inc.
MoSU: 1865; Jan-Nov 14, 1868 inc.

Gut Heil
MoSHi: Scattered copies 1889-1892. Official
organ of St. Louis Turnverein. Became
St. Louis Turner 1891.

Hausfreund   w   1851?
Noted in G-AN&P.

Herald   w   1876-1878?   d   1834, 1852-1876?
Sunday 1850?-?
MoHi: d, Dec 31, 1856; Nov 18, 1860; Jly 26,
1861. Sunday, Oct 26, Dec 7, 21, 1856; Jan
25, Feb 8, Apr 5, 1857; Sep 6, 1896. Monthly,
Jan 1870.
MoS: d, Dec 20, 1852-Aug 13, 1854; Jun 1855-
1856; Feb 5, 1859; Sep 2, Nov 11, Dec 1876.
MoSM: d, Jun 5-Nov 9, 1835 inc.
MoSHi: 1852-Jly 2, 1853; Mar 9, 1854; Jan 20,
1856; Sep 1857-Jun 1859; Mar 9, 1854; Feb
18, 1855; Jan 20, 1856; Jly 16, Aug 10, 1861.
MoHi: Herald of the Fair, Oct 5, 1876.
DLC: Aug 18, 1861.
NbHi: Sep 16, 1876.
NHi: May 26, 1877.

Herold des Glaubens   w   1850-1920?   m   1894?
MoHi: w, Film, Oct 16, 1889-Sep 27, 1899.
MoSHi: Mar 27, 1870; Feb 13, 1878; Sep 26,
1900; Dec 29, 1920.
MoS: Nov 30, 1898-Dec 29, 1920.
ICHi: Aug 23, 1876.
Monthly listed in Ayer 1895.

Hirlap   w   1913?
MoSHi: Aug 15, 1913. Hungarian.

Hesperion   w
MoSHi: Apr 20, 1867.

Hlas   w, sw   1873-1905?
MoS: 1917.
MoSHi: 1901-1926. Bohemian.

Hodiamont Herald
MoSHi: Feb 15, 1917.

Home Journal   w   1867-1873
MoHi: Nov 17, 1867-Nov 8, 1868; Jun 5, 1865.
Became Commercial Gazette Nov 1, 1873.
Rowell 1873 lists as Home Journal and
Commercial Gazette.
MoSHi: Scattered issues 1867-1869, 1871, 1874.

Home Journal and Commercial Gazette
w   1872?-1873
MoHi: Aug 2, 1872-Oct 25, 1873. See Home
Journal. Became Commercial Gazette
Nov 1873.

Hornet   w   1880-1882
  MoSHi: Oct 16, Dec 4, 1880; Aug 6, 27, Sep 3,
    17, 24, Oct 22, Nov 19, 26, Dec 10, 24, 1881;
    Jan 7, 21, 28, Feb 4, 11, Mar 4, Apr 1-29, May
    6, 13, Jun 24, 1882.

Hotel Reporter   w   1880-1891?
  MoHi: Oct 28, 1890. Organ of Western Com-
    mercial Travelers' Assn.
  NHi: Copy Daily Hotel Register Jan 26, 1884.

Humorist   w   1879-1891?
  MoHi: Oct 30, 1890. In Rowell 1892.

Hustler
  MoHi: Sep 15, 1891; Jan 15, 1892.
  MoSHi: 34 issues, no dates given.
  T: Dec 15, 1891.

Illustrated Graphic News   w   1885?-1886?
  MoS: Mar-Dec 1886.

Illustrated Home Journal   m   1890-?
  T: Dec 1890.
  KHi: Dec 1890.

Immigration and Investment Journal   ?
  Nameplate dated 1886 noted as Vol IV, No 19.

Imperial State
  MoHi: May 1881.

Independent Livestock Reporter   d   1904-1905?
  MoHi: Dec 29, 1905.

Independent Clarion   w   1914-1922?
  Negro publication.

Industrial Advocate   w   1866-1867?
  MoHi: film, Aug 4, 1866-Feb 9, 1867. .
  CSmH: Oct 13, 1866.

Industrial New Era   w   1892-1894?
  Populist paper.

Industrial Times
  MoSHi: Mar 23, 1901.

Inquirer
  See Enquirer.

International
  T: Sep 24, 1890.

Intelligencer   d, w, tw   1850-1857
  MoHi: d, Apr 11, 1856. Film, 1850-1851. W, Feb
    27, 1852-Jun 28, 1853; Jan 8, 1856-Oct 13,
    1857; Jly 18, 1854; Dec 5, 1856. TW, Jly 27,
    1852; Jun 3, 1854.
  MoS: Jan 1, 1850; Dec 31, 1851. Film,
  MoSHi: d, Jan-Sep 2, 1853; Aug 29, 1850; May
    10, Jun 9, 26, 1851; Nov 1, 1856. W, 1850-
    1851. TW, Jun 7, 1854; Dec 19, 1855.

ST. LOUIS (continued)

Intelligencer (continued)
  MoSM: d, 1850-1857 inc. Some morning, evening
    editions.
  MWA: d, Nov 24, 1852; Jun 7, Dec 23, 1853. W,
    Sep 28, 1852.
  IHi: Feb 15, Apr 29, Aug 12, Dec 30, 1853; Feb
    10-24, Apr 7, May 5, Jun 9, Jly 28, Aug 11,
    Nov 3, 17, 1854; Jan 19, Feb 9-16, Mar 2,
    16, Aug 17, 1855; Feb 29, Apr 4, Jun 20,
    1856; Mar 20, Apr 10, 1857.
  ICHi: D, Feb 25, 1851. W, Feb 29, 1856; Jan
    16, 1857.

Interstate Manufacturer
  MoSHi: Apr 10, 25, Mar 10, 25, 1901.

Jeffersonian   w   1884?
  WHi: Sep 26, 1884.

Jennings Bulletin   w   1916
  Listed in Ayer 1917.

Jewish Record   w   1915-?
  MWA: Feb 22, 1918. In English, Yiddish.

Jewish Voice   w
  MoHi: Jly 26, 1901-1926; Oct 24, 1890.
  MoSHi: 1888; Some in 1889, 1899, 1909, 1919,
    1921, 1922. Printed in English, Yiddish.
  NN: Film, 1888, 1890-1921.

Journal   d, w   1857-1876?   d, w   1895-1899?
  MoHi: d, Jun 9, 1877.
  MoS: Jly 1896-Jun 1897.
  MoSHi: d, Mar 24, 1874.
  MWA: w, Aug 17, 1876.
  DLC: d, Nov 9, 1874; 1875-Nov 15, 1878.
  ICHi: d, Oct 6, 1876. W, Aug 10, 1876.
  MnHi: d, Jly 24, 26, 1896.
  NHi: Apr 3, 1873; May 3, Dec 1, 1877.
  NcD: d, Sep 22, 1877.
  KHi: d, Oct 29, 1876-Oct 2, 1877 inc; Mar 18,
    Apr 18, Oct 11, 1878.

Journal of Agriculture and Farmer   w   1866-1895?
  MoHi: Jly 13, 1882; Mar 11, 1887; Dec 4, 1890;
    Feb 5, Mar 12, 1891.
  MoSHi: As Journal of Agriculture, Feb 27, Mar 13,
    1869. Fuller title, Mar 17, May 12, Nov 10,
    1881; May 4, Aug 17, 1882.
  ICHi: Sep 7, 1876.
  IHi: Jan 4, 1894-Dec 26, 1895 inc.
  KHi: w, Jun 26, 1879. SM, Oct 15, 1917?
  PHi: Aug 24, 1876.

Journal of Commerce   w, d, sm, m   1857-1875
  MoHi: Jun 22, 1872.
  MoSM: w, Apr 24-Jly 30, 1862; Mar 8-Dec 1866;
    1867-1869 ex Sep 24, 1869.
  MoSHi: d, Feb 19, 1862. Rowell 1871 lists d, w;
    1875 lists w, sm, m.

Kladderadatsch   w   1890?
  In Ayer 1891.

Kosmopolit   1847?
  Noted in G-AN&P.

Krieger-Zeitung   1892?
  Noted in G-AN&P.

Kunst und Literatur Blatt
  Noted in G-AN&P.

Labor   w   1893- 1930?
  MoHi: 1903; 1913-1930; Feb 1,15,1896; Jan 2,
    1904. Film,1903. See Progressive Press.
  MoS: Apr 29,1893-Apr 20,1895; 1901-Nov 1,
    1902; May 1907-Nov 8,1930. Film,Apr 29,
    1893-Apr 3,1897; Dec 10,1898; Jan-Apr
    1899; 1901-Nov 1,1902; 1903-1906; May
    1907-1912.
  MoSHi: 1914-1915; 1923-1925. Scattered issues
    for 1893,1895-1896,1899,1903,1905,1917,
    1919,1920,1925,1929.
  MoU: Film,Apr 29,1893-1912.
  MnHi: Mar 31,Apr 7,21,May 19,26,1917; Feb
    28,Mar 13-Apr 24,May 8-Jly 10,31,Sep 13,
    1920; Jan 1,15,29-Feb 26,Mar 19-Apr 9,
    1921.
  KHi: May 13,1893,Vol I,No 3.

Labor Campaign
  MoSHi: Oct 7,28,1894.

Labor Compendium   w   1896-?
  MoHi: Film,Jly 28,1901-Jan 1,1905. Published
    by National Building Trade Council.

Labor News   w   1904-1911
  Noted in Ayer 1909-1912.

Labor-Tribune   w   1936+
  MoHi: Film, Jun 25,1937+.
  MoS: Film,1945+.
  MoSHi: Nov 4,1939-1953; 1954+.
  Microfilm Cen: Film,1945-1961.

Lacherlich   w   1879?
  Listed in Rowell-Ayer 1880.

La Republique   w   1876?
  In Pettengill 1877. French.

Laterne   w   1877?-1904?
  MoS: 1-3,5-18. Noted in G-AN&P.

La Lega Italiana   w   1914-1920?
  MoHi: Oct 9,1914-1920.

Las Dos Naciones   w   1894-1895
  Spanish paper, in Dauchy 1896.

Leader   w   1855-1858   d   1857-1858
  MoHi: w,Oct 16,1856; Jan 4,1857; Apr 16,
    1858.
  MoS: w,Sep 1-6,Oct 16,24,1856.
  MoSW: d,Apr 13,1857-May 11,1858; w,Dec 6,
    1856-Feb 6,1858.
  MoSM: w,1855-Mar 1,1856. d,Oct 13,1856-
    Feb 3,1858 inc.
  MoSU: w,Oct-Dec 1856 inc. d,Jly-Dec 1856 inc.
  MoSHi: d,Mar 10,Jly 7,14,Sep 1,1855; Sep 8,
    1855-Mar 1,1856; Mar 8-Oct 5,1856; May 27,
    1857.
  MWA: May 16-Jun 13,Aug 1,Sep 12-19,1857.
  NHi: Jun 30-Jly 14,1855.
  DLC: w,Jan-Dec 18,1857.

Legal Record   d
  MoSM: Mar 11-Dec 1861; 1862; Jun 10-Sep
    8,1863.
  MoSHi: Apr 4,1861; Oct 28,1862; Oct 29,
    1863; Feb 13,1866.

Le Telegraphe   sw   1840
  Mentioned in Union List.

Liberia Advocate   m   1846-?
  NN: Vol 2,No 5,Jun 1847; Sep 1849.
  IHi: May 22,1846.

Library Docket   m
  MoHi: Oct 1,1873.
  MHi: Jly 1,1879.
  MnHi: Sep 28,1875.

Lichlputze   w   1852-?
  MoS: May 30,Jun 13,1852.
  KHi: Sep 28,1875; Apr 22,1878.

Life   w   1882-1885   w   1888-1895?
  Apparently two. Rowell 1884-1885 lists first,
    founded 1882. Rowell 1891-1896 lists second,
    a pictorial publication.

Light
  MoSHi: Feb 20-Jly 11,1947; Oct 13,1947-Jun
    25,1948; Sep 24,1948-Jly 8,1949; Oct 14,
    1949-Jun 24,1950; Oct 14,1950-May 26,
    1951.

Lightning Express
  MoSHi: Oct 9,1880.

Lightning-Rod Herald   m   1868-1878?
  MoSHi: Scattered issues, 1868-1870; 1876-1878.

Listy   w   1902-
  Bohemian.

Little Watchman   w,m   1870-1875
  Listed in Rowell 1876.

Live Stock Reporter & Weekly Price List
  MoSHi: Jan-Dec 1877. Later Livestock and
    Tobacco Review, Livestock and Produce Review.

Log Cabin Hero   w   1840
  MoSM: May 7, 1840. DLC also has copies of this
    first issue. Only 13 numbers planned for 50¢.

Louisiana Gazette   w   1809-1812
  See Missouri Gazette. Name used briefly.

Luminary   w   1854-1855
  MoS: Film, Nov 22, 1854-Dec 15, 1855.
  MWA: Nov 22, 1854.
  CSmH: Nov 22, 1854-Dec 15, 1855.

Lutheran
  MoSHi: Scattered copies, 1948-1955.

Mail   w   1870
  Listed in Rowell 1870.

Maplewood News   w   1909-1919?
  Listed in Ayer 1911-1920.

Maplewood Observer   w   1934-1951
  Ayer 1952 lists Observer. Earlier under fuller title.

Maplewood Regulator   w   1906
  Listed in Ayer 1907.

Mardi Gras News   1889?
  MoSHi: One issue, 1889.

Market Reporter   d, w   1866+
  MoHi: d, Aug 29, 1870; w, Oct 18, 1873.
  MoSHi: 1866-1905; 1907-1932; 1939-1944; 1946+.

Merchants Exchange & Price Current   1856?-1872?
  MoHi: Nov 16, 1864; Mar 29, 1865; May 11, 1872.
    Newspaper Record 1856 lists Price Current.
    American Newspaper Directory 1861 lists d, w.

Mid-Continent   w
  MoHi: Oct 30, 1890. Formerly Evangelist.

Midwest Labor World   bw
  MoHi: Film, May 12, 1943-Dec 6, 1950.
  MoSHi: May 1943-1950. Mostly complete.

Mill Boy   w   1844-1845
  MoHi: Film, Feb 10, 1844-Jan 21, 1845.
  MoSHi: Mar 1844-1845; Jan 21, Apr 20, May 4,
    18, Jly 13, Aug 24, Sep 28, 1844.
  MoSM: Feb 10-Dec 1844; Jan 21, 1845.
  MWA: Feb 10, 1844-1845.
  DLC: Feb 10, 1844. Campaign paper, supporting
    Clay.

Miner and Artisan   w
  WHi: Dec 23-30, 1865.

ST. LOUIS (continued)

Mining News
  MoSHi: May 7, 1887.

Mirror   w   1875, 1891-1913?   d?
  MoSHi: Jun 19, 1855. (No data on this date)
  MHi: Several for 1881?
    Rowell 1875 lists a Sunday Mirror. Rowell 1896-
    1908 list Mirror, founded 1891, as society pub-
    lication. Later Ayer lists as literary and political.
  Microfilm Cen: Film, 1957-1959.

Mississippi Blatter   w   1857-1938?
  MoHi: May 3, 1914-1920.
  MoS: Jly 1903-1929.
  MoSHi: May 5, 1901; Mar 11, 1905; Jan 1, 1918;
    Jly 22, 1923-Sep 18, 1927.
  KHi: Nov 10, 1918. Sunday edition of Westliche
    Post.

Mississippi Handels-Zeitung   w   1857-1861?
  In American Newspaper Directory 1861.

Mississippi Valley Review and Journal of Commerce
  w   1845-1870?
  MoSHi: May 19, 1870. Under full title in Rowell
    1870.

Missouri Advocate and St. Louis Advertiser
  w   1825-1827
  MoHi: Apr 2, 1825. Sold to Enquirer.

Mississippi Valley Democrat & Journal of Agriculture   ?
  KHi: Feb 3, 1898-Apr 13, 1899.

Missouri Advocate and St. Louis Enquirer
  w   1825-1827
  MoSHi: Dec 10, 1825; Feb 15, 1827.
  MoSM: Feb 28-Dec 1825; 1826.
  NN: May 27, 1826, Vol 2, No 75.
  DLC: Sep 7, 1826. Title used briefly for Enquirer,
    according to Union List.

Missouri Argus   w   1835-1841   sw   1835-1841
  d   1838-1841?
  MoHi: d, Jly 4-Sep 14, 1839; Mar 5-Dec 31, 1840;
    May 3, 1839. sw, Jun 6-Nov 11, 1837. w, May
    22, 1835-May 26, 1837; Nov 18-Dec 23, 1837;
    1838-Nov 22, 1839.
  MoS: May 22, 1835; Nov 22, 1839.
  MoKc: Film, May 22, 1835-May 26, 1837; Nov 13,
    1837-Dec 20, 1839; Jan 31-Nov 23, 1839.
  MoSM: w, May 26-Jun 2, Nov 25, Dec 9, 1837;
    Jan 20, 1838; Aug 19, Dec 2, 1841, sw, Jun
    9-Oct 18, 25-Nov 15, 29-Dec 9, 13-20, 1837;
    Jan 8-13, 23-29, 1839. D, Jly 31, 1838-Jan
    1839; 1841 inc.
  MoSHi: d, May 1835-Nov 1836; 1837-1839; Jly
    4-Aug 9, 1839, photostat; Feb 27, 1840; Jly
    16, 1841.
  MWA: d, Feb 26, Jun 6, 29, 1840.
  AzTP: Film, May 22, 1835-Nov 4, 1836.
  IHi: Jly 4, 8, 10, 11, 13-18, 22, 23, 25, 27, 30-Aug
    9, 1839.

Missouri Argus (continued)
    IaHi: w,Film, 1835-1839.
    NbHi: w,Film,May 22, 1835-Nov 22, 1839.
    WHi: w,Film,May 22, 1835-Nov 22, 1839. d,
        May 16,20,Oct 14,28,Dec 16,17,1840; Feb
        24,25,1841.
    Micro-Photo: film,sw,1835-1840.
    KHi: w,Film,May 22, 1835-Nov 22, 1839. D,film,
        Jly 4,1839-Dec 31,1840.
    DLC: w,May 22-Dec 1835; 1836; Jan-May,Nov
        18-Dec 1837; 1838-Nov 22,1839. sw, Jun-
        Nov 1837; Jly-Sep 1839.
    Ct: Jun 12,Jly 17,Sep 25,Oct 3,1835; Jan 29,
        1836.

Missouri Blatter   w   1874
    In Rowell 1874, Sunday edition of Courier.

Missouri Cascade   w   1854?-1855
    MoHi: Feb 11,25,May 18,Jly 29,Aug 5-Dec 30,
        1854; Jan 6,13,27,1855. Merged with
        Shepherd of the Valley,became True Shepherd
        and Cascade Feb 10,1855.

Missouri Citizen   w   1888-1889
    Listed in Rowell 1889-1890.

Missouri Democrat   w,d   1852-1875   tw   1860-1875
    MoHi: d,1855; Sep 1866-Jly 1874; Feb 10,1855;
        Mar 20,Apr 7,16,Oct 9,14,1858; May 16,
        1859; Jan 12,13,Mar 12,14,May 10,Jly 3,
        Dec 15,1860; Jan 8,10,16,Feb 27,Mar 5,27,
        28,Apr 16,27,May 21,27,31,Jun 14,Jly 16,
        31,Aug 5,14,19,22,Sep 10,20,23,Nov 26,
        27,Dec 17,1861; Jan 1,3,12,16,28,Feb 4,
        7,14,28,Mar 17,21,24,26,31,Apr 16,28,May
        3,6,9,21,22,27,28,30,Jun 14,Jly 4,14,Aug
        25,Nov 20,1862; Jan 1,14,26,Feb 2,4,7,19,
        21,Mar 10,13,16,19,25,Apr 16,21,25,27,28,
        May 4,7,21,26,Jun 1-4,13,17,Jly 20,30,Aug
        6,18,Sep 4,14,17,23,24,Oct 13,20,27,31,
        Nov 10,1863; Jan 13,Apr 27,May 6,23,Jun 16,
        Oct 26,Nov 9,Dec 19,21,26,30,1864; Jan 11,
        Feb 22,Mar 1-4,6-8,11,16,17,Apr 4,11,17,
        20-22,24-29,May 2-4,6,8-10,13,15-17,19,
        20,22-25,Jun 1-3,21,Dec 7,12,16,27,1865;
        Jan 3,Mar 6,20,Apr 26,Jun 5,14,Jly 6,7,Aug
        14,29,Oct 9,Nov 29,Dec 25,1866; Jan 1,Feb
        28,Nov 16,Dec 20,1867; Feb 20,Mar 7,10,
        Apr 6,7,10,18,20,May 11,Jun 20,Jly 22,Aug
        12,26,Dec 28,30,1868; Jan 4,May 6,8,Jun
        10,19,21,Jly 7,Aug 16,Oct 20,Nov 18,1869;
        Jan 17,May 9,20,Jun 25,Jly 22,26,Aug 11,
        Oct 14,16,17,19,23,27,Dec 6,20,1870; Jan
        1,4,5,17,18,24,31,Feb 1,3,16,23,Mar 7-10,
        23,Apr 3-7,17,18,21,22,25-27,May 2,3,6,
        16-18,20,30-31,Jun 1-3,7,8,15,Jly 17,Aug
        24,28,Sep 18,26,28,Oct 5,9,10,12,14-21,
        23,31,Nov 1,3,13,17,18,21,23,24,27,Dec
        2,4-9,11-16,18-30,1871; Jan 6,11-13,15,22,
        Feb 1,3,5-10,12-16,19-22,24,27,28,29,Mar
        14,18,22,30,Apr 1-6,8-13,15-18,20,22-24,

Missouri Democrat (continued)
    27,29,30,May 1-3,13-15,25,26,28,31,Jun 1,
        3-6,8,11-15,17,18,22,Sep 9,10,Nov 13,Oct
        11,14,Dec 2,1872; Film,Apr 5,1853-1857;
        Jun 30,1858-Jun 1861; Jly 1-Dec 1864. TW,
        1863-Jun 29,1864; Sep 12,1864-1867; Feb 28,
        1868-Jun 1870; Jan-Dec 2,1871; 1872; Nov
        23,1860; Nov 18,1861; Dec 31,1862. W,1858;
        Nov 1,Dec 20,1859 inc; Feb 26,1861-Feb 13,
        Apr 29,Dec 23,1862; Jan 1,Sep 11,25,Oct 9,
        16,23,30,Nov 6,13,27,Dec 11,25,1857; Jly
        14,1863; Apr 25,1865; Apr 28,1868; Dec 7,
        1869. Film,Feb 26-Dec 31,1861.
    MoSHi: d,Oct 15,1859-Apr 18,1865 inc; Apr
        1865-Jun 1875. Scattered copies 1855,1859,
        1860-1866,1870,1872-1875. W,Dec 11,1860;
        Dec 10,1867.
    MoS: 1855-1857; 1858-1859; 1861-1872.
    MoSG: w,1854-1875.
    MoSM: d,Jly-Dec 1857; 1858; 1861-1865 inc;
        1867-May 31,1875. Merged with Globe Jun
        1,1875.
    CoU: Film,May 25-Dec 31,1857; Jun 30,1858-
        Dec 31,1861; Jly 1,1862-Dec 31,1868.
    DLC: d,Oct 13,17,29,31,1852; 1855; Mar 24,
        1857; Mar 28-Dec 1861; 1863-1865; Feb 19,
        1866; Jan-Feb,Sep 6,1867; Jan-Jun 23,1868;
        Jan-Feb,Oct-Dec 1869; 1870; Jan-Mar,Sep-
        Dec 1871; 1872. W,May 5,Jly 28,Dec 15,22,
        1854; Jly-Oct 1856; Jan 20,Feb 17,1857; May
        19,Jun 16,1863; Aug-Dec 1864; 1865-1867;
        Oct 13-27,Nov 17,1868.
    ICHi: w,Jan 30,1855; Nov 27,1861; Apr 17,24,
        Aug 10,Sep 28,1865; Jly 3,31,1866; Oct
        10,1871. D,Dec 27,1862.
    KHi: d,Nov 13,14,1857; Feb 3,10,Dec 7,1864;
        Jan 29,Sep 15,1866-Jan 3,1875. Film,Mar 2,
        1843-Sep 2,1844. W,Feb 24,May 5,Sep 1,
        1863. TW,Jan 6,1861-Apr 17,1865.
    IHi: w,Feb 18,Mar 11-Apr 1,1862; Apr 3,1865.
        TW,Jan 29-31,Mar 14-17,24,31,1862. D,
        Jly 1,1861-Jly 31,1866 inc; Sep 18,1867;
        Mar 28,Oct 11,1871; Aug 30,Oct 16,21,
        Nov 25,1872.
    MWA: w,Dec 9,1856; May 30-Aug 1,29,Sep
        26,Oct 17-24,Nov 7,21,1865-Nov 6,1866;
        May 14,1867-1875.
    MnHi: d,Jun 29,Jly 10,1865; Jan 9,1872.
    NcD: d,Jun 15,1865.
    NN: Aug 27,1858.
    NbHi: Dec 9,1869; Dec 12,1873.
    NHi: Sep 1,1862; Dec 24,1863; Sep 16,1868;
        Mar 4,1873.
    NcU: Oct 5,1870.
    PHi: May 14,Aug 12,13,1861.
    WHi: Apr 2,1861; Feb 18-Oct 12,1864; Jan 31-
        Dec 21,1865; Mar 6-Dec 21,1866; Mar 23-
        Oct 11,1867; Jan 9-Nov 25,1868; Jan 1-Sep
        14,1869; TW,Aug-Dec 1861; Feb-Dec 1862;
        Apr-Jun 1863; Jan-Feb 1864.
    Micro-Photo: Film, 1845.

Missouri Demokrat   w   1843-1845?
   MoSHi: Sep 2, 16, 1843.

Missouri Farmer   w   1841?
   MoHi: Aug, Sep 1841.

Missouri Free Press   w   1832
   ICHi: May 24, 1832. See Free Press.

Missouri Gazette   w   1808-1822
   MoHi: Jly 26, 1808-Mar 6, 1822; Jly 26, 1808;
     Oct 4, 1809.
   MoSM: Feb 7, Mar 14, 1821; Jly 26, 1808; Feb
     22, 1817.
   MoS: Film, Jan 3, 1821; Mar 6, 1822.
   MoSHi: Jly 26, 1808-Sep 13, 1820; Mar 27, 1822.
   Univ. of KC: Jly 26, 1808; Mar 2, 1821.
   CSmH: Jly 26, 1808.
   DLC: Jly 26-Dec 1808; 1809-1822.
   GHi: Jly 26, 1808, reprint copy.
   AzTP: Film, Aug 2, 1808-Aug 1814; Nov 4, 1815.
   ICN: Jly 26, 1808-Dec 25, 1818 inc.
   IHi: Jly 26, 1808-Sep 18, 1818 inc.
   IaHi: Film, 1821-1822.
   IU: Film, Jly 26, 1808-Dec 25, 1818.
   KHi: Jly 26, 1808; Jan 1, 1819-Mar 6, 1822.
   LNT-MA: Jly 26, 1808.
   MHi: Feb 7, 1821.
   MnHi: Jly 26, 1808-1818 photostat.
   NbHi: Jan 1-Sep 15, Oct 20-Dec 22, 1819; Dec
     29, 1819-Jan 26, Feb 9, 23, 1820; Mar 8-Jun
     7, Jly 5-Aug 23, Sep 6-20, Oct 3-Nov 8, 22-
     Dec 20, 1820; Jan 3-17, 31, Mar 14, 28-Oct
     10, 31-Dec 12, 1821; Jan 2-Mar 6, 1822.
   NN: Jly 26, 1808-Dec 25, 1818 photostat.
   PHi: Apr 24, 1818.
   WHi: Film, Jly 26, 1808-Mar 6, 1822.
   Micro-Film: Film, w, 1819-1822.
   Microfilm Serv, Dallas: Film, Jly 26, 1808-Sep
     18, 1818.
   Under several titles: 1808-Nov 23, 1809 Missouri
   Gazette; Nov 30, 1809-Jly 11, 1812, Louisiana
   Gazette; Jly 18, 1812-Feb 19, 1814, Missouri
   Gazette; Feb 26, 1814-Jly 8, 1815, Missouri
   Gazette and Illinois Advertiser; Jly 15, 1815-
   May 1, 1818, Missouri Gazette; May 8, 1818-
   Jly 3, 1818, Missouri Gazette and Illinois
   Advertiser. Became Missouri Republican Mar
   20, 1822.

Missouri Herald and St. Louis Public Advertiser
  w   1826-1827?
   MoHi: Nov 22, Dec 6, 13, 1826; Jan 3, 17, 31,
     Feb 21, 28, Mar 7, 14, 1827.
   MoSHi: Nov 8, 15, Dec 27, 1826; Feb 7, 21, Mar
     28, Apr 1, 1827.
   Ct: Jan 24, Apr 25, 1827. Under Missouri Herald,
     Nov 8, 1826.

Missouri and Illinois Baptist   w
   MoHi: Mar 1, May 15, 1844.
   ICHi: Jly 12, 1876.

Missouri Journal   w   1865
   According to G-AN&P this is successor to
   Missouri Radical.

Missouri Land Register and Advertiser   w   1866
   MoHi: Jan 1866.
   MoSHi: Jan 1866, Vol I, No 1.

Missouri Observer   w   1826-1828
   MWA: Nov 21, 1827; Jan 30, 1828.
   Ct: Sep 12, 26, Oct 3, 10, 31, Nov 21, Dec 12,
     1827; Jan 16, 1828; Feb 6, 1828.
   MoSHi: Jly 25, 1827 under fuller title.

Missouri Post   w   1879-1881
   In Ayer 1882, Greenback paper.

Missouri Presbyterian
   MoSHi: Scattered issues for 1867, 1882-1883,
     1890-1891, 1894.

Missouri Reporter   d   1841-1846   tw, w   ?
   MoHi: Feb 3, 1845-Aug 15, 1846; Mar 28, 1842;
     Aug 22, Sep 8, 12, 14, 16, Nov 27, Dec 2, 1843;
     Jan 13, 25, Feb 12, Nov 28, 1844; Mar 19, Aug
     14, Jly 31, Sep 3, 10, 12, 15, Nov 22, Dec 6,
     1845; Jan 12, 15, 16, Jly 13, 1846.
   MoSM: d, Jly 27-Aug 1846, inc.
   MoSHi: d, Jan 4, Sep 30, 1843; Jun 17, 1842; Jly
     1, 1845-Aug 14, 1846. W, Jan 6-Jun 29, 1842;
     Jan 4-Jly 31, 1843.
   WHi: Nov 1843-Aug 1846.
   DLC: d, Mar 7, 1842; Feb 3-Dec 1845; Jan-Aug
     15, 1846. W, Jan 4-25, 1845. TW, Mar 28-Dec
     1845; Jan-Mar 25, 1846.

Missouri Republican   d, w, tw   1822-1888
   Formerly Missouri Gazette, later Republic.
   MoHi: d, Mar-Dec 1841; Mar 1849-1850; 1862-
     1864; 1866-Jly 1874, inc; 1875-Jun 1879;
     Oct 16, 24, 26, 29, Nov 6, 24-26, Dec 13, 15,
     25, 27, 1856; Jan 15, 17, 20, 26, Feb 6, 16,
     Mar 11, Jly 30, Oct 18, Nov 5, 18, Dec 9, 14,
     1857; Feb 6, 23, Mar 18, 20, 29, Apr 3, 9, 17,
     28, 30, May 6, Oct 3, 9, 10, 1858; Jan 5, 30,
     Jly 12, 14, 16, 17, 19, 20, Aug 6, 16, 23, Sep
     13, Nov 29, Dec 22, 1859; Jan 31, Mar 14,
     Aug 15, Dec 4, 7, 1860; Feb 4, Mar 7, 8, Jun
     21, 23, 26, Jly 16, 17, 30, Aug 3, 6, 17, 19, 31,
     Sep 3, 7, 12, Oct 7, Dec 15, 24, 25, 28, 1861;
     Aug 20, 1863; Feb 1, 2, 9, 10, 16-18, Mar 4,
     20-22, 24, 25, 27-31, Apr 11, 14, 15, 17, 18,
     26-28, May 24-31, 1, 5, 15, Jun 3, 5-8, 10,
     13-17, 20-24, 26, 27, 29, 30, Jly 8, 10-12, 17-
     22, 25, 27, Sep 21, Nov 13-17, 28, 1865; Mar
     11, 1866; Jun 1, 3, 11, 30, Sep 20, 29, Oct 6,
     10, 20, 28, Nov 3, 6, 13, Dec 3, 1872; Feb 23,
     Apr 28, 1876; May 24, Jun 10, Nov 27, 28,
     Dec 7, 14, 21, 24, 1878; Jan 4, 11, 17, 22, 24,
     Aug 9, 18, 24, 26, Sep 2, 4, 14, 16, 20-23, 30,
     Feb 16, 22, Oct 5, 9, 25, 1879; Jan 9, Mar 9,

Missouri Republican (continued)

30, Apr 30, May 4, 1873; Nov 29, 1881; Aug 31, 1882; Apr 14, 1883; Dec 31, 1862; Jly 25, Dec 21, 26, 1864. Film, Oct 27-Nov 9, 1872; Jan 21-Aug 1873; Nov 11, 1873-1875; May 1876-May 1888. TW, est 1823: Jly 8-Sep 14, 1859; Nov 11, 1859-Feb 10, 1860; Apr 28, 1860-Jun 30, 1865; Jan 3, 1866-Jun 28, 1867; Jan-Jun 10, 1868; Feb 8, 1844; Sep 5, 10, 1850; Apr 17, 19, Aug 28, Sep 4, 9, 25, 27, Oct 31, Nov 17, 1851; Jly 19, Aug 6, 9, 11, 16, 18, Sep 10, Oct 6, 15, 25, Nov 5, 8, 1852; Mar 11, 14, 21, Apr 8, May 18, 20, Aug 19, 31, Oct 27, 1853; May 15, Jly 26, Sep 6, Nov 8, 1854; Sep 14, Nov 12, 14, 16, 26, 28, 30, 1855; Jan 7, 14, 16, 18, 25, 1856; Jan 21, Nov 2, Dec 9, 14, 1857; Apr 22, 1858; Apr 20, 22, 25, 27, Aug 1, 26, 31, Sep 2, 16, 19, 21, 1859; Jan 30, 1860; Feb 18, Mar 6, 8, 11, 18, 22, 25, 27, Apr 1, May 20, Sep 16, 30, Oct 10, 21, Nov 4, 11, 18, 25, 28, Dec 3, 1861; Jan 1, 3, Feb 3, 14, 21, Jly 4, Sep 2, 23, 1862. W, est 1822: Jan 1822-Dec 1828; Jun 7, 1836; Dec 16, 1837; Apr 14, May 26, Sep 22, 29, Oct 13, 20, 1838; Mar 2, Sep 28, 1839; Aug 28, Oct 5, 1849; Sep 29, 1854; Oct 30, Nov 9, 20, 27, Dec 3, 11, 25, Feb 9, 1855; Jan 1-May 27, Jun 10, Jly 15, 22, Aug 5, 19, 26, Sep 2, 23, 30, Oct 7, 14, 28, Nov 4, 18, 25, 1856; Jan 3, 10, 31, Feb 7-Mar 6, 20, 27, Apr 3-24, 1860; Feb 11, 1862; Sep 1, 1863; Jan 5, May 27, 1864; Sep 13, 27, Oct 4, 18, Nov 29, 1867; Jan 1, 1868; Mar 4, 1869; Jan 27, 1870; Mar 27, 1872.

MoS: 1848; 1851-May 1888. Film, Mar 20, 1822-Jly 14, Oct 6, Nov 17, Dec 15, 29, 1829.

MoSW: d, 1847-Jun 1853; 1854-1855; 1857-Jun 1869; Jan-Jun 1863; 1865-1866; Jun 1870-Sep 1873; 1877-Jun 1888. TW, 1851-Oct 1853; 1856.

MoKc: w, film 1828-1829.

MoCaT: w, Nov 29-Dec 6, 27, 1867.

MoSM: w, 1848-1851 inc; 1852-1857 inc; 1858; 1859-1860 inc; 1862-1864; 1865 inc; 1866-1867; 1869-1870 inc; 1871-May 31, 1888.

MoSHi: w, Mar 27, 1822-Apr 2, 1833; Dec 22, 1843-Jan 1, 1847; Jly 10, 1884-Oct 16, 1870. TW, Feb 16, Mar 22, 1827; Mar 25, 1828-Mar 22, 1855; Feb 5, 1861-Apr 2, 1863. SW, Apr 9, 1833-Apr 28, 1835. Evening, Apr 20, May 5, 1862; May 25, Jly 27, Oct 26, 1863; May 5, 16, 1864; Feb 17, 1865. Film, 1826-1829.

AzTP: Film, Mar 20, 1822-1829; 1849.

CoU: Mar 20, 1822 inc.

DLC: Mar 20-Dec 1822; 1823-1828; Jun-Dec 1829; Jan 4, 1831; Aug 17, 1839; Mar-Dec 1841; Dec 5, 1845; May 27, 1846; Mar 3-Dec 1849; 1850-1854; Sep 23, Dec 23, 24, 1856; Mar 18, Aug 22, 1857; 1858-1859; Sep 3, 1861; Feb 8, 14, 1865; Feb 14, Sep 25, 1866; Jan 18, Feb 26, Mar 6-121867; Jan 30, Feb 13, 15, 16, Aug 7, 1869; Feb 18, 1870; 1873-1876. W, Mar 19-Dec 1852; 1853-Jun 1855;

Missouri Republican (continued)

Aug 8, Sep 12, 19, 1856. TW, Aug 5-19, Sep 14, 1859; Mar 4, 15, 18, 1861.

IHi: w, Oct 30, 1846; Sep 7-14, 28, Oct 12, 1860; Jan 20, 1870. TW, Dec 23, 1851; Mar 18, 1852; Dec 20, 27, 1862; May 26, 1865-Oct 15, 1866 inc. D, May 30, 1859; Jly 8, 1861; Jly 6, 1862-Jan 31, 1866 inc; Oct 11, 1871; Jly 31, Oct 31 Nov 22, 26, 28, 1872; May 11, 1877; Mar 1, No 27, Dec 13, 1878; Nov 22, 1879; Jan 15, Sep 17 21, 24, 1881; Jun 27, 1886.

IaHi: Film, Mar 20, 1822-1829.

KHi: d, Jly 28, 1848; May 16, 18, 1850. Film, Mar 1-Dec 31, 1841. W, Apr 7, 1871. Film, Mar 20, 1822-Dec 23, 1828. TW, Feb 9, 1849; Nov 3, 1856-Sep 15, 1863 inc.

LNT-MA: Aug 24, 25, 1878.

MHi: Oct 15, 1823; Sep 6, 1824; May 7, 1880.

MWA: w, Mar 29, Apr 26, May 17-24, Jun 14, Jly 26, 1824; Feb 22, 1827; Dec 11, 1832; extra 1838; Jun 20, Nov 28, 1840; May 21, Jly 4, 1849; Jan 15, 1850; Feb 27, Dec 10-31, 1852; Jan 28-Feb 11, May 23, 1854; Jan 16, Oct 26-Nov 2, 1855; Feb 22, Aug 22, Oct 10, 1856; Sep 10, 1858; Jly 10, 1863. TW, Dec 19, 24-31, 1835, Jan 5-23, 30, Feb 4, 9, 1836; Feb 18, 1847; Jan 14, 1852; Mar 10, 1863.

NcU: Apr 20, 1852; Oct 7, 1870; Jan-Mar, Jly-Sep, Oct-Dec 1877; Jan 1878.

NjR: TW, Jly 8, 1861. W, scattered copies, 1858, 1859, 1860.

NHi: d, Oct 12, 1863; Jly 26, 1867. W, Jun 1-8, 1849; Mar 20, May 1, Jly 6, 1873; Apr 9, 1875; Feb 2, Mar 6, 1877; Jun 22, 25, Jly 17, 31, Oct 7, 1878; Mar 6, 11, 25, May 4, 7, Dec 8, 1879; Feb 19, Mar 27, 1880; Jan 12, 30, Feb 16, 20, 22, 24-26, Mar 3, 17, Apr 4-7, 20, 21, May 4, Jun 30, Sep 29, Oct 3, 4, 10, 15, 16, Dec 31, 1883

NcD: Feb 25, 1877; Feb 21, 1888.

ICHi: w, Nov 26, 1823; Sep 14, 1876. D, Jun 8, 1863; Apr 8, Oct 16, Nov 6, 21, 1865; Oct 11, 15, 1871; Oct 15, 1876; Sep 10, 1877. TW, Jly 15, 1851; Jun 17, 22, 1852.

PHi: d, May 14, Jly 6, 27, Aug 7, 12, 1861.

T: May 1, 1873; Jly 17, 1884; Feb 26, Jly 9, Aug 6, 1885; Feb 10, 1887.

WHi: d, May 28, 1860; 1865. W, film, Mar 20, 1822-Dec 23, 1828; Jun 16, 23, Jly 7, 14, Oct 6, Nov 17, Dec 15, 29, 1829.

Micro-Photo: Film, w 1822-1828.

Changed to sw Apr 9, 1833; d, Sep 20, 1836.

Missouri Saturday News   w   1838-1839
WHi: 1838; Jan 5, 12, 19, 1839.

Missouri Staats-Zeitung   d   1872-1873?
MoSHi: Apr 2, Nov 9, 1873. In Rowell 1872-1873.
NHi: Copy for 1873.

Missouri State Atlas   w   1871-1872
DLC: Sep 7-Dec 1871; Jan-May 9, 1872. In Rowell 1872.

Missouri State Journal d 1861 w 1868?
  MoHi: d, Jly 6, May 16, Jun 19, 25, 1861.
  MoSHi: d, Mar 12-Jly 12, 1861.
  MoSM: d, complete.
  MoS: d, Apr-Jly 1861.
  CSmH, w, Apr 6, 1868. Suppressed Jly 1861.

Missouri State Republican w, tw, d 1901-1909
  MoHi: Jun 18, 1901; Feb 18, Mar 17, Jly 14, Aug
    11, 1904. Film, w, 1903-Sep 28, 1906. TW,
    Jly 17-Oct 23, 1903.
  MoSHi: Jan 31, 1902-May 23, 1907.
  IU: May 1906-1907.
  WHi: Apr 13, 1906-Apr 28, 1907. W to 1903;
    d, tw 1903-1904; w 1904.

Missouri State Review w 1871
  In Rowell 1872.

Missouri State Sentinel d 1868-?
  MoSHi: Jan 1, 1868.
  CSmH: Jan 1, 1868.

Missouri Submissionist w 1886
  MoSHi: May 13, 1886, Vol I, No 2.

Missouri Transcript w 1892-1898?
  Populist. In Ayer 1897, Rowell 1896-1899.

Missourian w 1843-1846
  MoSM: d, Oct 21-23, 1844.
  MoSHi: w, Dec 14, 1843-Feb 1845. D, Oct 7,
    1845-Jly 28, 1846.
  DLC: w, Nov 8, 1843; Apr 5-23, May 28, 1845.
    D, May, Nov-Dec 1845; Jan-Jly 1846.

Missouri Zeitung w 1854-?
  G-AN&P says this is continuation of Demokratische
  Presse and Der Deutsche Pionier.

Modern View
  NN: Sep 18, 1908-May 1943.

Monitor w 1887-1895
  People's Party paper.

Missouri Voice w 1892-1894
  Prohibition organ.

Mound City Review w 1881-?
  MoHi: Aug 30, 1886.

Naborhood Link News w 1930+
  Microfilm Cen: Film, Jun 1930+. Mostly free
    distribution.

Nation-wide Protest
  MoSHi: Jly 1937.

National w 1892-1900?
  Prohibition. Listed at times as National Weekly.

National American w 1882-1884
  NHi: May 12, 1883. Prohibition.

National Issue m 1909-1910?
  MnHi: Sep 1909; Mar, Apr, Aug 1910.

National Rip-Saw
  MoSHi: Jun 1907.

National Tribune w 1876-1881?
  Sunday. In Ayer, Rowell 1881-1882.

National Live Stock Reporter d
  MoHi: Dec 1, 1905; Dec 27, 1907.

National Prohibitionist
  MoHi: Oct 27, 1870.

Native American Bulletin d 1842-1843
  MoHi: Jan 3-Sep 29, 1842. Became Old School
    Democrat and Weekly Herald Mar 2, 1843.
  DLC: Jan-Sep 1842.

Negro World w 1875?-1889?
  Sunday publication.

Neighborhood News w 1922+
  Free distribution paper.

Neue Welt d, w 1868-1871?
  MoS: Nov 16, 1868-Nov 13, 1869. Sunday, Nov
    15, 1868-Nov 7, 1869.
  MoSHi: Oct 1868; Nov 15, 1868; Oct 7, 1870.
  In Rowell 1869-1871.

Neue Zeit d, w 1862-1864?
  MoHi: Dec 2, 9, 11, 1863; Mar 31, 1864.
  MoSHi: Jan 13, Dec 9, 18, 1863; Mar 31, 1864.

New Era w, d 1840-1850?
  MoHi: d, Aug 19, 1846. Film, Mar 6-Dec 29, 1849.
  MoSHi: w, Sep 25, 1841; Apr 28, 1842; May 25,
    Jly 13, 1848; Mar 6-Dec 29, 1849. D, Mar 17,
    1847; Mar 4, 1848.
  MoS: Apr 17, 1841; Jun 26, 1845. Film, Mar 5-
    Dec 29, 1849 inc.
  MoSW: w, Jan 1, 1846-Dec 31, 1846.
  MoSM: d, Apr-Sep 1840; Mar 30, 1841-Mar 1842;
    1843; Jan-Mar 1845; 1846-Jun 1848; 1849;
    Feb-Dec 1850.
  MoSU: Apr 1845-Mar 1846 inc.
  MWA: Jly 13, 1842; Jly 27, 1843.
  DLC: d, Jly 9, 1840; Jun 29, 1841; Mar 3, 8, 30,
    1842; Jly 28, Dec 12, 23, 1845. Film, Mar 5-
    Dec 1849. W, May 26, 1841; Mar 5, 1845.
  KHi: d, Film, Mar 6-Dec 29, 1849.

New St. Louis Star d 1913-1914
  See Star-Times. This title used briefly.

News d 1852-1867, 1898-1908? w 1850-1867
  MoHi: d, Jly 6, 1852; Sep 18, 20, 22, 23, 25, 26, 27,
    Oct 22, 31, Nov 24-28, Dec 1, 2, 26, 1856; Jan
    19, 20, Feb 16, 1857; Jan 20, Aug 14, 1858; Apr
    26, Aug 2, 1859; Dec 18, 1860; Feb 16, Apr 20,
    May 23, 24, 28, Aug 8, 24, 28, Sep 4, 5, 9, 11, Oct
    2, 1861; Feb 20, Jly 10, Aug 23, 25, 1862; Feb 9,
    1863; May 12, Jun 2, 1865; Nov 26, 29, Dec 6,
    12, 23, 1881; Jan 6, 1882; Nov 22, 1908. W,
    Jly 20, 1854-Aug 2, 1855; Jly 14-Aug 11, 1859;
    Nov 10, 1859 as Weekly St. Louis Evening News;
    Oct 20, 1857-Feb 8, 1858; Jan-Jun 23, 1859 as
    Weekly St. Louis Evening News and Intelligencer.
    Merged with Dispatch 1867.
  MoS: d, Jly-Dec 1859; Jly 8, 1861; Apr 15, 1865.
    (Note: a daily under this title published Sep 1-
    6, 1945, during strike at Post-Dispatch.)
  MoSHi: d, Mar 8, 1855; Jun 14, Aug 13, Dec 4,
    1856; Feb 14, Oct 9, 1861; Feb 20, 1862; Aug
    1, 28, Sep 22, 26, Nov 9, 1863; 1866-Jan 19,
    1867; Feb 1, Jun 7, 1903; Apr 1, 1908. Under
    Daily News, 1906-1907.
  MoSM: Under Evening News, 1852-1863 inc.
  MWA: d, Dec 22, 1853; Jun 3, 1859; Nov 23, 1881.
  DLC: d, Sep 30, 1853; Aug 11, 1865; Jan 8-Oct 5,
    1866; Nov 23, 1881.
  KHi: w, Oct 27, 1857.
  NHi: d, Nov 21-23, Dec 18, 1881.

News and Intelligencer
  MoSHi: tw, Sep 15, 1858; Jun 18, 1860. Weekly
    News and Intelligencer merged Oct 20, 1857.
    Several News listed in Ayer-Rowell, con-
    flicting data.

News and Hotel Register d 1905?
  MoHi: Dec 18, 1905.

News and Daily Hotel Reporter d 1906-1907?
  MoSHi: Jan 3-Jun, Oct-Dec 1906; 1907; Jan 15,
    1906; Mar 26, 1907.

News-Champion w 1909-1928?
  In Ayer 1921-1929. See Maplewood.

North County Journal ?
  Microfilm Cen: Film, 1957.

North St. Louis Community News w 1922+
  MoS: Film, 1931+
  Microfilm Cen: Film, 1931-1961.

North St. Louis Dispatch w 1897?
  In Ayer 1898, no founding date.

North St. Louis Leader w 1893-1895
  North End Leader in Ayer 1896.

North, South and West Journal w 1893-1899?
  Listed in Ayer 1898-1900.

Observer w 1833-1836, 1934+
  MoHi: Oct 30, 1890. Film, Sep 3, 1835-Aug 10,
    1836. Moved to Alton, Ill., as Observer.
    MoHi has these copies for Sep 8, 1836-Apr
    1838 on film.
  MoS: Film, May 1934-Mar 13, 1957; Sep 3, 1835;
    Jly 21, 1836.
  MoSHi: May 5, Jun 9, 1836; Jly 31, 1837.
  Microfilm Cen: Film, May 1934-1961.
  MWA: Dec 26, 1833; Nov 5, 1835.
  NcD: Dec 20, 1860; Aug 1, 1861.
  ICHi: Feb 11, 1836.
  IHi: Jan 2-Dec 25, 1834 inc; Sep 3, 1835-Jly
    21, 1836.
  T: Jun 11, 1885. Current Observer is a shopper.
    Rowell 1892 notes an Observer, founded in
    1877, and published by the Cumberland
    Presbyterians.

Old School Democrat and St. Louis Weekly Herald
w 1842-1844 d 1843
  MoHi: d, Mar 2-Dec 30, 1843.
  DLC: Dec 9, 1842; Jan-Feb 1843. D, Mar-Dec 184.
  ICHi: Nov 8, 1843.
  KHi: Mar 2-Dec 30, 1843 inc.
  MWA: Jan 13, 1843. Formerly Native American
    Bulletin, changed to Democrat Feb 1844.

Omnibus 1851?
  Noted in G-AN&P.

Organ and Reveille d 1839-1852
  MoCaT: Oct 28, 1851.
  MoS: Jan 31, 1842-Feb 20, 1845; Jan-Jun 9, 1846.
  MoSHi: Jan 31, 1844; Jun 29, 1847; Jan 29, 1852.
  MoSM: Jan-Oct 1844 inc.
  ICHi: Feb 25, 1851. Listed by Kennedy 1852, both
    as d, w, 1850. Also called Daily People's Organ.

Organisator 1890
  Campaign paper noted in G-AN&P.

Our Country w 1863-?
  MoHi: Apr 1, 1863. Issued by Democratic Central
    Committee.

Paladin w 1918
  Apparently survived a few months.

Palladium w 1884-1911?
  MoHi: Aug 15, 1908. Film, Jan 10, 1903-Oct
    1907. Negro.
  MoSHi: Jan 10, 1903-Oct 5, 1907.
  DLC: Film, 1903-1907.
  WHi: Film, Jan 10, 1903-Oct 5, 1907.

Parole w 1884-1891?
  MoHi: Nov 15, 1890. German.

Patriot w 1923-1928?
  MoHi: Jly 1923-Dec 1924. Filed under Washington, D.C., Missouri Klan Kourier.
  MoSHi: Dec 6, 1923; Jan 3, 1924; Dec 6, 1928.

Patriote et le Phare des Lacs w 1878-1887?
  MoS: 1878; 1886-1887. French.

Pedal w 1895
  Missouri Editor notes founding May 1895.

Pennant w,d 1839-1840?
  MoSHi: d, Apr-Oct 19, 1840. May 29-Oct 19, 1841 as Daily Pennant and Native American.
  DLC: d, Dec 6, 1839. W, Dec 7, 1839.

Pensiero w,sm 1904+
  Italian, Currently sm.

People w 1887
  Prohibition. In Rowell-Ayer 1888.

People's Advocate w 1879-?
  Greenback paper, little data.

People's Organ and Reveille d,w 1839-1851?
  MoSHi: (People's Organ) Sep 23, 1842; Jan 6, 31, 1844; Nov 8, 1845; Jun 29, 1847; Aug 29, 1850.
  MoS: d, Jan 31, 1842-Jun 9, 1846; Apr 25, 1848 inc. W, May 4-Oct 5, 1842.
  DLC: Nov 29, Dec 23, 24, 1845.
  ICHi: Apr 2, 1845.
  ICU: d, Aug 24, 1846. See Organ and Reveille. Also known as People's Weekly Organ, Daily People's Organ and Reveille.

Peoples Voice w 1892-?
  MoSHi: Mar 12, 1911; Oct 25, 1914; Nov 3, 1918. Rowell 1894-1895 lists Missouri Voice, prohibition paper founded in 1892. May be continuation.

Picket Guard d 1842? 1899? 1888
  DLC: Aug 19, 1842, Vol 1, No 2, Clay for President.
  IHi: Apr 25, 1899. Apparently published in E. St. Louis, Ill., as well as St. Louis.
  KHi: Mar 29, 1888, Vol 1, No 1.

Pilot d,w 1854-1856.
  MoHi: Film, Jan 6, 1855-Nov 15, 1856.
  MoS: Film, Jan 6, 1855-Nov 15, 1856.
  MoSHi: Film, Jan 6, 1855-Nov 15, 1856.
  DLC: Film, 1855.
  KHi: Film, Jan 6, 1855-Nov 15, 1856.

Pithy Sayings ?
  MoSHi: 1901.

Political Review w 1901-1905
  Last listed in Rowell 1906.

Post w 1846-1847? d 1878
  MoHi: Jan 11, Feb 7, 15, 20, 23, 1878. Film, Jan 10-Dec 11, 1878.
  MoS: Jan 10-Dec 11, 1878.
  MoSHi: Jan 10-Jun 29, 1878.
  MoSM: Jan 10-Dec 12, 1878.
  MWA: May 28, Jly 13, 1878.
  DLC: May 28, Jly 13, 1878.
  MHi: Dec 12, 1878.
  NHi: May 4, 25, 28, Jun 17, Jly 13, Sep 12, 18, Nov 9, 1878.
  NcU: Aug 26, 1878.
  WHi: Film, Jan 10-Dec 11, 1878.

Post-Dispatch d,w,tw 1878+
  MoHi: d, 1920-1942; Jan 18, Feb 22, Mar 19, Sep 1, 17, 1879; Nov 16, 1881; May 11, 1882; Jan 2, Feb 24, 1883; Sep 23, 1884; Feb 7, Apr 1-3, Jun 9, 16, 17, 20, Jly 7, 9, 11, 13-16, 20-25, 29-31, Aug 3-8, 10, 19, 20, 29, 31, Sep 9, 21, 30, Oct 3, Dec 2, 1885; May 1, 11, Jun 1, 8, 11, Jly 20, 27, 28, Aug 19, 21, Sep 8-10, Nov 19, Dec 11, 1886; Oct 18, 1887; Oct 23, Dec 1, 2, 1889; Jan 12, 13, May 4, 14, 16, 22, Jun 1, 13, 20, Aug 18, Sep 3, 4, 6, Oct 18, 20, Nov 3, 7-10, 19, Dec 23, 1890; Jan 1, 7, Feb 21, May 21, 25, Aug 9, Sep 10, 17, 1891; Nov 13, 1892; Apr 23, 1893; Jan 21, 1894; Jun 9, 1895; May 29, 1896; Apr 9, Aug 16-18, 21, Sep 6, 1904; Feb 16, 1906; Feb 27, 1916. Under Post and Dispatch, d, Dec 12, 1878-Feb 15, 1879; Dec 12, 1878. Film, Dec 12, 1878-Mar 7, 1879. Film, Mar 8, 1879+.
  MoSHi: Jly 1884-Sep 1885; Apr-Sep, Oct 28, Dec 27, 1886; scattered issues 1878, 1882, 1885-1888, 1891, 1893, 1896-1900; 1900-Apr 1918; Jly 1918-Oct 1919.
  MoMary T: 1934+.
  MoS: 1878-1960 inc. Film, 1864+.
  MoSM: 1879-1883 inc; 1884-1887; 1888-1897 inc.
  MoJcL: Feb 1950+.
  MWA: Mar 13, 1879; Jun 2, 1881; Sep 18, 1882; Dec 14, 1913.
  CoU: Oct 15, 1929; Oct 21, 1921 inc.
  CSmH: Mar 31, 1955.
  DLC: Mar 13, 1879; Jun 2, 1881; Oct 10, 1883; Sep-Dec 1893; 1894; Sep-Dec 1918; 1919; 1950.
  IaHi: Sep 3-Oct 4, 1887; Jun 24, 1880-Jly 14, 1881.
  IHi: Dec 20, 1914; Jan 30, 1925; Apr 13, Aug 15, 1945; Apr 6, 30, 1947; Nov 3, 1948; Feb 13, 1949. Film, Jan 1, 1953+.
  IU: 1927-1947. Film, 1934-1935; 1947.
  KHi: Dec 13, 1878; Jly 23, 1883; Dec 25, 1888; Feb 10, 1889; Mar 13, 1904; Jun 3, 1906; Mar 2, 1913; Jly 28, 1918; Apr 6, 1919; Dec 23, 1923.
  LNT-MA: Aug 28, 1938; Mar 23, Jun 18-20, Jly 11, 16-21, Sep 1-Dec 31, 1940 inc; 1941-1942 inc.
  LU: Film, 1940+.
  NHi: Jan 16, 31, Feb 11, 18-20, Mar 4-5, 10, 13-14, May 1, 9, Jun 14, Aug 4, Sep 29, 1879; Nov 24, 1880; Jan 3, Mar 19, Apr 30, May 26, Jun 2, Sep

Post-Dispatch (continued)
17,1881; Jun30,Sep 18-22,25,Oct 3-10,1882;
Jan 9,14,18,26,Feb 16,Mar 3,10,30,1884.
NN: 1938-1956. Film,1956+.
MnHi: Feb 24,1892; Jly 23-26,1896.
NcD: Jly 1-Dec 1932; Jan-Jun,Jly 1-3,5-13,
Aug-Dec 1933; 1934+.
NjR: Film,1874-1900,1935+.
WHi: Film,Dec 12,1878-1904; 1920; 1941+.

Presbyterian w
MoHi: Mar 31,Sep 29,1876; Feb 22,1878; Mar
14,21,1884; Oct 24,1890.
MoSHi: Feb 10,Apr 7,28,May 12,Jun 23,Aug 4,
Nov 3,10,1853.
IHi: May 29,1851.
ICHi: Aug 25,1876.
NcD: May 30,1850; Jly 31,1856; 1858-1859 inc;
1875-1891.
NcU: Aug 19,1858; Oct 14,1887.

Press d 1864-1866?
MoSHi: Apr 16,Dec 19,1865.
MoS: Film,Dec 17,1864-Aug 19,1866.
MoSW: Dec 1864-Aug 1866.
ICHi: Oct 1,Nov 26,1865.
WHi: Jly 6,10,1866.

Press-News w 1879-1881
Representative attended press session 1879-1881.

Price-Current w 1850-1874?
MoSHi: Mar 9,1850-Dec 11,1852; 1855-Jan 1,
1856; 1866-Jan 5,1870; Jan 3,1871-Dec
30,1893.
MWA: Mar 31,1864.
NjR: Jan 1,1855.
PHi: Jan 4,1851.
WHi: May 9,1856-Apr 30,1857. Also known
as Price Current and Merchants' Commercial
Record and other variations.

Price Current and Trade Journal w 1874-1877?
DLC: Nov 22,1877.
MWA: Nov 22,1877.
ICHi: Jly 6,1876.
NHi: Nov 22,1877.

Progressive Exponent w 1913-1914
MoHi: Oct 10,17,24,28,1914. Progressive Party.

Progressive Press w 1930-1932 m 1932-?
MoHi: Film,Dec 12,1930-Feb 1932.
MoSHi: Feb 13,Aug 28,1931. Replaced St.
Louis Labor.

Przewodnik Polski w 1899-
MoSHi: 1903-1910; 1913-1926; scattered copies
for 1927-1929.

Public Ownership Leader w 1898-1901?
Concerned with railroads.

Puck w 1871-1872?
MoHi: No 44 inc.
MoS: Nos 1-52.
MoSHi: Complete set.
MoSM: Complete set.
Humorous German-language weekly.

Quarterly Review q 1880-?
MoHi: Sep 1880; Oct 1881. Published by
Farmers and Mechanics' Mutual Aid Assn.

Radikale 1864?
Noted in G-AN&P.

Rainbow w 1875
MnHi: Jly 4,1875.

Raritatenkasten 1850?
Noted in G-AN&P.

Real Estate Bulletin & Building News
MoSHi: Dec 13,1919.

Real Estate Register
MoHi: Jun 15,1869.
MoSHi: Feb 1,1850.

Record d,w 1879 d 1890+
MoHi: 1962+.
MoSHi: May 24,1884.
MoS: Jly 25,1901+.
MnHi: Oct 16,1940.
Microfilm Cen: Film,Jly 1908+. I.F. Guiwits
Represented Record at press association meet-
ing in 1879. Present Record is legal pub-
lication.

Referendum w 1902?
MoSHi: Apr 23,1902.

Reform w,d 1891-1899
MoHi: Sep 4-Dec 9,1899. Changed from d to w,
moved to Kansas City Dec 1899. German
paper started as w, became d later.

Reformer w 1847?
Noted in G-AN&P.

Register w 1821-1957?
MoHi: Film,Jun 4,1854-Jan 25,1957.
MoSHi: Photostat,Dec 8,1821.
MoS: Film,1942-Jan 25,1957.
MoSM: Dec 8,1821.
Microfilm Cen: Film,1941-1961.
WHi: Oct 12,1867 copy of Daily Fair Register.

Reporter tw,w,d 1846-1847?
MoSM: Jly 28-Aug 21,1846. See Missouri
Reporter.

Republic   sw   1888-1919   d   1836-1919
  MoHi: d, Sep 2,9,13-16,1825; 1888; Apr 29,
    May 4, Feb 2,1889; Feb 22,1891; Apr 16,17,
    24, Jun 26, Jly 10,17, Aug 21, Dec 16,19,
    1892; May 20,31, Jly 8,1893; Mar 20, Dec
    23,1894; Jan 23,25, Jly 9,1898; Feb 9,1908;
    Feb 12,1914; Aug 31,1916. Film, May 31,
    1888-Dec 4,1919. SW, film, Feb 23-Dec 1892;
    May 16-Dec 1893; 1894; Jan-Mar 18,1895.
  MoS: sw, Jun 1888-Dec 1919. D, 1851-1853;
    Apr-Dec 1854; Mar 1855-1859; Sep 1860-
    Jun 1869; 1870-1884; Jly 1885-1919.
  MoSW: sw, Jly 1,1888-1894; Sep 1,1895-Feb
    28,1914; 1916-1918. D, 1847; 1849-1855;
    1857-Jun 1869; May 1870-1914.
  MoCaT: d, Dec 3,1843; Jly 27,1882; May 2,
    1889; 1913-1919.
  MoJ: d,1901-1919.
  MnHi: d, Jly 23,26,1896; May 3,1903; Jly 3,
    10,1905; Apr 2-3,1908.
  MoK: d, Apr 15-Nov 1904; Jly 12,1908.
  MoSHi: d, complete. SW, Oct 23,1890-Jun 28,
    1894; Jly 1909-Jan 13,1910; 1912-1914.
    W, Sep 6,1888-Oct 16,1890.
  MoSM: d, 1847-1848 inc; 1850-1851 inc; 1853-
    Jun 1862; 1863-Jun 1869; May 26,1870-1919.
    SW, 1906-1913 inc.
  MoSU: d, 1859-Sep 1916.
  MWA: d, May 6,1841; May 10,1848; Mar 6, Jly
    10-23, Oct 6-13,21, Nov 11-Dec 9,1849; Jan
    1,6-13, Feb 6,10, Nov 4,17-24, Dec 22,1850;
    Dec 7,1852; May 14, Oct 6, Dec 23,1853;
    Nov 9,1854; May 28,1856; Jun 26,1857; Jun
    6,16, Jly 20, Aug 17-18,21,24,29-Sep 1,6-11,
    29, Nov 11,1858; Mar 27, Apr 16,19, Jly 10,
    13, Sep 10,25,1859; Jan 10,1861; Jan 28,
    1862-1863; Sep 14,16,1867; Sep 14,1868; Mar
    13,15, Oct 22,1869; Jan 9,1873; Feb 11-Mar
    29,1874; Apr 2, Oct 15,1876; Sep 10,1877;
    Feb 5-Dec 1879; Mar 15,1882; Sep 29,1883;
    Mar 2,1884; Oct 5,1885.
  CSmH: d, Apr 17,1865; Sep 16, Oct 11,27,1867;
    Feb 3, Jun 26, Aug 8,1868.
  DLC: Under Republican, 1877-1898; Jan-Mar
    1899; 1900-Dec 4,1919.
  ICHi: d, Jly 12,1908.
  IU: May 1909-Nov 1919.
  IaHi: May 18,1899-Aug 6,1903.
  IHi: Oct 23,1888; Jly 7,1896; Mar 4,1897; Jun
    18,21,27-28,1900; Jly 12,1908; Jly 10,1910;
    Apr 22,1914.
  KHi: d, May 8,1898; Jly 18,1893-Jly 10,1910 inc;
    Aug 7,1904-May 3,1907; Aug 11,1907; Jly 12,
    1908. W, Mar 22,29,1914.
  LNT-MA: Sep 21-24,26, Oct 2-3,1904.
  NcD: May 1,1904. World's Fair Ed.
  NbHi: Apr 5, Jun 24,1892; Apr 4,5, Jun 16,30,
    1893; Feb 16, Mar 9, Aug 16, Sep 2,12,14, Nov
    15,19,1894; Jun 1,1903; May 13,1904; Aug
    26,1906.
  OrHi: 100th anniversary ed., 1908.

Republic   (continued)
  T: Oct 16, Dec 24,1891; Nov 3, Dec 8,1905;
    Mar 5,9, Apr 2, Sep 21,1908; Feb 15, Oct 28,
    Nov 1,4,1909; Jan 31, Mar 24, Aug 15,18,22,
    Sep 1,1910; Jly 1,1912; Sep 21,28, Oct 1,8,
    26, Nov 5,9,16,19,1914; Jly 1,5,26,29,1915;
    Sep 14, Oct 30, Nov 2,6,9,13,20,1916; Jly 12,
    Aug 30, Oct 1,1917; Mar 7,25,28, Apr 4, Jun
    27, Jly 4,11,18,22,25, Aug 12,22,26, Sep 2,5,
    12,16,19,23, Dec 16,1918.
  WHi: sw,1892-Oct 1893; Jly 12,1908.
  Formerly Missouri Republican. Sold to Globe-
  Democrat Dec 4,1919.

Republican   w   1823-?   d   1830-?,1940-?
sw   1833-1836
  MoHi: d,1875-Dec 15,1876. Film, Nov-Dec 1874.
  MoSW: d, Oct 1,1873-Dec 15,1876.
  MoSHi: Jun 7, Sep 1,1874; Apr 11, Aug 2,1875.
  CSmH: Feb 3,1834.
  ICN: Feb 1-Dec 31,1873.
  IHi: Mar 1,1875.
  ICHi: d, May 14, Oct 18,1876.
  KHi: d, Apr 13,1874-Jun 23,1895.
  MnHi: Jan 17,1901.
  NcU: Jan 26-Aug 4,12,31, Dec 15,1876; May
    19,1885.
  NHi: d, Sep 25,1875; May 28,1876; Oct 21, Nov
    18,1877; Jan 8, Feb 23-24,26, Nov 20,22,24,
    Dec 11,18,1881; Jan 10-11, Mar 18,23, Apr
    18-19,29, Jun 18, Aug 2, Oct 8,1882; Feb 25,
    Mar 23, Apr 15,22-23,26, May 6, Jun 14, Oct
    19-21, Nov 28,1883.
  NcD: Aug 25,1861. TW, May 24,1865.
  T: May 20,1875.
  Rowell 1874-1880 refer to w as Missouri
  Republican. At times d,w,tw listed. Rowell
  1880 lists all under Missouri Republican.
  MoSHi: lists Vol I, No 1 of a Republican dated
  May 1940.

Repudiator   w   1868
  MoHi: Feb 27,1868.
  MHi: Apr 2,1868.
  MWA: Mar 12,1868. "Repudiated" state debt.

Retailers Market News   1930?-1952
  MoSHi: Jan 4,1930-Oct 18,1952.

Retriever   w   1893-1896
  Single-Tax publication.

Reveille   d,w   1844-1850
  MoHi: d, Jan 19,21-22,25,26, Feb 1,10,14,17-
    19,21,23,24,1848. W, film, Jly 15,1844-Jly
    6,1846.
  MoSHi: w, Aug 3-Sep 28,1846-Jan 11,1847; Jan
    25-Mar 22, Apr 5-Jun 14,1847. D, Jun 8, Aug
    7,16, Oct 4, Dec 18,1847; Jan 24, Feb 22,
    1848; May 20, Sep 11, Oct 7,15, Nov 11,1849;
    Oct 5,1850.
  MoS: d, Dec 30,1847. W, Jly 15,1844-Jly 6,1846.

Reveille (continued)
MoSU: d, 1844-Nov 13, 1845.
MoSM: w, 1844; 1845 inc; 1846-Jly 5, 1847.
Univ of KC: d, Nov 5, 1845. W, Oct 27, 1845.
MWA: Nov 2, Dec 14, 1846-Jan 4, Apr 5, 19,
May 24, Jun 7, 21, Jly 5-12, Aug 2, 15, 30-
Sep 20, Oct 4, Dec 12, 1847.
CSmH: d, Sep 9, 1846.
ICN: May 14, 1844-Oct 6, 1850.
MHi: w, Sep 27, 1847.
NHi: Oct 22-29, Nov 5, Dec 17, 1848; Jan 29,
Jly 2-16, Aug 20, Sep 3, Oct 29, Nov 26, Dec
24-31, 1849; Jan 7-Apr 15, 1850.
WHi: d, film, May 14, 1844-Oct 6, 1850. W, film,
Jly 22-Sep 30, 1850.

Review   w   1941+
MoHi: Film, Feb 1, 1957+. Catholic.
MoS: Film, Feb 1, 1957+. Formerly Register to
Feb 1, 1957.

Revue de Lanst   w   1851-1852
Press formerly used for Ste. Genevieve Creole.

Revue de l'Ouest   w   1854-1865?
MoHi: Film, 1854.
MoSHi: 1854. In American Newspaper Directory
1861.

Revue Icarienne   w   1858
LNM: Oct 15, 1858.

Rolling Ball   w   1850-?
MoHi: Jun 23, 1850.
MoSHi: Jun 16, 1860. At times a funny paper
yet ironical, critical.

Randschau (Die)   w   1880?-1895?
MoSCHi: Aug 31-Nov 16, 1880.

Rural World   w, m   1848-1916
ICHi: m, Aug-Nov 1865.
NcU: Jly 22, 1886. See Colman's Rural World.

St. Louis   w   1895
In Rowell 1896. Office in courthouse.

Sales   w   1869
In Rowell 1870.

Saturday Blade   w   1891-1894
In Rowell 1893-1894, Ayer 1892-1895.

Saturday Evening Post and Temperance Recorder
w   1846-1847?
MoSHi: Jun 3, 1846; Jly 17, 1847.

Saturday Night   w   1920-1921
MoHi: Mar 6, 1920-Sep 10, 1921.
MoS: May 22, 1920; Nov 1921.
MoSHi: May 29-Jly 31, Aug 14, 28, Sep 11, 25,
Oct 9, 16, Nov 6, Dec 4, 18, 1920; Jan 1, 15,

Saturday Night (continued)
Feb 5, 19, Mar 12, 26, Apr 9, 23, May 7, 21,
Jun 11, 25, Sep 10. 1921.

Saturday Union Record   w   1888-1899
MoSHi: Aug 3, 1918. In Rowell 1899-1900.
In Ayer 1918-1919, founded 1889?
Sayings   d   1887-1888
See Star-Times. Union List says this name used
from Nov 20, 1887-Apr 15, 1888.

Schalk (Der)   w   1879?-1896?
Noted in Ayer 1891-1896.

Sentinel   w   1855, 1864
MoHi: Mar 24, 30, Jly 13, Aug 17, 1855; Jun 15,
22, 1864.
MoSHi: Mar 26, 1864. Formerly True Shepherd and
Cascade to Mar 24, 1855. First was temperance
paper; second had sermons, catechism comment
etc.

Signal   d   1851-1853?
MoSM: Jan-Jly 8, 1852. Formerly Barnburner,
merged with Missouri Democrat.

Signet   w   1856?
In Newspaper Record 1856.

Slasher   w, d   1844
MoSM: Apr 27, 1844. (D, Missouri Reporter)
MWA: Aug 24, 1844.

Sonnenschein (Der)   1899-1900
Listed in G-AN&P.

Sonntagsblatt   w
Other titles used included:
Sonntagsblatt der Amerika 1872-1924; Sonntagsblatt
der Missouri Staats-Zeitung, 1872-1875?; Sonn-
tagblatt der Neuen Zeit, 1862-1864?; Sonntagsblatt der Volks-Zeitung, 1900-1902?; Sonntagsblatt der St. Louis Tageblatt, 1888?-1897?;
Sonntagsblatt der St. Louis Tribune, 1880-1897?;
Sonntagsblatt der Stadtbote, Aug-Oct 1853.

South and West   sm   1883-1884?
MoHi: Oct 1, 1883.
MoSHi: May 15, 1884.

South County Journal   w   1960+
Free distribution paper.

South Side Journal   w   1935+
MoS: Film, Oct 1935+. Free paper.
Microfilm Cen: Film, Oct 1935-1961.

South Side Reporter   w   1895-1898
In Rowell 1896-1899.

South St. Louis Blade   w   1876?
MoS: Aug 20, 1876.

South St. Louis Carondelet Review   w   1872-1875?
    In Rowell 1876, Sunday paper.

South St. Louis News   sw   1875-1876?
    In Rowell 1876.

South St. Louis County News
    Microfilm Cen: Dec 1947-1961.

South St. Louis Progress   w   1899-1902?
    MoHi: Film, May 6, 1899-May 19, 1900. Was
    Carondelet Progress to May 6, 1899.

South-Western Methodist   w   1885?
    MoSHi: Aug 29, Dec 5, 1885.

Spectator   w   1880-1892
    Saturday society paper.

Spirit   w   1878-1880
    MoSHi: May 4, 1878. In Rowell 1881.
    NHi: Sep 28, 1878; Jly 10, 1880.

Spotlight   w   1948
    MoHi: Jly 18, 1948.
    MoSHi: Jly 18, 1948. (Only edition?)

Sporting News   w   1886+
    MoHi: Oct 11, 1890. Film, 1902-1904.
    MoU: Film, Mar 17, 1886-1961.
    MnHi: Nov 29, 1945.
    Microfilm Cen: Film, Mar 17, 1886+.

Squatter   w   1848
    MoHi: Oct 14, 1848. For daily edition see
    Daily Union.

Standard   w   1880
    Sunday, in Rowell 1881.

Star   d   1878-1879?, 1884-1905, 1908-1932 w 1960
    MoHi: Oct 14, 1903-Feb 1904; 1914-1931; Jan
    2-Jun 22, 1932; May 10, Jun 15-18, 1896; Dec
    7, 1903. Film, 1910-1914; Dec 26, 1922-1925;
    1931.
    MoSHi: May 28, Jun 14, 1896; Feb 16, 1897; Mar
    6, 17, Apr 27, Jly 14, 31, 1898; Feb 27, May 8,
    Sep 23, 1900; Oct 3, 1909; Jan 30, Feb 27, Mar
    27, 1910; Nov 12, 1911; Apr 22, May 5, Jun 9,
    Oct 9, 1912; Oct 15, Nov 7, Dec 8, 1917; Feb
    4, 1918; Jly 17, 1919; Aug 24, 1920.
    IU: d, 1909, 1914-1918.
    KHi: Dec 30, 1900; Feb 1901; Jly 29, 1925.
    MnHi: Jly 22-24, 26, 1896.
    NHi: d, Jan 31, Feb 4-6, 8, 14, 17-19, Mar 6, Apr
    12, 1879.
    MoS: Film, 1869-1909.
    Microfilm Cen: Film, 1896-1909 inc. Became
    Star and Chronicle Jun 6, 1905. Renamed
    Star Oct 24, 1908. Merged with Times Jun
    23, 1932. Weekly controlled circulation
    tabloid started 1960.

Star-Chronicle   d   1884-1905
    MoHi: Jly-Sep 1905. See Star.
    MoSHi: Feb 17, 1906; Aug 22, 1908.
    MnHi: Apr 2-3, 1908.
    Microfilm Cen: Film, Jun 6, 1905-Oct 1908.

Star Sayings   d   1884-1895?
    MoHi: Nov 20, 1891; Feb 27, 1892; Nov 15, 1894.
    MoSHi: Aug 18, 1891; Apr 11, 1894.
    MnHi: Feb 22, 1892.
    Microfilm Cen: Film, Mar-Dec 1895. Evening, Oct
    29, 1888-1895. Listed as Star Ayer 1897; found-
    ing dates vary in Ayer-Rowell.

Star-Times   w, d   1884-1951
    MoHi: d, Dec 10, 1933-1948. Film, 1937; 1949-end
    Jun 15, 1951; Jun 23, 1932-Dec 3, 1933 as Star
    and Times.
    MoSHi: Film, 1939-1945; Oct 31, 1946; Jun 6,
    1934; Dec 30, 1947; Dec 29, 1950; Jun 15, 1951.
    MWA: Oct 23, 1887. See also Sayings, Star-Sayings,
    Star-Chronicle, Times.

States   w   1868
    Sunday paper in Rowell 1869.

Statesman   w   1847?
    MoHi: Extra, Oct 9, 1847.

Steamer, City of Memphis Reporter   d   1858
    CL: May 1, 1858.

Suburban Review   w   1947-1952?
    In Ayer 1952, founding date of 1947.

Suburban Home Journal   w   1889-1909?
    In Ayer 1904-1910, Rowell 1905-1906.

Sunday Herald   w   1896
    Start noted in Missouri Editor, Jun 1896.

Sunday Mirror   w   1891-1894
    In Rowell 1892-1894, Ayer 1891-1895.

Sunday Morning   w   1872-1873
    In Rowell 1872-1873. Published in South St. Louis.

Sunday Sayings   w   1884-1887
    In Ayer 1887, Rowell 1885-1888, Dauchy 1884.
    Microfilm Cen: Film, May 3, 1885-Apr 26, 1886.

Sunday Telegraph   w   1909-1913?
    Listed in Ayer 1913-1914.

Sunshine Journal   w, sm   1936+
    In Ayer 1955-1956; fortnightly in 1963.

Tageblatt   d   1888-1898
    MoHi: Oct 28, 1890.
    MoS: Apr 30, 1888-Jun 1897.
    MoSHi: Mar 3, 7, 27, 1893; Feb 27, 1895; Feb
    15, 1897.

Tages-Chronik d 1860-1861 sw 1849-1861?
  MoS: Apr 24-Dec 27, 1859. Weekly, Wochen-
    Chronik, MoSC: Jun 6, 1861.

Tax-Payer
  MoSHi: Mar, Apr 1917.

Telegraph w 1861?
  WHi: lists Telegraphe, sw, Apr 11, 29, 1840. In
    American Newspaper Directory 1861.

Temperance Battery
  MoHi: May 14, 1853.

Texas w 1871-1872, 1878
  In Rowell 1873, 1879. Apparently two.

Times w 1866-1881? d 1895-1932,
1866-1881?, 1850 w 1829-
  MoHi: d, 1876-Sep 1877; Jan-Mar 1878; Jly-Dec
    1878; Jan 12, 1868; May 13, Nov 19, 1869;
    Sep 4, 1870; Apr 14, 1872; Oct 8, 1876; Feb
    18, 1877; Jun 7, 1878; Oct 24, 1880; Oct 8,
    1921. Film, Sep-Dec 1870; Apr 15, 1907-Jun
    29, 1916.
  MoSM: w, Jly 10-Dec 1830; Jan-Mar 1832; Jly
    1877-Jun 1880. d, 1866; 1867-1868 inc; 1870,
    1872, 1875 inc; Jun 1880; May 27-Dec 1850.
  MoS: Apr 15, 1907-Jun 23, 1932.
  MoSHi: Mar 27, 1830; Feb 11-May 19, Jun 2-Jly
    14, Aug 11, Sep 15, Oct 6, 13, 27, Nov 3-Dec
    29, 1832; Jan 5-19, Feb 2-May 11, 25-Jly 13,
    Aug 3, 10, Oct 5, 19, Dec 7, 21, 28, 1833; Jan
    4, 1834. (Jacob R. Stine, pub., Lovejoy and
    Miller editors.) Aug 29, 1850; Mar 21, 1851;
    Jly 21, 1866-Jan 25, 1867; Jan 3, Mar 29,
    1868; May 3, 23, 1874; Dec 10, 1876; Aug
    14, 1897. Vol 1, No 1 under Preetorius
    appeared Apr 15, 1907; Oct 22, 1907; Apr
    15, 1908; Jly 30, 1910; Mar 19, Apr 6, 7, 14,
    19, 21, Aug 7, Oct 6, 15, 27, Nov 21, Dec 15,
    1917.
  MWA: Apr 10, 1830; Feb 12, Dec 10, 1831; May
    5, 1832; Feb 23-Mar 2, 30, 1833; Nov 26,
    1870; Sep 30, 1875.
  ICHi: d, Dec 7, 1833; Oct 10, 15, 1871; Oct 22,
    1876.
  NcU: Jly 1, 1869; Mar 25, 1870.
  CSmH: w, Aug 28, 1830; d, Oct 27, Dec 20, 1867;
    Jan 4, Apr 29, 1868.
  IHi: Oct 30, 1878; Jan 23, 1912; Apr 22-23, Aug
    3, 29, 31, 1914; Aug 11, 1915; Apr 3, 1917.
  NHi: d, Dec 23, 1875; Feb 3, Mar 28, Oct 28,
    1877; Jan 12, 1878; Jan 4, 1881; w, Jan 9,
    May 4, 1873; Oct 21, 27, Nov 16, 19, Dec 19,
    1877; Jan 23, 1880.
  KHi: d, Aug 26, 1869; Mar 22, 1870; Jly 23,
    1872; Sep 29, 1919; Aug 15, 1921.
  WHi: w, Feb 4-May 12, 1832.
  CT: Jly 17, Sep 18, 25, Oct 2, 9, 30, Nov 6, 1830;
    Mar 5, Apr 16, 1831.

Times (continued)
  NcD: d, Oct 23-31, Nov-Dec 26, 1879.
  DLC: d, Jan-Mar 1868; Feb 17, Sep 14, 1869; Oct
    15, 1871; Nov 3, 1872; Oct 12, 1873; Feb 19,
    Jun 7, 27, Dec 5, 1874; Nov 28, 1875; Jan 4,
    10, 1880; w, Jly 7-21, Aug 21, 1829; Jan 8, 1880.
  MnHi: Apr 2-3, 1908.

Times-Journal d, tw, w 1866-1879
  MoSM: w, d, Jan-Oct 23, 1879. Apparently name
    used for Times for some years. Under full title
    in Rowell 1879.
  MoHi: d, Dec 7, 20, 21, 1878; Apr 13, May 4, Mar
    17, 1879.
  NHi: d, Nov 25, 28, Dec 4, 1878; Jan 6, 26, 31, Feb
    9, 16, 19, Mar 6, 9, 17, 20, 22-23, 25, Apr 13, May
    2, Jun 4, 14, 26-27, Jly 6, Aug 4, 19, Oct 30, 1879.
  NcD: Jan, Feb 1-16, 18-28, Mar 1-3, 5-24, 26-31,
    Apr 1-14, 16-26, 28, 30, May 1, 3-11, 13, 15-20,
    22-31, Jly-Sep, Oct 1-22, 1879.

Trade Journal
  MoSHi: May 1872.

Trade Review m 1876-?
  Wv-Ar: Mar 1891, Vol 15, No 41.

Transcript w 1844
  Mentioned in Brown thesis.

Traveler w 1861? m 1896-?
  MoSHi: Oct 4, 1879. Noted in American News-
    paper Directory 1861.
  KHi: m, Sep-Nov 1896, Vol 1, Nos 2, 4.

Tribune w 1838-? d 1869-1871, 1880-1897?
  MoHi: d, Nov 25, 1869; Aug 31, 1870. w, Jan 15,
    1870.
  MoS: d, 1880-1897? German.
  MoSHi: Sep 5-Dec 31, 1880; Jan 2, Apr 2, 14,
    1881; 1881-Dec 31, 1897. German.
  MoSM: d, Oct 26, 1869-Jun 1870.
    Newspaper Record 1856 lists Tribune. German
    paper for 1838. noted in G-AN&P. Rowell
    1870 lists d, w Tribune, founded 1869. Ayer
    1881 lists German daily, founded 1880. Later
    Sunday and weekly editions noted in Ayer.
  KHi: d, Aug 29, 1888.

True American w 1893-1897
  Publication of American Protective Assn.

True Democrat 1895?
  Suspension in Missouri Editor, Oct 1895.

True Shepherd and Cascade w 1855
  MoHi: Film, Feb 10-Mar 24, 1855. See Cascade.
    Became Sentinel Mar 24, 1855.

Truth w 1888-1897
  Weekly society and drama publication. Country
  Editor, Mar 1897, said "Truth is dead. Truth was out
  of place in a St. Louis newspaper office."

Turner   w   1891-1892?
    MoSHi: Jan 31-Dec 26,1891; 1892.

Union   w   1846-?,1881-1884?   tw   1847
d   1846-1867?
    MoHi: d, Jly 25,27,29, Aug 1,11,26,27, Dec 24,
        25,1863. Film, Aug 17,1846-Apr 6,1849. TW,
        Jun 22,1847; Apr 7,10,1848.
    MoS: Jun 10,1862-Jun 19,1863. Film, Aug 17,
        1846-Apr 6,1849 inc.
    MoSW: Jun 9,1863-Nov 19,1864.
    MoKc: d, Film, Aug 17-Oct 26,1846.
    MoSM: d,1846-1851 inc; Jun 9,1862-Jun 8,1863.
        W, Aug 25,1846-1847.
    MoSHi: w, Mar 27,1847; Jly 28,1848. d, Aug 27,
        1846; Apr 21,1847; 1863-1864 scattered. Film,
        Aug 17,1846-Apr 6,1849. Under Daily Morning
        Union MoSHi has Aug 29,1850; Sep 12,1851.
        Union List says formed by union of Daily Morn-
        ing Missourian and Missouri Reporter. Rowell
        1884 lists a weekly trades union paper, founded
        1881.
    MWA: d, Dec 12,1846; Nov 22,1852; May 9,
        1848; Apr 24,1852.
    DLC: w, Apr 19,1850; Oct 1,1852; Feb 18,1853.
        TW, 1847. D, film, Aug 17,1846-Aug 6,1849.
    KHi: d, Film, Aug 17,1846-Apr 6,1849.
    IHi: May 18,1849.
    IaHi: Film, Oct 24,1846-1849.
    NHi: Feb 13, Apr 14,1883.
    WHi: d, Film, Aug 17-Oct 26,1846; scattered issues
        for 1846,1847; Jan 10,1848; May 21,1850.

Union Labor Advocate   1934-?
    MoHi: Jan 18,1946.
    MoSHi: Film, 1955-1956. Some for 1934,1935;
        1936+?

University City Tribune   bw   1939?-1956?
    Noted in Ayer 1955-1957.

Unser Blatt   w   1872
    MoSHi: Complete set.

Unsere Zeit   tw,d   Nov 1850-Mar 1851
    Noted in G-AN&P.

Unterhaltungsblatter   1854
    Noted in G-AN&P.

Valley Farmer   w   1856?
    In Newspaper Record 1856.

Vanguard   w,sm   1881-1913?
    KHi: w, Jan 1889. Early weekly prohibition
        paper, later semi-monthly radical holiness.

Vehme (Die)   w   1869-1870
    MoHi: Nov 20,1869; Apr 2,16,1870.
    MoS: Nos 1-52. German.

Verein Deutscher Arzte   1916-1918
    Noted in G-AN&P.

Videke   bw   1912+
    Hungarian.

Volksanwalt (Der)   1902-1903
    In G-AN&P. Published by Arbeiter Zeitung.

Volksblatt   d   1855-1857,1875
    MoSCHi: Scattered issues. 1875 edition survived
        five weeks.

Volksstimme des Westens   d   1877-1880
w   1878-1880
    MoS: Complete set daily editions.
    MoSCHi: Scattered issues. Apparently Sunday
        edition 1877-1880.

Volkstribune (Die)   d   1861?
    Noted in G-AN&P.

Volkszeitung (Tagliche)   d   1865-1869?
1898-1902?
    MoSHi: Sep 26,1869.
    WHi: Mar 21-Jly 13,1866. German. In Rowell
        1869. Evening Volks-Zeitung noted in Ayer
        1900, founded 1898.

Vorsteher (Der)   1907-1913
    Noted in G-AN&P.

Vorwarts   w   1845-1846?
    Noted in G-AN&P.

Vox Populi   w   1894
    Populist. In Missouri Editor, Jun 1894.

Wage (Die)   w   1844
    MoSHi: May 30,1844. Weekly campaign paper,
        May-Jun 1844.

Wahre Republikaner (Der)   w   1870
    Weekly campaign paper.

Wahrheit (Die)   w   1871
    MoS: Complete set, Jan 6-Jun 30,1871.
    MoSHi: Complete set. Jewish weekly, in German.

War Bulletin
    MoSHi: Jly 23, Aug 6,8,1861.

Washingtonian   w   1842
    MWA: Jly 16,1842.

Watchman   w   1887?-?
    MoHi: Film, Sep 6,1903-1904. Sunday edition of
        Western Watchman.
    KHi: Feb 13,1898.

Watchman Advocate   w,d   1881?-?
    Listed in Rowell 1906 with 1881 founding.

Waterways Journal w 1887+
Inland waterway publication.

Wellston Journal w 1914+
MoS: 1950+.

West End News w
MoSHi: Nov 22,29,1905.

Western Atlas and Saturday Evening Gazette
w 1839-1842?
MoSHi: Jan 11,1840.
MoSM: Jan 16,1841-Jun 1842.
MWA: Dec 12,1840; Jan 5,19-26,1842.

Western Banner w 1858-1860?
MoS: Jan 14,Apr 21,1860.
MoSHi: Nov 27,1858.
MoSU: Oct 1858,Sep 1860.
MoScR: 1858-1859.

Western Barmah w 1861?
In American Newspaper Directory 1861.

Western Celt w 1870-1874?
Rowell 1872 said "Only Irish national newspaper
between New York and San Francisco."

Western Commercial Gazette w 1869-1871?
MoHi: Sep 9,1869.
MoSHi: Mar 16,1871.

Western Emigrant w 1817-1818
See Emigrant. In Union List as name used for
Enquirer, May 17,1817-Aug 1818.

Western Home Press w 1860
In Union List. DLC has 1860 copies.

Western Journal w 1815-1817
Followed by Western Emigrant, Enquirer.

Western Junior w ?
MoHi: Jan 29,1903-1904.

Western Stage d ?
MoHi: Nov 15,1869; Mar 21,1870.

Western Trade Journal w ?
MoHi: Jun 8,1882.

Western Watchman w 1849?-1933
MoHi: Sunday, film, Sep 6,1903-1904. W,
1902-Nov 30,1933; Mar 22,Sep 20,Dec 20,
1849; Mar 21,28,May 9,23, Jun 6,13,27,
Jly 4,11,25,Aug 1,8,1850; May 1,1851;
Mar 31,1853; Jly 13,1854; Jun 4,Nov 26,
1857; Dec 9,1858; Jly 21,Jun 16,1859.
MoSM: w,Nov-Dec 1846; 1847-1849; 1851-
1859.
MoSU: film,Sep 1869-1875; 1882; 1885-1886.

Western Watchman (continued)
MoSHi: w,1875-Mar 4,1876; Apr 1-Dec 30,1876;
Jan 13-Dec 29,1883; 1884; Jan 3-Sep 26,
1885; 1886; Jan 15-Feb 12,26,Mar 12,19,
Apr 2,1887; 1888; Dec 16,1915; Jan 17,
1919; Jun 1,1923. Sunday,1889-1890; 1908-
1909 inc; 1911; 1915-1933; Oct 21,1915-Sep
1923; Jly 4,1924.
Kenrick Seminary: film, 1875-1933 inc.
ICHi: Aug 12,1876.
IHi: Jun 23,1859.
KHi: Nov 27,1851.
WHi: Oct 12-19,1854.
American Newspaper Directory 1861 lists w,
as does Newspaper Record 1856. Organ traces
it to Edina Knox County Gazette which became
Missouri Watchman, Democratic-Catholic, in
1866 and in 1869 moved to St. Louis as
Western Watchman. Various founding dates
listed.

Westliche Blatter w 1835-1860? later?
MoS: Jly 24,1864-Jun 5,1898.
MoSHi: Dec 2,1860.
G-AN&P lists from 1859-1912? as Sunday ed
of Abend-Anzeiger.

Westliche Post d 1857-1938 w 1858-1898?
MoHi: d,Jly 1,1914-1920. Under Westliche
Post and Mississippi Blatter: Jun 16, 1869;
May 24,Aug 2,Oct 17,Dec 6,27,1874; Feb
27,28,Mar 1,2,12,13,16-20,23,30,31,Apr
1-4,13-17,19-24,26-30,May 1-8,10-14,18,
27,Jun 6,20,Sep 12,Oct 3,24,1875; Dec 31,
1876; Jan 1,Feb 4,18,25,Mar 24,Apr 25,May
13,Jly 1,22,Aug 12,19,26,Sep 2-30,Oct 7-
9,14-28,Nov 4,11,15,18,20,25,Dec 1877;
Jan 6,13,17,20,27,29,Feb 3,5,6,8,10,12,
14,16,17,24,Mar 3,10,17,24,31,Apr 7,21,
28,May 5,12,19,23,26,Jun 2,9,16,30,Jly
14,20,Aug 1,4,13,16,20,22,24,Sep 12,16,
17,19,20,21,23,Oct 20,27,30,Nov 24,Dec
3,8,12,18,27,1878; Jan 12,18,Feb 7,9,16,
Mar 30,May 18,Jun 1,22,Jly 7,26,28,Aug 6,
9,26,31,Oct 12,23,Nov 23,Dec 28,1879;
Jan 7,11,14,Feb 1,11,15,Mar 21,28,Apr 4,
11,May 13,30,Jun 6,9,11,13,28,Jly 12,18,
Aug 1,8,13,15,19,22,29,Sep 4,5,7,8,12,
15,20,Oct 2,3,5-7,13-19,25,29,31,Nov
1-4,6,12-16,18-25,27,29,30,Dec 1,2,4,5,
7-9,19,31,1880; Jan 14,17,19-21,30,Feb
2,19,Mar 4-6,8,11-13,21,22,26,27,Apr 2,
4,10,24,May 11,15,22-24,29,Jun 17,19,24,
26,29,30,Jly 2-16,18-29,Aug 1,6,14,17,21,
Sep 4,11,Oct 19,22-24,26,30,Nov 20,23,24,
27,29,Dec 1,2,4-7,9,11,1881; Jan 1,Feb 3,
May 4,9,16,18,21,28,Jun 1,7,9,11,Jly 31,
Aug 10-12,16,17,23,24,Sep 2,4,5,8,12,25,
Oct 7,1882; Feb 11,21,22,Mar 1,18,25,29,
Apr 13-16,18,19,23,May 4,6,13,19,24,26,
Jun 6,24,Jly 1,2,22,Sep 11,19,21,27,28,
Oct 1,3,8,10,13,14,20,21,23,24,Dec 13,

Westliche Post (continued)
    22,23,25,30,31,1883; Jan 1,2,5,1884; Feb
    22,26,27,Mar 3,Apr 3,4,6,8,10,18-20,22,
    26-30,May 1-5,8-12,15,17,19-20,22-25,
    28-31, Jun 3-6,8, 12-16,24, 28-30, Jly 2,4-
    10,13,15,Aug 14,Sep 15,Oct 4-13,Dec 16,
    1885; Feb 8,1891; Mar 26,1899; Jan 17,25,
    1906; Sep 26-28,Dec 18-20,22,1905.
    MoS: d,Sep 27,1857-1859; Sep 18,Dec 13,1860;
        Dec 1898-1939.
    MoSHi: d,Oct 26,1861; Sep 20,1881; Jan 30,
        1899; Feb 26,Apr 24,1900; Dec 13,1915; Jan
        1,1918. W,d 1856 on fairly complete to last
        issue Sep 11,1938. Sunday, 1858-1863 mostly
        complete; 1866-1870; Apr 2,1871; Mar 9,
        Oct 5,1873.
    ICHi: w, Jly 12,1876. D,Oct 5,1876.
    KHi: d,Aug 24,1888.
    MnHi: Mar 13,1932.
    NHi: Mar 5,May 2,Oct 9,1873.

West St. Louis w 1895-1896?
    In Ayer 1896-1897.

Wetmore's Weekly w 1904-1905?
    KHi: Aug 17,1904-Oct 19,1905.

Wheel w 1896
    Start noted in Missouri Editor, Jun 1896.

Windmuhle (Die) w 1868
    German humorous weekly in G-AN&P.

Woche w 1891-1895?
    Mentioned in Dauchy 1896.

Wolfs-Augen w 1900
    Noted in G-AN&P.

Women's National Daily d 1906-1911
w 1911-1916
    MoHi: d,Dec 2,1908-Mar 16,1911. W,Apr 1,
        1911-May 1915.
    MoSHi: Jun 6,8,1908.
    KHi: d,Oct 20,1907. W,Sep 20,Nov 22,1913;
        Mar 20,1915.
    LNT-MA: Jun 11,1908.
    MnHi: d,Feb 26,Mar 10,26,30,1910. W,Apr 15,
        1911-May 6,1916. Renamed Women's National
        Weekly Apr 1911.

Word and Works m 1888-?
    MoHi: Film,1899-1903.
    KHi: Jun 1888-Aug 1889 inc.

World d 1902-1918
    MoHi: 1903; May 15,18,Jun 26,1903; Nov 8,
        Dec 3,5,9,15,1904. Film,1904.
    MoSHi: Mar 3,1918.
    MoSL: Jun 1902-Sep 1906.

World Blind
    MoSHi: Sep 1916.

Zeitung sw 1848
    Noted in G-AN&P,published Jun 10-Oct 25,
    1848.

Zeuge der Wahrheit 1904-1909?
    MoSCHi: Complete file.

(NOTE: KHi, Topeka, has many other copies of
specialized Missouri publications.)

ST. MARYS (Ste. Genevieve County)

Progress w 1893-1898?
    Last listed in Rowell 1898.

Review w 1907+
    MoHi: Sep 26,1935-1944. Film,1945+.
    MoSHi: Nov 16,1933; Sep 13,Oct 25,1934;
        Oct 1,Feb 6,1936; Feb 25-Mar 18,Apr 1-
        29,May 13-Jly 15,Jly 29-Aug 19,Sep 2-
        Dec 30,1937; 1938-1942 inc.

Times w 1903-1905?
    In Rowell 1904, Ayer 1904,1906.

ST. THOMAS (Cole County)

Saturday Morning Visitor w
    MoHi: Nov 13,1858-Jan 14,1860. See Waverly.

SALEM (Dent County)

American Eagle w 1893
    Listed in Rowell 1894.

Democrat w 1880-1884 w 1902-1907?
    Also as Dent County Democrat. Hammond says
    first Democrat renamed News about 1884 and
    Mountain Howitzer 1886. Rowell 1902 lists
    second Democrat.

Democrat-Bulletin w 1899-1931
    MoHi: W,Apr 1930-Oct 28,1931; 1908. Film,
    1902-1911. Suspended 1912-Mar 1930.
    Ceased Oct 28,1931,sold to Post.

Democratic Bulletin w 1899-1904
    Apparently name used several years for Democrat-
    Bulletin.

Dent County Courant w 1891
    Listed in Ayer-Rowell 1892.

Dent County Post w 1912-1916
    MoHi: Oct 3,1912-May 4,1916. Renamed Post
    May 11,1916.

Headlight w 1895
    Listed in Dauchy 1896.

SALEM (continued)

Herald   w   1891-1894
    Same publisher as Dent County Courant.
    Missouri Editor, Jan 1895, reports "Herald is dead."

Leader   w,sm   1886-1906?
    Listed as sm in Rowell 1891.

Monitor   w   1868-1920?
    MoHi: 1911-1920; Jly 9,1903. Film,May 4,
        1872; Mar 8,1873; Apr 12,1873-1876; 1881-
        1889; 1901-1910.
    ICHi: May 18, Jly 6,1876.

Mountain Howitzer   w   1886-1889?
    In Rowell 1886-1889, Ayer 1886-1887.

News   w   1896+   w   1880-1885
    MoHi: Aug 12,1909-Jly 13,1911; Jun 1918-1944.
        Film,1945+. Rowell 1885-1886 lists earlier
        News.
    KHi: Nov 4,1926.

Post   w   1912+
    MoHi: May 11,1916-Oct 28,1931. Merged with
        Democrat-Bulletin Nov 5,1931 as Post and
        Democrat-Bulletin.

Post and The Democrat-Bulletin   w   1912+
    MoHi: Nov 5,1931-1944. Film,1945+. See Post.

Republican   w   1884,1895-1918
    MoHi: Oct 27,1880; Jun 1,1906-May 1918; Apr
        17,1908; Mar 5,1909. See Republican-Head-
        light. Hammond says a campaign paper under
        this title appeared in 1884.

Republican-Headlight   w   1895-1906
    MoHi: Jan 6,1905-1906. Became Republican
        Jun 1,1906.

Southern Missouri Argus   w   1860-1861
    MoHi: Jun 30,1860. To Farmington 1861.

Spirit   w   1878
    Listed in Rowell 1879.

Western Weekly Success   w   1873-1876
    ICHi: Feb 2,1876. Also in Rowell as Western
        Success.

SALISBURY (Chariton County)

Bulletin   w   1869
    MoHi: Mar 4-Dec 30,1869.

Chariton County Democrat   w   1883?-1890?
    MoHi: Oct 24,1890. Also as Democrat. Founding
        dates include 1881,1882.

Charitonian   w   1883?-1900
    Listed in Rowell-Ayer 1901.

SALISBURY (continued)

Chariton Courier   w   ?-1953
    Sale announced MPN, Feb 1953. Courier then said
        to be 84 years old. Purchaser had started Chariton
        Shopper about 1951. Not in Ayer.

Democrat   w   1883-1917
    MoHi: Jan 9,1903-1917;   Sep 22,29,
        Oct 20,Nov 24,1905. Film,1913-1915.
    MoSHi: Dec 4,1908. Sold to Press-Spectator Dec
        1917.

Enterprise   w   1890
    "Unsectarian" paper,Rowell 1891.

Journal   sm   1887
    In Ayer 1888.

Press   w   1870-1881
    MoHi: Film,Dec 1877-Dec 10,1879; 1880-Jly
        7,1881.
    MoSHi: Jan 15,1875.
    ICHi: Jan 21, Jly 7,1876. Merged with Spectator
        Jly 15,1881.

Press-Spectator   w   1869+
    MoHi: 1911-1944; Dec 23,1892. Film, Jly 15,
        1881-1887; Jan 13,1888-Feb 28,1890; Mar
        14,1890-1910; 1945+. See Press.
    MoSHi: Dec 4,1908.
    KHi: Jun 8,1888.

Spectator   w   1880-1881
    Consolidated with Press.

SANTA FE (Monroe County)

Advertiser   w   1897-1899
    In Ayer 1900.

Herald   w   1894
    Missouri Editor, Apr 1894,tells of start.

Progress   w   1916-1917
    In Ayer 1917-1918.

Record   w   1906
    In Rowell 1907.

SARATOGA (McDonald County)

Sentinel   w   1883
    In Rowell 1884.

SARATOGA SPRINGS (McDonald County)

Eagle   w   1882
    In Ayer 1882.

SARCOXIE (Jasper County)

American-Tribune   w   1893-1902
    MoHi: Film, Jly 12, 1901-Dec 12, 1902. Formerly
    Tribune to Jly 12, 1901. Renamed Tribune Dec
    19, 1902.

Argus   w   1877
    In Rowell 1878.

Democrat   w   1875
    Listed in Rowell 1875.

Farm Record   w   1890-1901?
    In Ayer 1902 under this title. See Record, same
    publisher, Bernard Finn.

Leader   w   1893-1908
    MoHi: Dec 27, 1907; Jan 3-31, Feb 14-28, 1908.
    Film, Feb 13, 1903-Dec 20, 1907. Formerly
    Tribune.

Quid Nunc   w   1881
    In Ayer 1881. Succeeded by Vindicator.

Record   w   1901+
    MoHi: Oct 30, 1903-1905; 1914-1944. Film,
    1945+.

Siftings   w   1893?-1900?   sw   1894
    Missouri Editor, Feb 1894, tells of sw issues. Dir-
    ectories vary on founding, 1882, 1883, 1881. No
    listings before 1894.

Tri-County Republican   w   1891-1892
    Also referred to as Republican.

Sun   w   1888-1891
    In Rowell 1889-1892, Ayer 1888-1891.

Tribune   w   1893-1903
    MoHi: Film, Dec 1, 1898-Jly 5, 1901; Dec 19, 1902-
    Feb 6, 1903. See American-Tribune.

Vindicator   w   1881-1891?
    MoHi: Oct 23, 1890. In Rowell 1882-1893, Ayer
    1882, 1889.

SAVANNAH (Andrew County)

American Eagle   w   1857
    Anti-Benton paper, according to Organ.

Andrew County Advance   w   1876-1879
    Listed in Rowell 1877-1879.

Andrew County Advocate   w   1877
    Mentioned by Hammond.

Andrew County Democrat   w   1876-1925
    MoHi: Jan 21, 1921-Sep 18, 1925. Formerly
    Democrat. Merged with Reporter Sep 25, 1925.

Andrew County Herald   w   1899-1900
    In Rowell 1900-1901, Ayer 1900.

SAVANNAH (continued)

Andrew County New Era   w   1864-1872
    Listed in Rowell 1871-1872.

Andrew County Reporter   w   1876-1908?
    See Reporter.

Andrew County Republican   w   1871-1876, 1890-1913
    MoHi: Feb-Dec 1876; 1905-Aug 1913; Jan 31,
    1896. Film, Nov 1, 1871-1875.
    ICHi: Jly 6, Aug 10, 1876.

Andrew County Union   w   1868
    Campaign paper, Hammond notes.

Courier   w   1868
    In Rowell 1869.

Democrat   w   1876-1921
    MoHi: Nov 25, 1898-1910; 1912-Jan 14, 1921;
    Oct 24, 1890; Sep 22, 1905. Film, Apr 2-Dec
    1880; Feb 11, 1881-Dec 22, 1882; 1883;
    1883-Mar 23, 1888; Aug-Dec 1889; 1890-
    Jly 24, 1891; Jly 29, 1892-Jly 20, 1894; Aug
    10, 1894-Jly 14, 1899. Became Andrew
    County Democrat Jan 1921.

Family Intelligencer   w   1856
    Follows Sentinel. Later Northwest Democrat.

Missouri Plaindealer   w   1860-1861, 1864
    MoHi: Apr 2, 1864. Anti-slavery paper seized
    1861, press-type molded into bullets.

Monitor   w   1891
    Farm and Labor Union, in Ayer 1891.

New Era   w   1864-1870
    MoHi: May 19, 1870.

News   w   1934
    MPN, Nov 1934, tells of start.

Northwest Democrat   w   1854-1857
    MoHi: Film, Jly 12, 1856-Jly 4, 1857.
    KHi: Film, Jly 12, 1856-Jly 4, 1857.
    NbHi: Film, Jly 12, 1856-Jly 4, 1857.

Patron of Husbandry   w   1874-1876
    ICHi: Feb 17, 1876. In Rowell 1875-1876.

Register   w   1882
    O.E. Taul press association member 1882.

Reporter   w   1876-1925
    MoHi: Jly 26, 1901-1906; 1909-Sep 25, 1925;
    Oct 24, 1890; Nov 4, 1904. Film, Apr 28, 1876-
    Apr 11, 1879; Apr 22, 1881-Dec 24, 1882; Jly
    1882-1889; Oct 1890-1891; May 1893-1902;
    1907-1908. Merged with Andrew County
    Democrat Sep 25, 1925.

SAVANNAH (continued)

Reporter and Andrew County Democrat   w   1876+
    MoHi: Sep 25,1925-1944. Film,.1945+. Formed
    by merger 1925.

Republican   w   1890-?
    Under this title in Ayer 1900, Dauchy 1896.
    See Andrew County Republican.

Saturday Democrat   w   1880
    In Ayer 1880.

Sentinel   w   1851-1856?
    MoHi: Film, Nov 1,1851-Oct 23,1852.
    MoSHi: Nov 1,15,22, Dec 6,20,1851; Jan 3,
    17,24, Dec 6,20,1852; Apr 9, May 21, Jun
    11,25, Jly 2,9,30, Aug 6,20,1853.
    DLC: Jan 10,1852.
    KHi: Film, Nov 1,1851-Oct 23,1852.

Tribune   w   1870
    MoHi: May 28,1870.

Union   w   1868
    MoSHi: Sep 5,1868.

Western Eagle   w   1849-1856?
    Hammond says followed by Family Intelligencer.

Western Empire   w   1845-1846,1847,1849
    All brief, according to Organ.

Wind Mill   w   1883-1884?
    In Rowell-Dauchy 1884.

SCHELL CITY (Vernon County)

Ledger   w   1947+
    First in Ayer 1948.

News   w   1880-1945
    MoHi: Oct 30,1890; Nov 17, Jly 10,1904.
        Sold to Nevada Mail and Herald 1945.
    KHi: Apr 13, May 4,1922; Oct 4,1923.

Times   w   1879
    In Ayer 1880.

Union Star   w   1881?
    In Ayer 1882, no data.

SCHLEY (Nodaway County)

New Conception Herald   w   1900-1904
    In Rowell 1902-1905.

SEDALIA (Pettis County)

An Easter Greeting   ?
    MoHi: Apr 1898.

SEDALIA (continued)

Advertiser   w   1864-1865,1877
    MoHi: Nov 15,1877.
    MoSe: Aug 20-Dec 1864. First closed after raid,
    sold, renamed Times.

Adviser   m   ?
    MoHi: Jun 1869. Real estate paper.

Advocate   w   1879-1880? 1891
    MoHi: Jan 24-Mar 7,1891. J.N.Pierce repre-
    sented paper at 1879-1880 press meetings.

A Flash O'Lightning   bi-m   1897
    Mentioned in Country Editor, Jun 1897, as
    starting. "So called because it is to appear at
    uncertain times." Two issues?

Bazoo   w   1869-1904?   d   1869-1895?
    MoHi: d, Sep 20,1869-Mar 16,1870; Jly 1873-
    Jun 1874; 1875; 1877-Jun 1880; Oct 12,
    1869. Film, Jly 1880-Jun 1887; Jan-Jun, Aug
    1888; 1889-Aug 11,1893; Nov 20-Dec 1893.
    Sunday, Aug 20,1876; Jan 5,1890; Aug 6,
    1893; Feb 17, Mar 17,1895. Film, Mar 16,1873-
    Mar 14,1875; Mar 18,1877-Mar 9,1879; May
    1879-Jly 1881; 1883-1885; 1889-1893; Jly 7,
    1895-Jun 16,1896. W, Jun 15,1869; Jly 12,
    1884; Oct 13, Mar 16, Apr 20, May 4,1886;
    Feb 21,1895; Jly 4,1893; Feb 12,1901; Jly
    19,1904. Film, Jun 1877-1887; 1889-1893.
    MoSe: w, May 30,1871-Mar 27,1873; Jly-Dec
    1873; 1874; 1875-1895 inc. D, Sep 20,1870-
    Jun 1872; Jan-Jun 1873.
    MoSHi: d, May 11,18,1879.
    ICHi: d, Mar 10,26,1876.
    KHi: w, Oct 2,1888. D, Dec 16,1888; Jan 21,27,
    1889.
    MnHi: d, Mar 2,1872.
    NHi: May 14,1874. Suspended Aug 12-Nov 19,
    1893. Later m.

Blue Ribbon   w   1877
    MoSe: Aug 15, Oct 6,1877.

Bulletin   w   1885
    MoHi: Oct 31, Nov 7,21,28, Dec 19,1885.

Capital   w   1889-1920?   d   1895+
    MoHi: d,1911-1921; Sep 1932-1949; Aug 15,
    1900; Dec 19,1901; Aug 13,1905; May 31,
    1908; Feb 23,1909. Film, May 1890-1897;
    Feb-Dec 1898; Jan-Mar, May-Sep, Nov-Dec
    1899; 1900; Feb 1901-1910; 1922-Aug 1932;
    1951+.
    KHi: d, Jly 30,1921; Jan 16,1924.
    MoSe: May 2,1895-Apr 30,1905.
    Micro-Photo: Film,1922-1932. Capital and
    Democrat merged 1907. Paper uses 1886
    founding date.

Central Missouri Sentinel   w   1886-1891
MoHi: Dec 22, 1888; Jan 9, 1889; Nov 1, 1890;
Jan 17, 24, Mar 14, 1891. Film, Nov 20, 1886-
Feb 2, 1889. Listed as w edition Evening
Sentinel. See Enterprise-Sentinel.

Conservator   w   1903-1909
MoHi: Jan 6-27, Feb 17-Mar 10, 24, Jly 21, Aug
4, Dec 24, 1906; Jan 7-28, Feb 11-Mar 4, 18-
May 13, 25-Jly 15, 19-Aug 5, 26, Dec 9-23,
1907; Jan 6, 20, 27, Feb 10-Mar 9, 23, Apr 5-
20, May 11-Jun 15, 29-Aug 31, Sep 14, 21,
1908. Film, May 8, 1903-Dec 23, 1905.

Democrat   w, d   1868+
MoHi: d, Jly-Dec 20, 1872; May-Jun 1883; Jan-
Feb 23, 1924; Feb 23, 1925-1950; May 24,
1873; Jun 3, 1874; Oct 3, 1875; Mar 2, May
26, 31, Sep 6-8, 16, 1876; Dec 26, 1880; Mar
28, 1881; Apr 4, Aug 29, 1882; Apr 12, May
1883; Dec 9, 1884; Jan 13, Sep 6, 11, 1885;
Oct 3, 1886; Jan 29, 1888. Film, Dec 19,
1871-May 1872; Dec 21, 1872-Dec 18, 1874;
Jan 26, 1875-Apr 28, 1883; Jly 1883-1885;
Jly 1886-Jun 1887; Apr-Jun 1888; Dec 1891-
Dec 27, 1923; Feb 24, 1924-Feb 22, 1925;
1951-1953; Sep 1-Oct 15, 1954; 1955+
Sunday, Feb 1881-1882; Feb 14, 28, 1897; Nov
6, Jly 24, 1904. Film, Jly 1884-1885. W, 1872-
Jan 1878; 1882; Jun 20, 1878; Feb 24, Mar 2-
May 24, Jun 9, Oct 6, 17, Nov 3, 1893. Film,
Mar 16, 1869-1878; 1882; 1892. Evening
Democrat, Feb 24, 29, 1892; Jan 25, Feb
12, Mar 26, Apr 13, 19, Sep 26, 1893; Aug 13,
Dec 5, 1894; Feb 7, May 14, Dec 5, 8, 1895;
Apr 15, 17, 30, 1896; Feb 3, 5, 8, 1897; Aug
21, 1900; Jun 17, 1901. Film, Dec 1891-1906.
MoSe: d, film, Dec 18, 1871-Apr 28, 1883; Dec 18,
1891+. Evening Democrat, Dec 19, 1871-Apr
30, 1901. W, 1870-1871; 1876-1884; 1886.
MoSHi: d, Mar 1, 1878.
ICHi: Jly 20, Oct 10, 1876.
Micro-Photo: Film, 1871-1883; 1912+. Under
Evening Democrat, 1891-1906.

Democrat-Capital   (Sunday)
See Democrat, Capital. Combined name used
for Sunday edition.

Democrat-Sentinel   w   1881-1911   d   1891-1911
MoHi: Film, 1907-1911.
MoSe: May 1, 1901-1906; Feb-Dec 1907; 1908;
Jan-Jly, Oct-Nov 1909; Jan-Jun, Oct-Dec
1910; Jan-Mar, Oct-Dec 1911.
Micro-Photo: Film, 1907-1911.

Democratic-Press   w   1867-1868
MoHi: Film, Feb 7-Dec 17, 1868. Name used
for Democrat briefly.

Dispatch   d   1882
In Rowell 1883.

District Advocate   w   1876-?
MoHi: Sep 1, 1880. Religious emphasis.

Druggist   m   ?
MoHi: Oct 1900. Free paper by drug firm.

Eagle   w   1878-1881
MoHi: Nov 14, 1880; Feb 13, 20, 1881 as Sunday
Morning Eagle. W, Aug 2, 1878-Jly 25, 1879;
Feb 27, Mar 9, Nov 14, 1881.
MoSe: 1879. Formerly Boonville Eagle; con-
solidated with Times Jan 18, 1881. Eagle-
Times sold to New Age 1883.

Eagle-Times   w   1878-1883   d   1881-1882
MoSe: Feb 22, 1882. See Eagle.

Earth   w   1885-1887
MoHi: Dec 19, 1885; Mar 27, Apr 3, 10, 24, May
1-15, Jun 26, Dec 18, 1886.

Enterprise-Sentinel   w, sw   1893-1895
MoHi: May 19, Jun 2, 9, 23, 30, Jly 14, Sep 15, 22,
30, Oct 8, 14, 21, 28, Nov 4, 10, 1893; Jun 16,
Sep 29, 1894; May 11, Oct 12, 1895.

Enterprising Merchant   m   ?
MoHi: Dec 1888.

Free Press   w   1877-1878, 1895
MoHi: Mar 2, 30, Apr 6, 1895.
MoSe: Mar 23, Jun 8, 1877.

Gazette   d   1888-1895   tw   1888-1889?
MoHi: d, Dec 1888-Sep 1890; Jly 24, 28, 1889;
Sep 6, Dec 6, 1891; Jan 3, Mar 20, May 8, 11,
1892; Feb 28, May 28, Aug 20, Sep 3, 30, 1893;
Jun 14, 1894; Jun 21, 1895. Film, Oct 1890-
Mar 1894; Jly 1894-Aug 1895. TW, film, Dec
16, 1888-May 31, 1889.
MoSe: 1888; Jan-Jun 1889; 1890; Jan-Mar
1891; 1892-1895. Merged with Daily Capital.

Grange and Labor Union   w   1885-1886
In Ayer 1887.

Herald   m   1892-?
MoHi: Jly 1892 first issue. Real estate firm.
Noted there were then 3 dailies, 10 weeklies
in Sedalia.

Humorist   w   1892

Independent   w   1882

Independent Press   w   1866-1868
MoHi: Mar 31, Apr 12, Jly 19, 1866; Jan 10, Mar
28, Apr 4, May 30, Sep 19, 1867.

International   w   1890?-1896
MoHi: May 2, 1896. In Dauchy 1896 with 1890
founding date.

Journal   w   1877-1917
MoHi: 1899-1906; 1909-May 10,1917. Film,
May 11,1887-May 3,1899; May 9,1906-
May 8,1907. German.
KHi: Sep 25,1888.

Labor Union   w   1885-1887?
MoHi: Jan 8,1887.

Leader   w   1914-1924?
Labor paper, in Ayer 1917-1925.

Liberator   w   1910-1914
MoHi: 1913-Aug 1914; Apr 8,22,1911. Film,
Aug 27,1910-Aug 1912; 1913-1914. Became
Railway Federationist Aug 29,1914.

Liberty Bell   w   1894-1896?
In Rowell 1895-1896.

Light of Life   w   1888?
MoHi: Aug,Sep 1888.

Missouri Dry   bm   1916?
MoHi: Jan 1,Feb-Apr, Jun-Aug 1,Sep-Nov 1,
Dec 1,1916.

Missouri Monarch   m   1885

Missouri Transcript   sw   1884
In Rowell 1885.

New Age   w   1882-1883
Temperance; also named Missouri New Age.

News   d   1880-1881,1885
MoHi: Feb 18,Mar 30,Apr 7,17,23,27,May 11,
24,25,27,Jly 15,Aug 30,1880. Rowell 1881
lists w, called Saturday Evening News. Another
Evening News began 1885.

Now and Then   w   1887-?
MoHi: Sep 28,1887. Devoted to Sedalia, past
and present.

Onward Republican   d   1888
MoHi: May 14,1888.

Opera Glass   w   1881

Opinion   w   1872-1876
ICHi: May 5, Jly 7,1876. In Rowell 1873-1876.

Pacific Enterprise   w   1863-1864
Brief life. Moved to Warrensburg.

Penny Earth   w   1900
MoHi: Jan 7,1900. "Original literary, society,
and family paper."

Pettis County Missouri   ?
MoHi: copy,no date, probably 1909.

Pettis County News   w   1885
First issue Jun 20,1885.

Play Bill   w   1869?
MoHi: Jun 5,1869. Theater paper.

Press   w   1867
MoHi: Oct 4,1867.

Pythian Banner   w   1883-1884?
MoHi: Dec 12,1883; Jan 2,16,Feb 13,27,Apr
30,1884.

Railway Federationist   w   1914-?
MoHi: Aug 29,1914-Oct 1923. See Liberator.

Register   m   1878-?
MoHi: Dec 1880; Jan-Jun,Aug,Oct,Dec 1883;
Jan-May,Sep 1884.

Republican   d   1870, 1884-1885,1925
MoHi: Oct 14,1870; Aug 25,30,Sep 1,3-6,
8-13,16-18,20,22-29,Oct 1-4,6,7,30,
Nov 18,1884. Evening, May 9,1884.
MoSe: Aug 25,1884-May 1885.
Rowell 1885 lists both d,w. E&P, Jun 27,
1925, tells of start of Republican.

Review and Plain Talk   m   1898
First issue May 1898.

Rosa Pearle's Paper   w   1894-1910?
Society publication.

Saturday Evening Call   w   1879-1881
MoHi: Jan 24,1880; May 7,1881. Greenback,
in Ayer 1881,Rowell 1882.

Seminary Observer   m   1887-1888?
MoHi: Apr 1887; Mar,May 1888.

Sentinel   d   1895-1906   w,sw   1886-1906
MoHi: d, Evening Sentinel,Feb 17,Dec 2,1897;
Jly 14,1898; Aug 14,1900; May 1,21,26,Jun
28,1901. Film,Feb-Apr 7,1890; Jun 5-Aug
1896; Jun 1897-1906. As Sentinel, Jun,Nov
1886; Dec 31,1906. Merged with Morning
Star to become Evening Star-Sentinel. Renamed
Evening Sentinel Jun 5,1896. Founded as
Central Missouri Sentinel 1886. Earlier founding
dates in Rowell with d 1895, w 1881.
Micro-Film: Film,d, 1898-1906. W, 1898-1906.

Signal   d   1873-1874
Short-lived, noted in county history.

Social Messenger   w   1912-1918
In Union List.

Star   d   1895
MoHi: Film,Nov-Dec 1895. Morning paper merged
with Evening Sentinel.

SEDALIA (continued)

Star-Sentinel   d   1896
  MoHi: May 27, 1896. Film, Jan-Jun 3, 1896.
  Apparently name used Jan-Jun 1896. W
  Enterprise-Sentinel in Rowell 1896.

Sun   w   1880?-1885?
  In Rowell-Ayer 1882.

Theatre News   w   1909?
  MoHi: May 1, 1909.

Times   d   1872-1881, 1936-1944   w   1872-1881,
1894-1905, 1865-1881, 1957-1962
  MoHi: d, Nov 1, 1872-Apr 30, 1873; May 1-3, 1873;
  Apr 3, 1875; Nov 7, 1881. W, Jan 21, Feb 4, 1905.
  Film, Aug 31, 1901-Dec 19, 1903; Jan 21-Feb 4,
  1905. W, Oct 8, 1937-May 16, 1941; Jly 18, 1941-
  Feb 1944.
  DLC: Film, Aug 31, 1901-Dec 19, 1903; Jan 21-Feb
  4, 1905.
  ICHi: w, Jly 27, 1876.
  WHi: w, Nov 24, 1865. Film, Aug 31, 1901-Dec 19,
  1903. Nameplate for Daily Times of Nov 8, 1881,
  is Vol I, No 2. Merged with LaMonte Record to
  become Sedalia Times-Record May 3, 1944. Suspended Apr 6, 1962. W, founded Mar 1865, MoHi
  has Feb 9, 1866-Sep 26, 1872; 1873-Oct 14, 1880;
  Mar 31, 1865; Sep 26, 1872. First Times eventually
  merged with Eagle. Times of 1894-1905 Negro.

Times-Record   w   1944-1957
  MoHi: Mar 3-Dec 1944. Film, 1945-1957. See
  Times. Became Times Dec 6, 1957.

Trade Review   mo   1881?-1887?
  MoHi: Aug, Oct 1884; Mar-Jun, Oct-Dec 1885; Jan,
  Jly-Oct, Dec 1886; Jan-Nov 1887.

Trader   ?
  MoHi: One copy, no date, 1900 or earlier.

Tribune   w   1923-1927
  In Ayer 1924-1928.

Truth   w   1889, 1891
  MoHi: Feb 21, 1889. Ayer 1892 lists Truth.
  People's Party paper founded 1891.

University Review   ?
  MoHi: Sep 1883; Aug 1884.

Up to Date   m   1893-?
  MoHi: Apr 1893, first issue. For "Home interests,
  society, secret societies."

Western World   w   1893-1894?
  MoHi: Oct 28, Dec 2, 23, 1893; Jan 13, Feb 10,
  17, 1894.

SELIGMAN (Barry County)

Herald   w   1900
  In Rowell-Ayer 1901.

SELIGMAN (continued)

News   w   1889-1890
  Republican and temperance paper.

Outlook   w   1916
  Short-lived publication.

States Gazette   m   1924-1925
  Mostly a booster journal.

Sunbeam   w, sm, tw,   1881-1897?
  MoHi: Nov 1, 1890. Near end of career was semi-
  monthly. Briefly tw.

Times   w   1914
  In Ayer 1915.

SENATH (Dunklin County)

Dunklin County Press   w   1946+
  First listed in Ayer 1944.

Dunklin County Republican   w   1910-1937
  Known as Leader 1921. In 1937 became Dunklin
  Tribune. In Ayer 1923-1938.

Dunklin Tribune   w   1937-1938
  Moved to Kennett Aug 1938.

Leader   w   1910-1921
  See Dunklin County Republican.

Sentinel   w   1905
  Listed in Rowell 1906.

Southeast Missouri Republican   w   1910-1911
  Listed in Ayer 1912.

Star   w   1903
  Listed in Ayer 1904; Rowell 1905.

SENECA (Newton County)

Armokan   w   1937-1942?
  Started to serve 20 counties, according to MPN,
  Dec 1937. In Ayer 1940-1943.

Dispatch   w   1882-1908
  MoHi: Sep 28, 1883. See Dispatch-Hustler.

Dispatch-Hustler   w   1882-1911.
  Apparently continuation of Dispatch. In Ayer
  1910-1912.

Hustler   w   1903-1908
  MoHi: Dec 22, 1904. Film, 1907-1908. Merged
  with Dispatch.

News-Dispatch   w   1882+
  See Dispatch. First under News-Dispatch in Ayer
  1914.

Observer   w   1871
  Lasted less than year. See Rowell 1871.

SENECA (continued)

Signal w 1879-1880?
In Rowell-Ayer 1880.

SEVEN STARS SPRINGS (Barry County)

Beacon Star w 1881-1882
In Rowell 1882.

SEYMOUR (Webster County)

Advocate w 1896
Listed in Ayer 1897.

Citizen w 1907-1954
MoHi: Aug 2, 1923-1944. Film, 1945-1954. Became Webster County Citizen Apr 1, 1954.

Enterprise w 1885-1895?
MoHi: Oct 10, 1890.

Flashlight w 1894-1907?
In Rowell 1895, 1902-1908, Ayer 1905.

Herald w 1896-1900
Last listed in Rowell 1901.

Independent w 1885-1886
In Rowell 1886-1887, Ayer 1886.

Sentinel w 1898-1899 w 1904
MoHi: Film, Jan 22-Aug 26, 1904. First Sentinel
listed in Ayer 1900. Second failed to survive
for Ayer listing, although name only in
Rowell 1905.

Webster County Citizen w 1907+
MoHi: Film, Apr 1, 1954+. See Citizen.

SHEFFIELD (Jackson County)

Blue Valley Record w 1888-1890
Listed in Rowell 1889-1891.

Free Press w 1897-1899
In Rowell 1898-1899, Ayer 1899-1900.

Jackson County Advocate ?
Rowell 1890-1891 refers to Independence.

News w 1895-1896
Listed in Ayer 1897.

Times
Rowell 1890 refers to Centropolis.

SHELBINA (Shelby County)

Democrat w 1869+
MoHi: 1904-1944; Jan 23, Apr 3, May 22, Dec 18,
1878; Jan 22, Feb 19, Sep 3, 24, Oct 1, 1879;
Oct 19, 1881; Sep 20, 1882; Oct 3, 1883; Jly
29, 1903; Oct 29, 1890. Film, Apr 7, 1870-May

SHELBINA (continued)

Democrat (continued)
28, 1873; 1874-Jly 17, 1901; 1945+.
KHi: Mar 2, 1932.
ICHi: Jan 26, 1876.

Gazette w 1866-1870?
Changed to Shelby County Herald before 1871.

Index w 1881-1885?
MoHi: Nov 18, 1881; Aug 18, Sep 1, 1882; Oct
5, 12, 1883. Later part of Torchlight.

News w 1933 w 1938
MPN, Aug 1933, tells of News started. MPN, Jan
1938, tells plans for first issue of News Jan 26,
1938. Apparently short-lived.

Shelby County Herald w 1867-1870
In Rowell 1871. See Shelbyville.

Shelby County News w 1882?-1919?
Listed in Ayer 1920.

Torchlight w 1882-1922?
MoHi: 1890-1892; Aug 9, 1901-1922; Nov 7, 1890.

SHELBYVILLE (Shelby County)

Shelby County Guard w 1892-1908?
In Rowell 1893-1908, Ayer 1892-1908.

Shelby County Herald w 1870+
MoHi: 1904-1905; 1925-1944; Dec 18, 1878; Jan
22, Feb 19, Oct 1, 1879; Oct 22, 1890; Sep 14,
1955. Film, Apr 5, 1871-Jun 15, 1881; 1888-Dec
1903; 1945+.
ICHi: Aug 23, 1876.

Shelby County Times w 1883-1884?
Hammond says Hunnewell Echo, founded 1883, moved
to Shelbyville as Shelby County Times Feb 1, 1884.

Shelby County Weekly w 1861
Although its motto was "Free as the wind, pure and
firm as the voice of nature, the press should be,"
paper was closed in three months by Union Home
Guards.

Spectator w 1853-1860?
First in county. Later named Star of the Prairie,
according to Organ.

Star of the Prairie w 1860?
Mentioned by Organ.

SHELDON (Vernon County)

Democrat w 1890-1892?
Listed in Rowell, Ayer 1891-1892.

SHELDON (continued)

Enterprise w 1881-1951?
    MoHi: Aug 1901-1903; 1906-1910; 1913-1944.
    Film,1904-1905; Jan 9,1911-1912; 1945-
    Feb 27,1947; Jun 5,1947-Nov 19,1948.

Herald w 1910
    Listed in Ayer 1911.

Index w 1881
    Listed in Ayer 1882.

News w 1889-1890?
    MoHi: Oct 31,1890. In Ayer 1891.

Record w 1911-1912
    Listed in Ayer 1912-1913.

SHERIDAN (Worth County)

Advance w 1888-1922
    MoHi: 1902-Nov 2,1922; Oct 30,1890; Feb 9,
    1905. Film,Jan 13,1893-Jun 12,1901; 1905.
    Suspended Nov 2,1922.

Advance-News w 1902
    Apparently name for Advance Feb 14-Apr 11,1902.

News w 1901-1902
    In Ayer 1902. Merged with Advance Jan 1902.

Northwest Missourian w 1887?-1942
    Discontinued Jan 7,1942. MPN, Jan 1942,refers
    to it as a 50-year-old weekly. First listed Ayer
    1939, founding date 1887.

Press w 1923-1927?
    Listed in Ayer 1924-1928.

SIKESTON (Scott County)

Budget w 1898-1901?
    In Rowell 1898-1902, Ayer 1900.

Clarion w 1900-1902?
    In Rowell-Ayer 1901-1902.

Enterprise w 1884-1909
    MoHi: Film,May 4,1906-1909.

Herald w 1900-1960
    MoHi: 1920-1944. Film,1917-1919; 1945-1960.
    Ceased Jun 9,1960.

Hornet w 1908-1910
    Listed in Ayer 1909-1911.

Scott County Agricultural Wheel w 1885
    Mentioned in county history.

Scott County Democrat w 1894-1904?
    MoHi: Jan 12,1895. Star renamed Scott County
    Democrat 1894.

SIKESTON (continued)

Scott County Reflector w 1881
    In Ayer 1881. Later named Southeast Reflector,
    succeeded by Star.

Scott County Republican w 1905
    Listed in Rowell-Ayer 1906.

Siskiyou Star w 1885?-1894
    Under this title in Rowell 1894.

Southern Sun w 1954?
    MoHi: May 9,23, Jun 13,27,1954. Negro.

Standard d 1911+ sw 1911-1947
    MoHi: 1947-1950. Film,1951+. SW, Jan 9,1914-
    1944; Jan-May 30,1947. Film,1945-1946.
    Changed to d, Jun 2,1947.
    Micro-Photo: Film,1913-1922; 1956+.

Star w 1883-1893?
    See Scott County Reflector.

SILEX (Lincoln County)

Index w 1893-1943
    MoHi: 1906-1920; May 12,1921-May 6,1943.
    Film, Jly 25,1901-Mar 16,1905; Mar 23-Dec
    21,1905. Merged with Troy Free Press May 6,
    1943.

Siftings w 1892-1893
    In Rowell-Ayer 1892-1894.

SILOAM SPRINGS (Howell County)

Banner w 1892-1893
    Listed in Ayer 1894.

Optic w 1895
    Listed in Ayer 1896.

Review w 1879-1880
    Listed in Ayer 1881.

SKIDMORE (Nodaway County)

Advance w 1886?-1887?
    In Rowell-Ayer 1887,Rowell 1888.

Herald w 1894-1896
    In Rowell 1895-1897,Ayer 1895.

New Era w 1905-1915
    MoHi: Feb 16,1905-Oct 1909; 1910-1915; Oct
    28,Nov 11,18,Dec 2,9,1909. Suspended Dec
    30,1915.

News w 1895-1955?
    MoHi: 1916-1917; 1920-Mar 1927. Film,1918-
    1919. Under Burlington Junction Post Ayer
    1956. Formerly Standard.

SKIDMORE (continued)

Patriot w 1892
    Listed in Ayer 1892.

Post w 1884+
    See Burlington Junction.

Standard w 1895-1905
    MoHi: Aug 12, 1898-1904.

Village Chronicle w 1887
    Listed in Ayer 1888.

SLATER (Saline County)

Bee w 1890-1901?
    Listed in Ayer 1901-1902.

Bulletin w 1880
    Listed in Rowell-Ayer 1881.

Call d 1893-1894
    Missouri Editor, Sep 1894, tells end of daily,
    "too much for the town."

Index w 1880-1899 d 1896
    MoHi: Film, Dec 1, 1898-Dec 21, 1899.
    MoSHi: Dec 15, 1898. Missouri Editor, Oct 1896,
    tells of death of Daily Index. Also known as
    Missouri Index. May be traced to Miami Index,
    1874, which moved to Slater, later to Marshall.

Monitor w 1876-1880
    Greenback paper founded in Marshall, published
    1880 in Slater, according to Hammond.

News w 1907-1936
    MoHi: 1919-Jan 3, 1936. Film, 1913-1918.
    Became News-Rustler Jan 10, 1936.

News-Rustler w 1885+
    MoHi: Jan 10, 1936-1944. Film, 1945+.

Rustler w 1885-1936
    MoHi: 1905-1914; 1916-1935. Film, May 12, 1888-
    May 1893; Mar 1894-May 29, 1896; Jun 1896-
    1904. See News.

Saline County Index w 1880-1884?
    In Rowell 1881-1885, Ayer 1881.

Saline County Republican w 1891-1894
    Also known as Republican.

Sentinel w 1879-1880?
    In Rowell 1880.

Topics w 1894
    Start noted in Missouri Editor, Oct 1894.

Western Interest w 1882
    In Ayer 1882.

SMITHTON (Pettis County)

Review w 1872?
    MoHi: Mar 19, 1872.

Sunbeam w 1896-1907
    MoHi: Film, Jan-Oct 18, 1907.

Times w 1908-1955?
    KHi: Jan 2, 1928. Last in Ayer 1956.

SMITHVILLE (Clay County)

Democrat w 1889-1908
    Union List says name used for Democrat-Herald
    for these years.

Democrat-Herald w 1889+
    MoHi: 1914-1944. Film, 1945+. First known as
    New Era.

Herald w 1889-1908
    MoHi: Jly 1901-1903. Film, 1904-1908. Rowell
    1891 lists Farmers' Herald.

New Era w 1886-1889
    In Rowell 1890.

Star w 1899-1908
    MoHi: Film, Aug 13, 1903-Aug 15, 1907. In Rowell
    1900-1908, Ayer 1900-1909.

Times-Herald w 1889-1901
    Listed as Herald in Ayer 1902.

SOUTH GREENFIELD (Dade County)

Dade County Journal w 1891-1898?
    Rowell 1896 notes edition printed for Everton.

Pointers w 1891
    In Rowell 1892.

Rustic w 1892, 1898
    Ayer 1894 lists one, founded 1892. Rowell-Ayer
    1899 has 1898 founding.

SOUTH ST. JOSEPH (Buchanan County)

Sentinel w 1898-1899
    In Ayer 1900.

SOUTH ST. LOUIS (St. Louis County)

Carondelet Review w 1872-1877?
    Sunday, in Rowell 1875-1878.

South St. Louis County News w - +
    Free distribution

South St. Louis Progress w 1899-1900?
    MoHi: Film, May 6, 1899-May 19, 1900. Formerly
    Carondelet Progress.

SOUTHWEST CITY (McDonald County)

Boomerang w 1907-1910?
In Rowell 1908, Ayer 1908-1911.

Christian County Leader w 1901?-1907?
In Ayer 1907. Paper with same listing under
Sparta 1908.

Corner-Stone w 1886-1887
In Rowell 1888, Ayer 1887-1888.

Enterprise w 1888-1899
See Enterprise-Herald.

Enterprise-Herald w 1888-1902
In Rowell 1900-1903, Ayer 1900.

News w 1903-1907
In Rowell 1905-1908, Ayer 1904-1907.

Plain Dealer w 1900
In Ayer 1901.

Republic w 1901?+
MoHi: 1919-Aug 2, 1935. Film, Sep 4, 1903-1904;
1905-Apr 1906 inc.

Republican w 1894-1907?
In Rowell 1902-1908, Ayer 1903.

Southwest Leader w 1888-1902?
Also listed as Leader.

SPARTA (Christian County)

Christian County Leader w 1900-1907
MoHi: Film, Aug 13-Dec 31, 1903.

Herald w 1893-1894
In Ayer 1895, Dauchy 1896.

News w 1910-1922?
In Ayer 1911-1923.

Pioneer w 1889-1890
In Rowell 1890-1891.

SPICKARD (Grundy County)

Grundy County Gazette w 1887-1907, 1910-1944?
MoHi: Jly 31, 1901-Apr 25, 1907; Jly 14, 1910-
Sep 1944. Merged with Herald Apr 25, 1907;
renamed Grundy County Gazette Jly 14, 1910.

Herald w 1906-1907
Under Herald Rowell 1907, Ayer 1908.

Herald and Grundy County Gazette w 1907-1910
MoHi: Apr 25-Dec 1907; Jan-Jly 7, 1910. Film,
1908-1909.

SPICKARDSVILLE (Grundy County)
(Same as Spickard?)

Sentinel w 1891
In Ayer 1892.

Grundy County Gazette w 1887-1894
Rowell 1895 lists under Spickard.

SPLIT LOG (McDonald County)

News w 1887
In Ayer 1887.

SPRING CITY (Oregon County)

Champion w 1879
Listed by Hammond, brief career.

SPRINGFIELD (Greene County)

Advertiser w 1844-1861, 1871-1876
MoHi: May 14, 1844-Jun 22, 1847. Film, Aug 8,
1848-Jun 15, 1850; Dec 23, 1874-Oct 4, 1876.
MoSp: film & bound, May 21, 1844-Apr 29, 1845;
May 31, 1845-Jun 22, 1847; Aug 8, 1848-Jun
15, 1850; Dec 23, 1874-Oct 4, 1876.
MoSHi: Jun 12, 1860.
ICHi: w, Aug 16, 1876.
IHi: Jly 6, 1858; Aug 30, 1859.
KHi: Film, May 21, 1844-Jun 15, 1850.
MWA: Apr 2, 1861. Merged with Daily Patriot,
continued as Patriot Advertiser, Oct 11, 1876.

American w 1891, 1912-1913
Rowell 1892 lists Farmers' Alliance paper.
Second was labor paper.

American Negro w 1890
MoHi: Oct 25, 1890.
DLC: Film, Oct 25, 1890.
KHi: Film, Oct 25, 1890.

Cain's Thomas Cat w 1898-1901, 1926-1936
Two periods, both same family. In Rowell
1900-1902, Ayer 1936-1937.

Chronicle w, d 1896
In Rowell 1896, Ayer 1897.

Clarion d 1895
In Ayer 1896.

Commercial Events w 1928-1933?
Union List says followed Express. Daily Events by
same firms.

Democrat d 1890-1895
MoHi: Oct 26, 1890. Film, Sep 1890-Jly 1895.
MoSp: Film & bound, Sep 17, 1890-Mar 31, 1892;
Jly 1, 1892-Jly 6, 1895. Merged with Leader
Oct 1895.

Democratic Spotlight w 1927?
In Ayer 1935, with 1927 starting date. Same
publisher as Cain's Thomas Cat.

Equal Rights Gazette w 1860-1862
IHi: Aug 25, Sep 8, 1860; Feb 7, May 16, 1861.
KHi: Sep 21, 1861.

Events d 1928+
See Commercial Events for w. Founding date 1880
in first Ayer listing 1929.

Express w 1881-1928?
MoHi: Apr 1, 1881-Mar 9, 1894; Jly 10, 1908;
Feb 11, 1916.
MoSp: Oct 19, 1883-Feb 22, 1884; Jun 22, 1888;
Aug 10-Dec 21, 1888; Jan 11, 1889-Feb 28,
1890; Mar 16, 1894. Film & bound.

Extra d 1879-1884
Named Journal 1884, brief career.

Farm Club News w 1919-?
Death of E&P, Walter Wadsworth, reported in 1935.

Examiner w 1960
MoSp: Jun 23-Nov 20, 1960.

Gazette w 1868
In Rowell 1869. Sold to Patriot.

Greenback News w 1878-1880
In Rowell-Ayer 1880-1881.

Headlight d 1888-1889
In Rowell 1889-1890.

Herald w 1906-1911? d 1883-1888?
MoHi: w, Jly 17, 1908. d, film, Mar 1883-Aug
1884; Dec 2-28, 1884; 1886-Sep 27, 1888.
Early daily Herald bought by Republican.
Second Herald was prohibition paper for
brief time. Early Herald published weekly
Patriot.
MoSp: Film & bound, d, Mar 22, 1883-Sep 11,
1886; Aug 28, 1887-Sep 27, 1888.
MoSHi: May 31, 1885.
KHi: d, Sep 1, 2, Aug 19, 1888.

Hornet w 1888
Listed in Ayer 1888.

Industrial Southwest w 1894
Start of "immigration journal", noted in Missouri
Editor, Dec 1894.

Journal w 1862-1867 w 1884-1885
w, d 1889-1890
MoHi: w, Sep 3, 1866; Feb 9, 1867. Rowell 1885
lists weekly, founded 1885. Rowell 1890 lists
morning and weekly, founded 1889.

Journal (continued)
MWA: Mar 31, 1863; Oct 2, 1865.
CSmH: w, Apr 17, 1865.
NcD: d, Oct 31, 1884.

Greene County Republican w 1919-1920
Listed in Ayer 1921.

Laborer d 1916-1917
MoHi: Dec 12, 1916-Jun 15, 1917. Labor paper,
in Ayer 1917-1918.

Lancet w 1852?-1858
Benton paper "as sharp and cutting as the in-
strument for which it was named."

Leader w 1867+ d 1870 (various titles)
MoHi: d, est 1870; Apr 29, 1903-May 14, 1933;
May 8, 1870. Film, May 3-Aug 31, 1870; Apr
20, 1886-Apr 5, 1887; May 1, 1888-Sep 29,
1894; 1895 inc. W, Oct 23, 1890; Dec 20,
1892; Feb 28, 1906; Mar 6, 21, 1916. Film,
Apr 4, 1867-Mar 23, 1871; Mar 9, 1876-Jun
6, 1878; Mar 10, 1887-Nov 12, 1891.
MoSp: film & bound, w, Apr 4, 1867-Aug 15,
1872; Mar 2, 1876-Jun 16, 1878; Mar 10,
1887-Oct 30, 1890; Nov 6, 1890-Nov 12,
1891.
MoSHi: w, Dec 2, 1886; Mar 3, 1912; Feb 25,
1819. Merged with Democrat as Leader-
Democrat Oct 1895. Resumed name Leader
Apr 1903. Merged with Press as Leader and
Press May 1933, name now used. See Leader
and Press.
T: Aug 7, 1886.
ICHi: w, May 4, 1876.
WHi: d, Jan 1, 1917-Dec 1919.
KHi: d, Aug 29, 1888-Jan 30, 1889 inc; Nov 26,
1924; Jun 27, Jly 11, 1927. Masthead for
Leader Jan 16, 1895 says 14th year.

Leader-Democrat d, w 1867-1903
MoHi: d, May 1902-Apr 1903. Film, Oct 1895-
May 1903. See Leader.

Leader and Press d 1866?+
MoHi: d, May 15, 1933-1947; Oct 18, 1954. Film,
1948+.
MoSp: Film and bound, May 3, 1870-Aug 31, 1870;
Apr 20, 1886-Dec 29, 1893; Feb 12-Sep 29,
1894; Dec 21, 1894-Dec 31, 1895, Apr 1-Jun
30, 1896; Oct 1, 1896-Mar 31, 1897; Jly 1,
1897-Jun 30, 1900. Film, Apr 14, 1887-Apr 30,
1888; Dec 21, 1894-Dec 31, 1895; Aug 1, 1900-
Jly 12, 1902; Dec 1, 1902-Jun 30, 1903; Oct
1, 1903-Jun 30, 1904; Oct 1, 1904-Sep 30, 1911;
Jan 1, 1912-May 30, 1914; Jly 7, 1914-Dec 31,
1931; Jan 1, 1936+. Unbound, Jan 1, 1932-Dec
31, 1935; 1939+.
Micro-Photo: Film, 1936-1947, 1956+.
Following names, dates noted in Springfield Public
Library listings:

Leader and Press (continued)
Weekly Leader, Apr 4, 1867-Aug 29, 1886.
Daily Leader Aug 30, 1886-Mar 3, 1892.
Leader Mar 4, 1892-Apr 1, 1894.
The Leader Apr 2, 1894-May 3, 1895.
Leader May 4, 1895-Jly 18, 1895.
Leader Democrat Jly 19, 1895-Apr 10, 1902.
Leader & Democrat Apr 12, 1902-Apr 28, 1903.
Leader Apr 29, 1903-May 15, 1933.
Leader & Press May 16, 1933+.
First in Ayer under long title 1941 with 1866 founding date.

Mail   w   1897-1899
Free Silver paper.

Military News   w   1861
MoSHi: Jun 29, 1861.

Mirror   w   1855-1862
Mentioned by Organ.
IHi: Jun 12, Jly 31, 1858; May 25, 1861.

Missouri Commoner   w   1895
Populist paper, in Ayer 1896.

Missouri Patriot   d, tw   1866-1876   w   1862-1876
s   1878
MoHi: d, tw, film, Sep 11, 1866-Sep 13, 1867.
w, Dec 20, 1866; Jly 1, 1869. Film, Jun 8, 1865-Oct 5, 1876.
MoSp: W, film & bound, Jun 18, 1865-Oct 5, 1876.
D, film, Sep 11, 1866-Sep 13, 1867. S, (Patriot) film & bound, Feb 3-May 12, 1878. Weekly merged with Advertiser as Patriot Advertiser Oct 12, 1876. See Patriot.

Missouri Populist   w   1894-1895
People's Party paper.

Missouri Presse   w   1892-1901?
In Rowell 1894-1901. German. Last in Ayer 1900.

Missouri Staats-Zeitung   w   1888
Noted in Ayer 1889.

Missouri Tribune   w   1857-1858
Devoted to "Union Democracy."
IHi: Jan 16, Jun 12, 1858.

Missourian   w   1862-1864
WHi: Jly 9, 1864. Irregular publication, renamed Missouri Patriot Sep 1864, merged with Patriot-Advertiser.

New Crusade   w   1887-1888
Organ of Knights of Labor and Farmers' Alliance, according to Ayer 1888, Rowell 1889.

News   d   1892+
MoHi: d, 1927-1947; Oct 18, 1954. Film, 1948+

News (continued)
MoSp: d, Film, 1927-1929; 1936+. Unbound, 1930-1935; Jly 1, 1937+. Formerly Republican to Jan 4, 1927. Published as part of Leader and Press Mar 28-Jun 22, 1947.
Micro-Photo: film, d, 1927-1929; 1936-1947; 1956+.
KHi: d, Apr 13, 1927.
W in Ayer 1928, no founding date.

News Digest   d   1951-1954
MoSp: Dec 1951-Mar 1954. Paper financed by ITU during printers' strike. Ended Mar 26, 1954.

News and Leader   w   1928+
Sunday edition. See Leader and Press.

News-Paper   w   1878-1885
Listed in Ayer-Rowell 1886.

Ozark Eagle   w   1838?-1842
Formerly Ozark Standard, later Advertiser.

Ozark Standard   w   1838
See Ozark Eagle.

Patrick Henry   w   1889
Anti-monopolist organ, in Rowell 1890.

Patriot   w   1862-1881?   sw   1866-1867   d   1878?
MoHi: d, film, Feb 3-May 12, 1878. w, film, Oct 20-Dec 1881; Sep 7, 1882-Sep 27, 1883.
MoSp: w, Film & bound, Nov 20, 1881-Sep 27, 1883. S, film & bound, Feb 3-May 12, 1878. See Patriot-Advertiser, Missourian.
MWA: Oct 19, 1865; Jan 18, 1866.
KHi: w, Film, Jun 18, 1865-Dec 15, 1870.

Patriot-Advertiser   w   1876-1881
MoHi: w, Film, Oct 12, 1876-Sep 9, 1880; Jan 13-Oct 8, 1881.
MoSp: Film & bound, Oct 11, 1876-Sep 9, 1880; Jan 13-Oct 6, 1881. Result of merger of Missouri Weekly Patriot and Advertiser, w, Oct 6, 1876. Superseded by Weekly Patriot Oct 20, 1881.

Press   d   1929-1933
MoHi: Mar 4, 1929-May 14, 1933.
MoSp: Film, Mar 4, 1929-May 11, 1933. Merged with Leader May 15, 1933, continued as Leader and Press.

Public Forum   w   1942
Listed among papers suspended in 1942, in MPN, Dec 1942.

Queen City Sun   d   1881
Listed in Ayer 1882.

Record   w   1896-1904?   sw   1897   d   1899-1904?
In Rowell 1900-1905, Ayer 1901.

Reflex w 1885
Listed in Rowell-Ayer 1886.

Republican w 1885-1915? d 1892-1927
MoHi: d,1920-Jan 2,1927; Jly 16,1908; Jun 11,
Jly 10,21,22,Sep 19,1909; Apr 6,1910; Aug
18-22,1915; Sep 14,1901; Jly 22,23,1896.
Film, Jly 5,1887-Jun 29,1890; Dec 3,1893-
Jly 20,1895; Jan 16,1896-Oct 30,1901; Jan
2,1902-Dec 31,1919. As Daily Republican,
Jun 5,1892; Jly 10,1894.
MoSp: d,film & bound, Jly 5,1887-Jun 29,1890;
Dec 3,1893-Jan 27,1899; May 4,1899-Aug
31,1902; Oct 2,1902-Dec 31,1926. W,film
& bound, Jan 2,1889-Dec 26,1889; Feb 8,
1894-Dec 27,1906; Jan 2,1908-Dec 29,1911.
MoSHi: Feb 16,1899.
Absorbed Daily Herald 1889. Title changed to
Daily News Jan 4,1927.
IHi: May 11,1889.
KHi: d,Sep 15-Dec 16,1888; Aug 18,1926.

Sixteen-To-One w 1895-1896
Free Silver paper, in Ayer 1897.

Southeastern Citizen w 1882
Greenback paper,according to Hammond.

Southwest w 1870? sm 1898-1907?
MoHi: Jly 29,1870. In 1882 press association
listed a Southwestern in Springfield. No other
data. In 1879 reference to Southwester.
ICHi: Jan 18,1876.
KHi: sm,Jan 5,1898-Jly 1907 inc.

Southwest Standard ?
MoSHi: Dec 19,1919.

Southwestern Flag w 1849-1852
Supported Benton,according to Organ. Hammond
says equipment used for Lancet.

South-West Union Press w 1866
MoHi: Jun 9-Sep 6,1866. Founded by J.West
Goodwin,who soon went to Sedalia and the
Bazoo.
WHi: Dec 20,1866.

Standard d 1874
In Rowell 1875 as "only daily paper in Southeast
Missouri."

Statesman w 1882
Greenback paper, in Rowell 1883.

Sun d 1881-1882?
Listed in Rowell 1882.

Sunday Democrat w 1900
In Ayer 1901, S edition of Leader-Democrat.

Sunday Review w 1894
Listed in Ayer 1895.

Texas Democrat w 1846-1848
Political paper,according to Organ.

Times w 1870-1879
MoSp: Film & bound, Jun 14,1876-May 8,1878.
Merged with Weekly Leader in 1879 as Times-
Leader. Times prefix dropped 1883.
ICHi: Oct 8,1875.

Times-Leader w 1867-1883
See Times.

Town and Farm
MoHi: Oct 1,1890.

Tradesman w 1902-1911?
MoHi: Jly 11,1908. In Rowell 1907-1908,
Ayer 1911-1912.

Tribune w 1884-1886 w 1898
Apparently two, both short-lived.

Triple Link sm 1880?
KHi: Apr 15,1892-Dec 15,1898.

Union w 1888-1889
In Rowell 1888-1890,Ayer 1888.

Union Labor Record w 1937+
MoHi: Film,Oct 20,1937-Dec 25,1952.

Western Sunbeams w 1887
Listed in Ayer 1888.

Whig w 1848-1849
MoHi: Film,Sep 11,1848-Sep 15,1849.

World w 1893-1894
People's Party paper.

SPRING GARDEN (Pettis County)

Herald w 1882
Listed in Rowell 1883.

Spy w 1881-1882?
Listed in Dauchy 1883.

Spy and Mirror w 1883-1884
Moved to Tuscumbia during 1884 campaign,
according to Hammond.

STANBERRY (Gentry County)

Alliance Unit w 1891
In Rowell 1892,Farmers' Alliance paper.

Democrat w 1902-1903
Listed in Ayer 1904.

STANBERRY (Gentry County)

Gentry County Headlight   w   1894-1899
   See Headlight.

Headlight   w   1894-1910, 1926+
   MoHi: Nov 23, 1898-Oct 4, 1899. Name changed
      from Gentry County Headlight to Headlight,
      Oct 13, 1899-1900; 1902-Aug 21, 1913; Feb 4,
      1926-1944. Film, 1945+. Merged with Owl Apr
      21, 1910 to become Owl-Headlight. Renamed
      Headlight Jan 1926.

Herald   w   1887-1925
   MoHi: Jan 8, 1914-Dec 3, 1925. Sold to Owl-
      Headlight Dec 25, 1925.

News   w   1880-1885?
   In Rowell 1880-1885, Ayer 1880-1882.

Nominee   d, w   1891-1894
   Both d, w listed Ayer 1892. Missouri Editor, Mar
      1894 tells of sale of paper to firm that started
      Headlight.

Owl   w   1900-1910
   MoHi: 1904-Apr 5, 1910. Film, Aug 26, 1902-
      1903. See Headlight.

Owl-Headlight   w   1910-1913
   MoHi: Apr 12, 1910-Aug 21, 1913. See Headlight.
   KHi: Nov 8, 1923.

Sentinel   w   1880-1897
   Sentinel and Headlight consolidated 1897. In
      Ayer 1880-1897, Rowell 1880-1897. In Rowell
      1903 with 1902 founding date.

STAR (Barry County)

Seven Star Beacon   w   1881
   Greenback paper, in Ayer 1882.

STEELE (Pemiscot County)

Enterprise   w   1921+
   First in Ayer 1924 founding date 1921. In Ayer
      1963 with 1908 founding.

News   w   1908-1912?
   Listed in Ayer 1909-1913.

STEELVILLE (Crawford County)

Crawford County Advocate   w   1870
   Listed in Rowell 1871.

Crawford County Democrat   w   1887-1905
   MoHi: 1902; Oct 30, Nov 20, 1890; Apr 14, Nov
      10, 1904; Jly 27, 1905. Film, Jan 1-Jly 9,
      1903; Jly 16, 1903-Oct 12, 1905. Became
      Ledger Oct 19, 1905.

STEELVILLE (continued)

Crawford County Express   w   1871-1874?
   Listed in Rowell 1872-1875.

Crawford County Mirror   w   1872+
   MoHi: 1903-Feb 1928; Apr 1929-1944; Dec 29,
      1898. Film, 1945+. Also referred to as Crawford
      Mirror.
   MWA: May 24, Jun 21, 1872.
   NHi: Apr 4, 18, 1873.
   KHi: Nov 11, 1926.
   ICHi: May 11, Jly 6, 1876.

Crawford Champion-Sentinel   w   1880-1885
   Listed in Rowell-Ayer 1886.

Crawford Sentinel   w   1880-1890?
   MoHi: Sep 24, 1880; Nov 5, 1890.

Democrat   w   1888-1894?
   Listed in Ayer 1895.

Ledger   w   1887-1954
   MoHi: 1906-1944; Jan 4, 18, 1906; Dec 24, 1908.
      Film, Oct 19-Dec 28, 1905; 1945-1946. Merged
      with Crawford Mirror and Cuba News & Review
      Jan 7, 1954.

Register   w   1875-1876
   ICHi: Feb 17, 1876.

Shield and Temperance Advocate   w   1876-1877
   Mentioned in county history.

STELLA (Newton County)

Enterprise   w   1928-1930
   Listed in Ayer 1929-1931.

Leader   w   1931-1933
   Listed in Ayer 1933-1934.

Record   w   1904-1916?
   Temperance publication.

STEWARTSVILLE (DeKalb County)

Democrat   w   1893-1895, 1899-1900
   Also known as DeKalb-Clinton Democrat.
   Apparently two papers.

Echo der Gegenwart und des Zeitgeists
bw, m, sm   1876-1885?
   Noted in G-AN&P.

Illinois Fifty-Second
   IHi: Jan 15, 1862.

Independent   w   1877-1890
   MoHi: Oct 25, 1890.

STEWARTSVILLE (continued)

Investigator w 1893-1905? w 1884
DeKalb-Clinton Democrat changed to Investigator,
according to Missouri Editor, Nov 1895. Rowell
1885 lists another Investigator.

New Era w 1891-
In Rowell-Ayer 1892. Tax reform paper.

News w 1886-1888, 1892-1895, 1924-1956
MoHi: Dec 24, 1936-1944; Sep 5, 1935. Film,
1945-1954. Several News listed in directories.
Subscription list sold to Cameron Sun Nov 1956.
ICHi: Jly 7, 1876.

Record w 1892-1928
MoHi: 1913-1922; 1925-Jun 28, 1928. Film,
Mar 10, 1905-Jan 1, 1909; Jan 9, 1909-1912.
Moved to Maysville Jly 1928.

Telegraph w 1858-1861
Mentioned by Organ.

STOCKTON (Cedar County)

Anti-Bulldozer w 1880
Campaign paper, short-lived.

Cedar County Republican w 1886-1944
MoHi: 1919-1944; Nov 11, 1909. Film, Jan 22,
1914-1918. (See Cedar County Republican and
Stockton Journal)

Cedar County Republican and Stockton Journal
w 1886+
MoHi: Film, 1945+. Papers merged 1940.

Journal w 1869-1940
MoHi: 1903; 1918-Nov 6, 1940; Jan 5, 1870;
Oct 16, 1890; Jan 7, 21, 1904; May 29, 1913.
Film, 1914-1917. Hammond says absorbed
Southwest Tribune. Suspended Nov 6, 1940.
ICHi: Jun 15, 1876.

People's Advocate w 1894-1895
Populist paper in Rowell 1895-1896.

Stalwart w 1879-1883?
In Rowell 1880-1883, Ayer 1880-1881.

Southwest Tribune w 1866-1874?
MoHi: Jly 31, 1868-Nov 26, 1869.

STOTESBURY (Vernon County)

Standard w 1895-1898?
In Rowell 1896-1899, Ayer 1897.

Tribune w 1905-1907
In Rowell 1906-1908, Ayer 1907.

STOTTS CITY (Lawrence County)

Index w 1895-1899
Free Silver, in Ayer 1897-1900.

Lawrence County Republican w 1910
Listed in Ayer 1911.

Searchlight w 1901
Listed in Ayer 1902.

Sunbeam w 1899-1907
MoHi: Jly 26, 1901-1907. See Pax.

Times w 1903-1907
In Rowell-Ayer 1905-1908.

STOUTLAND (Camden County)

Advocate w 1896-1897
Free Silver, Rowell 1897, Ayer 1897-1898.

Country Standard w 1875-1877
ICHi: Jly 29, 1876. In Rowell 1875-1878.

Camden County Herald w 1909-1910
MoHi: Film, 1910. In Ayer 1910-1911.

Camden County Rustic w 1873-1874
To Linn Creek 1874, according to Hammond.

Herald w 1916-1917
Listed in Ayer 1917-1918.

Journal w 1897-1898, 1911-1914
In Ayer 1899, 1912-1915.

Rustic w 1874-1876
ICHi: Apr 20, 1876. In Rowell 1874-1876.

STOUTSVILLE (Monroe County)

Banner w 1890-1914
MoHi: Nov 24, 1898-1899; 1903-Aug 1913;
Oct 30, 1890.

Journal w 1915-1916
Listed in Ayer 1917.

Monroe County Star w 1919-1921
Listed in Ayer 1920-1922.

STOVER (Morgan County)

News w 1911-1922
See Tri-County Republican. In Ayer 1913-1922.

Tri-County Republican w 1911+
KHi: Jun 9, 1922. Known as News until 1922.

STURGEON (Boone County)

Herald w 1894
Start noted in Missouri Editor, Jun 1894.

STURGEON (continued)

Independent   w   1867-1870
    MoHi: Film, Oct 1869-Aug 1870, inc. See
    Centralia House Circle.

Leader   w   1866+
    MoHi: Oct 25, 1890; Jly 20, 1905; Aug 1901-
    1944. Film, 1945+.

News   w   1858-1861
    First in county outside Columbia.

STURGIS (Livingston County)

Journal   w   1861-1868?
    In Rowell 1869.

SUGAR CREEK (Jackson County)

Jackson County Herald   w   1924-1954
    MoHi: Film, 1946-May 26, 1954. Combined with
    Fairmont Station Inter-City News Jun 3, 1954.

SULLIVAN (Franklin County)

News   w   1910-1951
    MoHi: Jun 9, 1910-1944. Film, 1945-Nov 1951.
    Merged with Tri-County Democrat Nov 29,
    1951. See Tri-County News.

Sentinel   w   1896-1914, 1955-1960
    MoHi: 1901-Jun 26, 1914; Feb 10, 1905. Merged
    with News. See Rowell 1897-1908, Apr 1898-
    1914, 1955+.

Sixteen-To-One   w   1896
    Campaign paper.

Star   w   1895-1896
    In Ayer 1896-1897.

Sun   w   1905
    In Rowell-Ayer 1906.

Tri-County Democrat   w   1916-1952?
    In Ayer 1919-1953.

Tri-County News   w   1896+
    MoHi: Film, Dec 1951+. Sentinel merged with
    News Apr 1, 1960.

SUMNER (Chariton County)

Courier   w   1889?-1951
    First in Ayer 1945, last 1952.

North Chariton Times   w   1899-1902?
    In Rowell 1900-1903, Ayer 1900.

Star   w   1891-1939
    MoHi: Jun 25, 1937-Mar 10, 1939.
    MoSHi: Dec 11, 1908. Became Keytesville
    Chariton Courier Mar 17, 1939.

SUMMERSVILLE (Texas County)

Beacon   w   1947+
    First in Ayer 1950.

Gem   w   1938-?
    Start noted in MPN, Aug 1938.

Leader   w   1897-1904, 1913-1921?
    In Rowell 1897-1905, Ayer 1900-1902, 1915-1922.

Mail   w   1907
    Listed in Rowell-Ayer 1908.

News   w   1939-1950?
    First in Ayer 1950. Mentioned in MPN, Dec 1939,
    Feb 1944.

Ozark Mountain News   w   1930-1937?
    Listed in Ayer 1933-1937.

SWEET SPRINGS (Saline County)
(Town earlier known as Brownsville)

Herald   w   1874+
    MoHi: May 27, 1904-Jan 1906; 1910-1944. Film,
    Dec 27, 1907-1909; 1945+.

Republican   w   1896-1898
    Republican purchased by Herald, Jan 1898.

Tri-County Eagle   w   1914-1917
    Listed in Ayer 1915-1918.

TANEY CITY (Taney County)

Taney County Star   w   1891-1893, 1897-1899
    Apparently two. Second was Silver Democrat paper.
    See Forsyth Star. In Rowell 1894, Ayer 1894, 1900.

Taney County Times   w   1887-1890
    MoHi: Oct 23, 1890. In Rowell 1891.

TANEYVILLE (Taney County)

Taney County Democrat   w   1897-1900
    In Rowell 1900-1901, Ayer 1901.

Taney County Sentinel   w   1890-1897
    Listed in Ayer 1897-1898.

Taney County Star   w   1897-1898
    Listed in Rowell 1897-1899.

TARKIO (Atchison County)

Atchison County World   w   1898-1903
    MoHi: Film, Jan 1-Jly 16, 1903.

Avalanche   w   1884+
    MoHi: Apr 23, 1897; 1911-1944. Film, Aug 15,
    1885-1890; 1899-1902; 1908-1910; 1945+.
    KHi: Apr 4, 1924.

TARKIO (continued)

Blade w 1881
    Listed in Rowell 1882.

Herald w 1906-1908
    In Rowell 1907-1908, Ayer 1907-1909.

Independent w,d 1890-1908
    MoHi: 1902-1908. Briefly, about 1894, was d.

Republican w 1880-1884?
    Last listed in Rowell 1885.

TEBBETTS (Callaway County)

Post w 1899-1900, 1913-1914
    Union List says first Post combined with Mokane
    Herald to form Herald-Post, later Missourian.
    Ayer 1915 lists another Post.

THAYER (Oregon County)

Fourteenth District w 1910-1911
    Listed in Ayer 1911-1912.

Gazette w 1914-1916
    Listed in Ayer 1916-1917.

Herald w 1886
    Listed in Rowell 1887.

News w 1900+
    MoHi: 1918-1944. Film, 1945+. Formerly Ozark
    News. First in Ayer 1919, founding date 1900.

New Era w 1889
    Listed in Ayer 1889.

Oregon County Democrat w 1930-1952?
    Listed in Ayer 1935-1953.

Oregon County Independent w 1884
    Listed in Rowell 1885.

Oregon County Observer w 1916
    Listed in Ayer 1917.

Oregon County Tribune w 1899-1904
    MoHi: 1899-1902; Mar 22, 1903. Film, 1903-
    Nov 18, 1904. Merged with Republican Nov
    25, 1904.

Ozark News w 1900-1917
    MoHi: 1917. Became News Jan 4, 1918.

Populist w 1894
    Start noted in Missouri Editor, Oct 1894.

Progress w 1895
    In Ayer 1896.

Republican w 1900-1904
    United with Oregon County Tribune.

THAYER (continued)

Republican-Tribune w 1888-1905
    MoHi: Film, Dec 2, 1904-Feb 17, 1905.

Telephone w 1888
    In Rowell-Ayer 1889.

Tidings w 1885-1887
    In Rowell 1888, Ayer 1887-1888.

Tribune w 1888-1899?
    MoHi: Oct 18, 25, 1890. Brief title may have
    ended in 1899. See Republican.

THOMASVILLE (Oregon County)

New Era w 1871
    In Rowell 1872.

South Missourian w 1873-1874
    In Rowell 1873-1875.

TIFF CITY (McDonald County)

News w 1897-1898
    In Rowell 1897-1899, Ayer 1898.

TINA (Carroll County)

Herald w 1884-1911
    MoHi: Oct 31, 1890. Merged with Interior
    Journal.

Interior Journal w 1912-1933
    MWA: Jun 19, 1924. Moved to Norborne.

Journal w 1922-1942?
    In Ayer 1942-1943.

TIPTON (Moniteau County)

Advance w 1871-1872
    MoHi: Aug 18, 1871-Sep 27, 1872.

First Division Proclamation ?
    IHi: Dec 4, 1861.

Fly w 1894-1895
    In Ayer 1895-1896, Rowell 1896.

Gazette w 1895-1896
    MoHi: May 16, 1895; Mar 19, May 14, Jly 30, Aug
    6, Sep 3, 17, 24, Oct 8, Nov 26, 1896. United
    with Times as Times-Gazette.

Missouri Mail w 1898-1906
    MoHi: Jun 1, 22, Jly 6, 12, Aug 10, 1905; Jan 4,
    11, 25, 1906. Film, Jly 26-Dec 1901; 1902 inc;
    1903-1906.

Moniteau Enterprise w 1872-1873
    In Rowell 1873, no starting date.

IPTON (continued)

Times w 1877+
  MoHi: 1911-1944; Mar 1, Jun 7, 28, Jly 12, 26, Aug
    2, Sep 13, Oct 4, 11, 25, Nov 1, Dec 6-20, 1877;
    Oct 31, 1889; Oct 30, 1890; Mar 28, Oct 17, 24,
    1895. Film, Jan 10, 1878-Jly 8, 1897; Oct 18,
    1906-1910; 1945+. First in Rowell 1877 with
    1877 founding date.

Times-Gazette w 1897-1906
  MoHi: Jly 15-Dec 23, 1897. Film, Jly 15, 1897-
    1900; Jly 19, 1906. Formed by merger Jly 15,
    1897; renamed Times Oct 18, 1906.
  MoSHi: Mar 20, 1902.

RASK (Wright County)

World's Cresset w 1906-1908
  MoHi: Sep 5, 1907-Aug 13, 1908.

TRENTON (Grundy County)

Christian Pioneer w 1854
  Organ says formerly Western Pioneer, moved to
    Lindley 1854.

Gazette w 1876
  Apparently Jamesport Gazette, printed in
    Trenton briefly.

Grand River News w 1861-1865
  Hammond says later named Grand River Republican.

Grand River Republican w 1866-1872
  Later named Republican.

Grundy County Gazette w 1887-1952
d 1950-1952
  MoHi: d, film, Dec 5, 1950-Jan 30, 1952. W, film,
    Oct 12, 1944-Nov 30, 1950. Became d Dec 5,
    1950. Moved from Spickard Oct 12, 1944.
    Merged with Republican-Times Jan 31, 1952.

Grundy County Missourian w 1933-1944
  Fire destroyed plant Apr 1944. Sold to Republican-
    Times.

Grundy County Times w 1871-1887 d 1887
  ICHi: w, Aug 10, 1876. Daily in Rowell 1888.

Grundy Farmer w 1891
  MoHi: Oct 8, 1891. In Rowell 1892.

Herald w 1852-1860
  MoSHi: Jun 7, 1860. Forced to suspend by Federal
    authorities.

Leader w 1915?
  MoSHi: Jun 10, 1915.

News w 1907-1911 w 1867
  MoHi: Nov 7, 1907-1911. N.T. Doane of News
    attended editors' meeting in 1867. No other
    data about this paper.

TRENTON (continued)

Rambler w 1954-1957
  MoHi: Film, Aug 30, 1956-Mar 28, 1957. Published
    at Fair Play Apr 4, 1957. Formerly Linneus
    Rambler.

Republican d 1881-1903 w 1861?-1903
  MoHi: d, Film, 1884-Feb 18, 1885; May 8, 1886-
    May 1902. w, Sep 1869-1889. Film, 1890-
    Mar 12, 1903.
  MoSHi: w, Jun 10, 1915; Nov 23, 25, Dec 2, 9, 16,
    1920; Jan 6, 1921. (See Republican Tribune)
  ICHi: w, Aug 17, 1876.
    Daily merged with Star Feb 19, 1885. Renamed
    Evening Republican May 8, 1886. Merged with
    Morning Tribune Mar 1903 as Republican-
    Tribune. Weekly merged with Weekly Tribune,
    as Weekly Republican-Tribune Mar 19, 1903.

Republican News w
  WHi: Dec 22, 1866.

Republican-Star d 1881-1886
  MoHi: d, Film, Feb 19, 1885-May 7, 1886. See
    Republican.

Republican-Times w 1861-1952 d 1881+
  MoHi: w, Jly 30, 1903; 1927-1944. Film, Mar 3-
    Dec 1927; 1945-1952. See Republican.
    Formed by merged Republican-Tribune and
    Weekly Times Mar 3, 1927. D, Feb 19, 1946-
    1950. Film, 1914-1930; 1951+.

Republican-Times and Grundy County Gazette
d 1864+ (Full name for Republican-Times)

Republican-Tribune w, d 1903-1927
  MoHi: d, Jan-Jun 1911; 1912-1913. Film, 1904-
    1910; Jan-Feb 21, 1927. W, 1911-1926. Film,
    Mar 19, 1903-1910; Jan 6-Feb 27, 1927. See
    Republican-Times.

Star w 1879-1885? d 1882-1885?
  Hammond says Star sold to Republican Mar 5, 1885.

Times w 1872-1927 d 1888-1927
  MoHi: d, Feb 9, 1898. w, Aug 1, 1901-1903; 1905-
    1910; 1919-Feb 22, 1927; Oct 30, 1890. Film,
    1904; 1911-Dec 18, 1912.
  KHi: w, 1888-Mar 21, 1889.

Tribune d, w 1889-1903
  MoHi: d, Film, Jan 23, 1891-1897. W, film, Dec
    31, 1890-1902. Merged with Republican 1903.

Western Pioneer w 1851-1854
  MoHi: Film, Jun 28, 1851-Jun 19, 1852.
  MoSHi: Oct 11, 18, 25, Nov 22, 29, 1851; Jan 24,
    31, 1852. County history says paper moved to
    Lindley 1854 as Christian Pioneer, back to
    Trenton 1859, merged with Herald, destroyed
    by fire 1862.

TRIMBLE (Clinton County)

Tribune w 1898-1901
In Rowell 1900-1902, Ayer 1900.

TRIPLETT (Chariton County)

Bazoo w 1894
Listed in Ayer 1895.

Daisy w 1895
Start noted in Missouri Editor, Oct 1895.

Herald w 1894-1895?
Missouri Editor, Feb 1895, tells of suspension of Herald. Still listed Rowell 1898, Ayer 1899.

Rustler w 1893-1894
In Ayer 1894-1895, Dauchy 1896.

Times w 1896
Missouri Editor, Dec 1896, tells of revival of Times.

Tribune w 1900-1917?
Last listed in Ayer 1918.

TROY (Lincoln County)

Dispatch w 1871-1873
In Rowell 1872-1873. Apparently absorbed by Herald 1873.

Free Press w 1878+
MoHi: Aug 2, 1901-1944; Oct 24, 1890; Jly 24, 1903; Sep 1, 1905. Film, 1882-1901; 1945+.
MoSHi: Dec 21, 1900.

Gazette w
WHi: Sep 21, 1865.

Herald w 1865-1890?
MoHi: Jun 18, 1873-1878. Merger of Dispatch and Lincoln County Herald Jun 18, 1873.
KHi: Sep 26, Dec 5, 12, 1888.

Independent w 1861
In American Newspaper Directory 1861.

Lincoln Gazette w 1854-1855
Apparently changed to States Rights Gazette in 1855. Forced to cease by Federal authorities, according to Organ.

Lincoln County Herald w 1865-1873
MoHi: 1866-Jun 4, 1873; Aug 24, 1866. See Herald.

Lincoln County News w 1885-1890, 1900?
MoHi: Oct 23, 1890. In Rowell 1886-1888, 1900-1901, Ayer 1887, 1901. Two papers?

Lincoln County Times w 1891-1893
In Rowell 1892-1894, Ayer 1891, 1894.

TROY (continued)

Record
MoSHi: Jly 2, Oct 1, 1900; Feb 16, Jun 1, 1901; Feb 15, Sep 15, 1902.

States Rights Gazette w 1855-1861
See Lincoln Gazette.

Republican w 1888-1889
In Rowell 1889-1890.

TRUXTON (Lincoln County)

Lincoln County Republican w 1898-1900
In Rowell 1898-1901, Ayer 1900.

TURNEY (Clinton County)

Hammer w 1896
MoHi: Aug 14, 1896. Also dated at Cameron.

Times w 1901-1903
MoHi: Dec 12, 1902. Film, 1903. In Rowell 1902-1903, Ayer 1902.

TUSCUMBIA (Miller County)

Banner Cresset w 1881-1882?
Listed in Dauchy 1883.

Eye Opener w 1889-1898
MoHi: Jan 14, 1892. In Rowell 1890-1899, Ayer 1891-1897.

Helmet w 1874-1877
MoHi: Film, Apr 6, 1876-Mar 29, 1877.
ICHi: Jun 1, 1876. In Rowell 1876-1878.

Miller County Autogram w 1883-1959
MoHi: Sep 10, 1885-Jly 1894; 1905-1944; Aug 27 1885; Sep 19, 1912. Film, Jan 22-Oct 15, 1885; 1894-Jly 19, 1900; Jly 25, 1901-1905; 1945-1959. Became Miller County Autogram-Sentinel Apr 2, 1959. See Iberia, Aurora Springs.

Miller County Autogram-Sentinel w 1883+
MoHi: Film, Apr 2, 1959+.

Miller County Republican w 1904
In Rowell-Ayer 1905.

Miller County Vidette w 1872-1878
MoHi: Dec 28, 1876; Aug 29, 1878. Film, Jan 15, 1875-1876; Mar-Dec 1878.
ICHi: Aug 31, 1876.

Miller County Vindicator w 1879-1888
MoHi: Sep 9, 1881-Apr 1, 1884; Mar 1885-1887. Film, Jan 31, 1879-1880; May 13-Nov 25, 1881; Mar 3-Dec 29, 1882.

Osage Valley Banner w 1879-1881
MoHi: Film, Jan 16, 1879-Nov 10, 1881.

USCUMBIA (continued)

Osage Valley Record   w   1889-1902?
    In Rowell 1900-1903, Ayer 1900.

Osage Valley Sentinel   w   1870-1872
    MoHi: Film, Jan 12, 1871-Dec 6, 1872.

Republican   w   1870-1871
    In Rowell 1871-1872. Hammond says changed to
    Sun and Republican.

Spy and Mirror   w   1884
    Campaign paper, according to Hammond.

Sun and Republican   w   1872
    Brief career. Noted by Hammond.

UNION (Franklin County)

Appeal   w   1865-1871?
    MoHi: Jun 10, 1869; Jan 20, 1870.
    MoSHi: Oct 6, 1870.

Clarion   w   1872-1874
    In Rowell 1873-1874.

Flag   w   1848-1849?
    First in county. Renamed Independent, ended
    1852, according to Organ.

Franklin County Democrat   w   1870?-1880?
    Apparently earlier known as Franklin County
    Tribune, founded 1865. Moved to Pacific,
    named Franklin County Progress. Later to
    Washington as Franklin County Democrat.
    Apparently returned to Union 1887. In 1891
    consolidated with Republican in Washington
    and Record in Union and named Republican-
    Tribune. Renamed Franklin County Tribune 1896.

Franklin County Progress   w   1865-1871?
    MWA: Mar 16, 1866. In Rowell 1872.

Franklin County Record   w   1874-1890
    MoHi: 1883-Nov 1890 inc. Film, Sep 3, 1874-1882.
    ICHi: Jan 13, Jly 27, 1876.
    Washington Museum Society: Sep 3, 1874-Dec 21,
        1876; 1879-1880; 1881-Dec 21, 1882; 1883-
        Dec 11, 1884.

Franklin County Tribune   w   1865+
    MoHi: 1911-Feb 28, 1919; Mar 12, 1937-1944;
        Feb 24, Mar 17, 1905. Film, Dec 18, 1896-
        1910; 1945+.
    MoSHi: May 7, 1915.
    Washington Museum Society: 1898-Feb 27, 1925.
        Formerly Tribune-Republican. Merged with
        Republican-Headlight to become Republican-
        Tribune Mar 7, 1919. Renamed Franklin County
        Tribune Mar 12, 1937.

Independent   w   1849-1852
    See Flag.

UNION (continued)

Progress   w   1865-1871?
    A. Ackerman attended first editors' meeting
    in 1867.

Polish Pielgrzym   w   1872-1874
    Krakow lists Polish Eagle that later moved to
    Union.

Record   w   1874-1891
    KHi: Oct 25, 1888.
    Washington Museum Society: Jan 13, 1887-Oct
        1890.

Republican-Headlight   w   1904-1919
    MoHi: 1916-Feb 28, 1919. Film, Mar 4-Aug 19,
        1904; Jan 23, 1914-1915.
    Washington Museum Society: Mar 9, 1906-Feb
        23, 1917.

Republican-Tribune   w   1887-1897
    MoHi: Mar 7, 1919-Mar 5, 1937.
    MoSHi: Mar 7, 1919-Feb 24, 1922.

Tribune   w   1887-1890
    MoHi: Film, Jun 17, 1887-Dec 5, 1890.
    Washington Museum Society: Dec 12, 1890-1895.
        Merged with Republican 1890.

Tribune-Republican   w   1887-1896
    MoHi: Film, Dec 12, 1890-Dec 11, 1896.
    Washington Museum Society: Dec 12, 1890-Dec
        27, 1895. See above.

UNION STAR (DeKalb County)

Comet   w   1883-1899, 1920-1940?
    Union List says Comet known as Toothpick 1883-
    1886. See MPN, Dec 1937.

Criterion   w   1896
    Start noted in Missouri Editor, Jun 1896; end
    Sep 1896.

Herald   w   1898-1929?
    MoHi: 1903-May 1920; Jly 1937-Nov 20, 1938.
        Film, Jly 1901-1902. See New Herald. Ayer
        1925-1929 lists Herald, founded 1920.

New Herald   w   1923-1925
    In Ayer 1922-1924. See Herald.

Pinhook News   w   1912-1914?
    In Ayer 1915.

Times   w   1940-1951?
    First in Ayer 1946.

Toothpick   w   1883-1886
    See Comet.

UNIONVILLE (Putnam County)

Argus w 1858-1861
In American Newspaper Directory 1861.

Democrat w 1886-1891
MoHi: Oct 30, 1890. In Rowell 1889 as Democrat-
Investigator.
IaHi: Jun 3, 1886-Jun 25, 1891.

Investigator w 1886-1888
IaHi: Feb 27, 1886-Jun 14, 1888. Apparently
name used for Democrat.

Journal w 1899-1903
Union List says name used these years for Putnam
County Journal.

New Century w 1876-1890?
MoHi: Dec 20, 1878; Jan 17, Feb 14-28, Mar 14,
Aug 1879; Sep 30, Nov 18, 1881; Sep 1, 22,
1882; Sep 7, 28, Oct 5, 12, 1883; Aug 28, Sep
4, Oct 30, Nov 6, 20, 1884; Apr 2, May 28, 1885;
Jun 9, 1890.
IaHi: Aug 12, 1876-Nov 12, 1880; Jly 8, 1881-
Apr 6, 1883; Mar 26, 1885-May 27, 1886.

News d 1897
MoHi: Dec 1, 21, 1897. No directory data.

Pantagraph w, sw 1897-1904 d 1897-1898
MoHi: d, film, Nov 1897-Jan 6, 1898. W, 1901-
1904, film 1900.
MoSHi: w, 1904.
IaHi: Jan 8, 1898-Jan 15, 1901.

Progress w 1891-1892
IaHi: Jly 9, 1891-Jan 28, 1892. In Ayer 1891,
Rowell 1892. Union List says name used for
Putnam Democrat Jly 1891-Jan 1892.

Putnam County Journal w 1889-1926
MoHi: 1903-1926. Film, Aug 22, 1901-1902.
IaHi: Feb 26-May 14, 1897; Aug 2, 1900-Oct
13, 1903.

Putnam County Leader w 1889-1898 w 1873
Rowell 1874 lists paper, founded 1873. Next in
Rowell 1890, founded 1889.

Putnam County Ledger w 1873-1876
IaHi: May 16, 1891-Dec 30, 1898.
ICHi: Jun 20, 1876. Rowell 1877 lists under
Republican and Putnam County Ledger.

Putnam County Leader & Journal
IaHi: Jan 6, 1899-Jly 26, 1900.

Putnam Democrat w 1876-1896?
IaHi: Mar 30, 1892-Jan 26, 1893; Feb 2, 1893-
Feb 19, 1897. Earlier known as New Century,
Democrat, Progress.

UNIONVILLE (continued)

Republican w 1865+
MoHi: w, Oct 5, 1892-1896; 1903-1944; Aug 28,
1884; Jan 11, 1905. Film, Sep 26, 1867-Oct 6,
1870; Oct 24, 1872-Sep 28, 1892; 1897-1902;
1945+.
IaHi: Nov 6, 1879-May 7, 1885; Apr 5, 1888-1890;
Feb 13, 1895-Jly 7, 1897.
NHi: Film, Sep 26-Nov 7, 21-Dec 19, 1867; Jan 2-
Mar 26, Apr 9-Jly 2, 16-Dec 24, 1868; Jan 7-
Sep 3, 17-Dec 31, 1869; Jan 7-Oct 6, 1870; Feb
20, 1873.
ICHi: Aug 3, 1876.

Republican and Putnam County Journal
See previous listings. MoSHi lists under this full
title: Sep 6, Dec 13, 20, 27, 1939; Jan 3-Feb 7, 21,
28, Sep 4-Dec 25, 1940; 1941.

Tribune d 1897
MoHi: Nov 22-30, 1897. In Ayer 1898.

UNIVERSITY CITY (St. Louis County)

Journal w 1934?
Combined with News in 1934.

News w 1934?
MPN, Dec 1934, tells of combining News and
Journal.

Western Journal and Civilian w 1951-1954?
University City Library lists papers for these dates.

UPPER ALTON (St. Louis County)

Independent w 1896
Start noted in MPN, Dec 1896.

URBANA (Dallas County)

Dallas County Republican w 1905-1912
In Rowell 1906-1908, Ayer 1907-1913.

Enterprise w 1915-1918?
Listed in Ayer 1919.

URICH (Henry County)

Chronicle w 1886-1892?
In Rowell 1887-1892, Ayer 1887-1892.

Herald w 1893-1957
MoHi: Film, May 17, 1893-May 3, 1900; Nov 6,
1952-1957. See Herald-Tidings. Also, Montrose.

Herald-Tidings w 1892+
MoHi: Film, Oct 18, 1957+. Herald and Tidings
combined Oct 18, 1957.

Home Talk w 1891
Listed in Ayer 1892.

UTICA (Livingston County)

Advance   w   1891
    Listed in Ayer-Rowell 1892.

Bugle   w   1899
    Start noted in Country Editor, Mar 1899.

Herald   w   1872-1885?   w   1896-1903?
w   1911-1914?
    ICHi: Jly 8, Aug 5, 1876. In Rowell 1876-1886,
    1900-1908, Ayer 1880-1882, 1900-1902, 1915.

News   w   1896-1898
    In Rowell 1897-1899, Ayer 1897-1898.

Times   w   1861   w   1897-1898
    In American Newspaper Directory 1861. Second
    Times in Rowell 1897, Ayer 1898, with death
    notice in Country Editor, Mar 1898.

VALLEY PARK (St. Louis County)

Dispatch   w   1903-1904
    In Ayer-Rowell 1905.

Messenger   w   1923-1924
    In Ayer 1925. Refers to Kirkwood 1926.

Sun   w   1906-1917?
    MoSHi: Jan 21, 1911. Last in Ayer 1918.

VAN BUREN (Carter County)

Carter County Journal   w   1912-1914
    MoHi: Film, Jan 9-Dec 4, 1914.

Carter County Herald   w   1904-1910, 1930-1946
    In Ayer 1911, 1933-1947.

Current Local   w   1884+
    MoHi: Jly 4, 1901-1910; 1913-1944; Aug 27,
    1908; Jan 25, 1951. Film, May 24, 1884-
    May 1886; Jly 1888-Jun 1889; Jly 11, 1891-
    Jly 1893; 1894-Jun 1896; May 1899-Oct
    1900; 1911-1912; 1945+.
    KHi: Jan 17, Feb 21, 1924. See Times.

Echo   w   1904-1905
    MoHi: Film, Dec 22, 1904-1905.

Times   w   1879-1884
    Followed by Current Local. In Rowell 1880-1884,
    Ayer 1880-1881.

VANDALIA (Audrain County)

Argus   w   1883-1884
    In Dauchy 1883, Rowell 1884.

Graphic   w   1890-1891?
    In Rowell 1891-1892, Ayer 1891.

VANDALIA (continued)

Leader   w   1875+
    MoHi: Jly 25, 1901-1943. Film, 1935-Nov 19,
    1936; 1943-1944; 1945+. Founding also
    given as 1872, 1874.
    ICHi: Jly 5, Sep 20, 1876.

Mail   w   1893-1945
    MoHi: 1905; 1908-Apr 5, 1945; Jly 13, Sep 14,
    1905. Film, 1906-1907. Ended Apr 5, 1945.

Mail and Express   w   1893-1903?
    MoHi: Aug 28, 1902. Film, Oct 8-Dec 31, 1903.
    Union List says name used for Mail for these
    years yet Rowell lists long title as late as 1908.

Press   w   1945
    MoHi: Film, May 17-Aug 17, 1945. Merged with
    Laddonia Press Aug 23, 1945.

Press and Laddonia Herald   w   1884-1961
    MoHi: Film, Aug 23, 1945-1960. Sold to Vandalia
    Leader Jan 5, 1961.

VERONA (Lawrence County)

Advocate   w   1892-1923
    MoHi: Film, Mar 9, 1917-Dec 20, 1918.

Banner   w   1873
    Mentioned in county history.

Gazette   w   1872-1873?
    In Rowell 1873.

Globe   w   1881-1882?
    In Rowell 1882.

Independent   w   1885-1890?
    In Rowell 1886-1891, Ayer 1886-1889.

Journal   w   1871
    "Only paper in town," Rowell 1872.

News   w   1878-1879
    Noted in county history as starting Dec 13, 1878,
    ended May 9, 1879.

Ozarkian   w   1938-1939
    In Ayer 1939-1940.

Republican   w   1878
    In Rowell 1879. Hammond says started Aug 31,
    ended Nov 9, 1878.

Sentinel   w   1885-1891
    In Ayer 1891, Rowell 1892.

VERSAILLES (Morgan County)

Argus   w   1871-1872
    MoHi: Jan 26, 1871-Jun 13, 1872.

VERSAILLES (continued)

Gazette   w   1871-1886
    MoHi: Feb 4, 1871-1873; 1877-Jly 1879; 1880-
        Jly 1881; Apr 1882-1886; Oct 13-Nov 3,
        1881; Feb 18, 1885. Film, 1874-1876.
    ICHi: Jun 22, 1876.
    T: Jun 12, 1873.

Journal   w   1882-1883
    MoHi: Jun 1, 15, Jly 20- Sep 29, Oct 13-Nov 17,
        Dec 1-22, 1882; Jan 1883.

Leader   w   1887-1948
    MoHi: 1887-1890; 1911-1944; Jly 7, 30, Aug 6,
        1891; Jan 19, 1906. Film, 1891-1894; 1897-
        1910; 1945-Sep 17, 1948. Formerly Morgan
        County Leader. Merged with Statesman Sep
        24, 1948.

Leader-Statesman   w   1886+
    MoHi: Film, Sep 24, 1948+. See Leader.

Messenger-Gazette   w   1871-1887
    MoHi: Jan 6-Mar 17, 1887. Organ tells of early
        years. Apparently consolidated with Gazette
        1886.

Morgan County Banner   w   1865-1870
    MoHi: Apr 6, 1867-1868; Apr 3-Oct 16, 1869;
        1870; Aug 4, 1866; Mar 16, 23, 1867; Mar 27,
        Jun 5, 1869. Later named Morgan County
        Gazette.

Morgan County Democrat   w   1900-1906
    MoHi: Jly 10, 1903-Aug 17, 1906. Renamed
        Morgan County Republican Aug 24, 1906.

Morgan County Forum   w   1858-1861
    First in county. Office abandoned, publishers
    entered Confederate Army.

Morgan County Gazette   w   1871-1874?
    Formerly Morgan County Banner, later Gazette.
    Mentioned by Organ.

Morgan County Leader   w   1887-1889?
    MoHi: Jan 3, 1889. Rowell 1890 lists Leader.
    KHi: Sep 13-Nov 22, 1888.

Morgan County News   w   1900
    Listed in Rowell-Ayer 1901.

Morgan County Republican   w   1900-1914
    MoHi: Aug 30, 1906-1912; Jan-Aug 1914. See
    Morgan County Democrat.

Morgan Messenger   w   1884-1886
    MoHi: Oct 9, 1884-Oct 21, 1886. Rowell 1887
    refers to Messenger-Gazette.

Optimist   w   1898
    Listed in Rowell 1899.

VERSAILLES (continued)

Ozark Chief   m   1895
    Start noted in Missouri Editor, Nov 1895.

Populist   w   1894
    Start noted in Missouri Editor, Jun 1894, end Jan
    1895.

Statesman   w   1887-1948
    MoHi: 1902-1916; 1919-1944; Mar 26, Apr 9,
        1897. Film, 1902-1905; 1917-1918; 1945-
        Sep 17, 1948. Combined with Leader 1948.

Vindicator   w   1866-1869
    MoHi: Jly 12, Sep 17, Oct 4-25, 1866; 1867-
        1868; Jan 1-29, Feb 12, 26, Mar 5-26, Apr
        9, May 7, Jun 11, 1869. Listed in Rowell 1870.
        Film, Jan 3, 1867-Dec 25, 1868.

VICHY (Maries County)

Chronicle   w   1881-1883?
    In Dauchy 1883. Hammond says Chronicle started
    in 1882, moved to Cuba two years later.

Herald   w   1884
    County history says moved to Vienna.

Hustler   w   1892
    Listed in Rowell 1893.

Post   w   1885-1886
    Vichy Springs Post in Rowell 1886-1887.

Times   w   1885
    Listed in Dauchy 1885.

VIENNA (Maries County)

Banner of Liberty   w   1873
    In Rowell 1873. According to Hammond later
    named Courier, Maries County Courier, and
    Maries County Gazette.

Central Missourian   w   1858-1861?
    MoHi: Feb 26, 1859; Apr 24, May 1, 1861.
    MoSHi: Feb 26, 1859 photostat. Organ says
        paper became Rolla Express, but dates
        appear in error.

Courier   w   1873-1876
    In Rowell 1874-1876, Pettengill 1877.

Home Adviser   w   1902+
    MoHi: May 17, 1906-1944. Film, 1945+.
    KHi: Nov 2, 1922.

Maries County Advocate   w   1873-1902?
    In Rowell 1873-1874, again 1902-1903, Ayer
    1899, 1894. Beginning uncertain.

Maries County Courier   w   1874-1884?
    In Rowell 1877-1885, Ayer 1881-1882.

VIENNA (continued)

Maries County Gazette   w   1872?+
    MoHi: Aug 1902-Nov 1905; Mar 1906-Jan 1907;
    Oct 30, 1890; Jan 9, May 1, May 15-Jly 10,
    31, Aug 14, 28, Sep 11, 18, Dec 18, 1914.

Maries County Herald   w   1884?
    In Dauchy 1884. See Vichy.

Maries County Times   w   1896-1904?
    In Rowell 1897-1905, Ayer 1897-1900.

Rolla Express   w   1860?
    Organ says printed briefly in Vienna before
    moving to Rolla Jly 1860.

WAKENDA (Carroll County)

Alert   w   1888
    KHi: Jly 20, 1888.

News   w   1899-1902
    In Rowell 1900-1903.

Record   w   1868-1878
    Union List says name used for Carrollton Re-
    publican Record for these years. Hammond says
    started 1862.

(Unnamed paper - 1896)
    Missouri Editor, Mar 1896, says "Wakenda has
    a new paper published by J.E. Moss."

WALKER (Vernon County)

Herald   w   1882-1935?
    Last in Ayer 1936.

Journal   w   1883
    Listed in Rowell 1884.

WALNUT GROVE (Greene County)

Bee   w   1886
    In Rowell 1887, Ayer 1886-1887.

Bulletin   w   1888
    Listed in Rowell 1889.

Comet   w   1889
    Listed in Ayer 1890.

Eagle   w   1896-1901
    In Rowell 1900-1901, Ayer 1898-1902.

Tribune   w   1903-1932
    MoHi: 1906-1914; 1917-1918; Jly 1, 1914. Film,
    Jun 7, 1904-Nov 29, 1905; 1915-1916.

WARREN (Marion County)

Vindicator   w   1878-1879
    Hammond says founded Mar 1878, moved to
    Bloomfield 1879.

WARRENSBURG (Johnson County)

Democrat   w   1871-1876
    MoHi: Dec 25, 1874; Jan-Apr 1876. Formerly
    Johnson Weekly Democrat. Merged with
    Journal as Journal-Democrat Oct 27, 1876.
    ICHi: Apr 14, 1876.

Herald   d   1880
    MoHi: Jly 28-Aug 12, 15-Sep 16, 1880. Organ
    notes another Herald that combined with
    Standard 1893.

Johnson County Democrat   w   1913-1918
    In Ayer 1915-1919.

Johnson County Eagle   w   1891-1899?
    In Rowell 1899, founding date 1891.

Johnson County Star   w   1882-1916
    MoHi: Jly 10, Aug 7, 28, 1886; Oct 8-22, 1887;
    Aug 19, Nov 3, 1888. Film, Aug 8, 1891-Aug
    6, 1892. Merged with Journal Democrat to
    become Star-Journal 1916.

Johnson County Union   w   1891-1897
    Populist. Became Quarry City Magazine, m, 1897.
    May have been d briefly.

Johnson Weekly Democrat   w   1871-1874
    MoHi: Sep 23, 1871-Mar 30, 1872; Apr 25-Dec
    18, 1874. Became Democrat Dec 25, 1874.

Journal   w   1865-1876
    MoHi: May 8, 1867-Jly 4, 1868; Jun 13, 1874-
    Oct 20, 1876; Apr 18, 1866.
    MoSHi: Jly 2, 1870.
    ICHi: Aug 25, 1876. Merged with Democrat Oct
    27, 1876.

Journal-Democrat   w   1865-1912?   d   1893-1895?
    MoHi: Oct 27, 1876-Dec 12, 1879; Jly 8, 1881-
    1882; Oct 31, 1890; Feb 29, 1884; Aug 6, 20,
    Sep 3, 1886; Oct 14, 1887; Sep 21, Nov 2, 1888.
    Film, Jan-Nov 18, 1892; 1894-1910; Jan-Sep
    1911. See above.

Jule Coe's Weekly   w   1897-1899
    Absorbed by Journal-Democrat and Weekly Star,
    noted Country Editor, May 1899.

Missouri Tribune   w   1864-1865
    MoHi: Jly 1, 1865.
    MWA: Oct 14, 1865.

News   d   1872-1878?   w   1855, 1876-1878
    MoHi: May 17, Jun 21, 1855. Rowell in 1877-
    1879 lists News as d, Republican w edition.
    IcHi: d, Jly 12, Aug 30, 1876.

Press   w   1878-1879
    Greenback. Rowell 1879-1880, Ayer 1880.

Republican   w   1876-1878
    See News.

WARRENSBURG (continued)

Sentinel   w   1853-1862
    Organ says forced to close in Civil War.

Standard   w   1865-1891   sw   1891-1893
d   1878-1893
    MoHi: d, film, May 1878-Sep 30, 1879. W, sw,
        May 10, 1867-Jan 27, 1870; Apr 26, 1867; Jun
        10, 1869; Apr 21, 1870; Jun 7, 1877; Jan 3,
        1879. Film, Jun 17, 1865-May 3, 1867; Feb 3,
        1870-Sep 30, 1875; 1880-1892. Merged with
        Holden Herald to become Standard-Herald
        Jan 3, 1893.
    ICHi: Jly 6, 1876.

Standard-Herald   w   1865+
    MoHi: Sep 25, 1903; Dec 1936; Oct 21, 1938-
        1944. Film, 1893-1905; 1945+. Ayer 1894
        lists sw. Country Editor, Oct 1898, tells of
        death of d.
    KHi: Feb 16, 1917; Jly 6, 1928.

Star   w   1881-1885?   d   1889-1892?
    CoD: Jun 14, 1892 (Vol 4, No 92). W, Jly 9, 1885
        is Vol 3, No 48.

Star-Journal   w, sw   1882+   d   1889+
    MoHi: d, 1938-1950. Film, Jan-Jun, Dec 28-30,
        1936; 1937-Jun 1939; Jan-Mar 1945; 1951+.
        W, sw 1917-Jan 1939; 1940-1944. Film, May
        5-Dec 29, 1916; 1945+. Paper uses 1865
        founding date.

Tribune   d   1895
    First issue Jly 13, 1895.

Union   d   1896
    Start noted in Missouri Editor, Dec 1896.

Union Standard   w   1862-1865
    Organ says followed by Standard Jun 17, 1865.

Western Missourian   w   1856-1861
    MoHi: May 22, 1858.
    MoSHi: Aug 21, 1858.

WARRENTON (Warren County)

Banner   w   1865+
    MoHi: Aug 29, 1902-1905; 1908-Feb 1910; Sep
        1910-1944; Nov 7, 1890; Jan 26, 1906. Film,
        1906-1907; 1945+. Shoemaker says Banner
        succeeded Nonpareil, founded 1857.
    ICHi: Jly 11, 1876.

Buerger (Der)   w   1865-1869
    Followed by Washington Citizen, which had a
    German section.

Chronicle   w   1869-1875?
    MoHi: Dec 9, 1869. In Rowell 1870-1875.
    Hammond says became Citizen, ended 1881.

WARRENTON (continued)

Economist   w   ?-1889
    Organ tells of combining Economist and Banner
    in 1889.

Economist-Banner   w   1889-1891
    Organ says name Banner resumed 1891. In Ayer
    1889-1890.

Herald   w   1898-1905
    MoHi: Sep 13, 1898-Aug 1902; Dec 14, 1905;
        May 31, Jun 7, 14, 1905. Film, Sep 10, 1902-
        Nov 15, 1905.

Missouri Conservator   w   1864-1865
    Mentioned by Organ.

Nonpareil   w   1857-1865
    MoSHi: Dec 25, 1862. Organ says Nonpareil re-
        named Warren County Banner in 1865, Banner
        in 1869.

Sentinel   w   1874?   1880-1882?
    Ayer 1881 lists Sentinel with 1874 founding date.
    Rowell 1881-1882 uses 1880 founding date.
    G-AN&P says a Sentinel, German-language,
    started about 1870.

Union (Die)   w   1875-1879
    MoHi: Aug 31, 1876. Data from Hammond.

Volksfreund   w   1880-1918
    MoHi: Feb 7, 1902-Apr 1918.

Warren County Citizen   w   1874-1880?
    In Rowell 1875-1880, Ayer 1880. Carried German
    section for many years.

Warren County Democrat   w   1891
    MoHi: Dec 11, 1891, souvenir edition. In Ayer
        1891, Rowell 1892.

Warren County Economist   w   1887-1889
    In Ayer 1887, Rowell 1887-1888. Also known as
    Economist.

WARSAW (Benton County)

Benton County Banner   w   1871
    In Rowell 1871.

Benton County Democrat   w   1871-1874?
    In Rowell 1871-1875.

Benton County Enterprise   w   1881+
    MoHi: 1903-1937. Film, Jly 26, 1901-1902; Mar
        1, 1956+.
    MoSHi: Jly 11, 1913.
        Merged with Times and Cole Camp Courier, be-
        came Benton County Guide Jan 1938. Changed
        to Benton County Enterprise Mar 1, 1956.

WARSAW (continued)

Benton County Guide   w   1938-1956
    MoHi: 1938-1944. Film, 1945-Feb 24, 1956. See
        Benton County Enterprise.

Benton County Index   w   1866-1869
    Listed in Rowell 1869.

Benton County Tribune   w   1898-1899
    Free Silver paper, in Rowell 1898-1900, Ayer 1900.

Bugle   d   1899
    KHi: Sep 20, 1899 is Vol I, No 1. Also, Sep 23,
        1899. As Bugle Call.

Democratic Press   w   1875-1876
    IChi: Aug 5, 1876. In Rowell 1876.

Democratic Review   w   1850-1853
    MoHi: Oct 9, 1851.
    MoSHi: Sep 30, Dec 9, 1852; Apr 14, May 12, Jun
        30, 1853. Organ says this followed Whig, later
        became Southwest Democrat.

Missouri Enterprise   w   1881-1897?
    In Rowell 1884-1898, Ayer 1882-1895. Renamed
        Benton County Enterprise.

Missourian   w   1841-1845
    Mentioned by Organ, Hammond.

Osage Banner   w   1840-1842
    First Whig paper in area. Organ says publisher
        walked into Osage River up to his neck, changed
        mind about taking own life.

Osage Valley   w   1842-1843
    Mentioned in county history.

Osage Yeoman   w   1843-1845
    DLC: Nov 28, 1844. Noted by Organ.

Register   w   1879
    In Rowell 1880. B. R. Lingle of Register press
        association member in 1881.

Saturday Morning Visitor   w   1845-1849
    MoSHi: Jun 10-Aug 19, 1848; Sep 2, 1848-Feb
        24, 1849; Mar 3, Apr 28, May 12-26, 1849.
        Organ says became Whig.

Signal   w   1841-1846
    Organ says was anti-Mormon paper.

Southwest Democrat   w   1853-1861?
    MoHi: Feb 15, 1855. Organ says followed
        Democratic Review.
    IHi: Feb 18, Mar 4, May 13, Jly 8, 1858; Sep 1,
        1859.

WARSAW (continued)

Times   w   1865-1938
    MoHi: Oct 5, 1905-1937; Apr 23, 1908. See
        Benton County Enterprise.
    IChi: Jly 6, Aug 3, 1876.
    KHi: May 3, 1923.

Whig   w   1848-1850
    Organ says followed Saturday Morning Visitor.

WASHBURN (Barry County)

Gazette   w   1875
    Mentioned in county history.

Journal   w   1895
    Listed in Ayer 1896.

WASHINGTON (Franklin County)

Advertiser   w   1858-1865
    Organ says Advertiser suppressed by Federal
        authorities in Civil War. Later became Observer.

Buyer's Guide   w   1939?-1940
    MoHi: May 25, 1939-Aug 1940.

Citizen   w   1905+
    MoHi: Aug 25, 1905-1944. Film, 1945+.

Courier   w   1859-1861
    G-AN&P says started 1858, Organ says 1859.
        Hammond says paper was suspended by Federal
        authorities in 1861.

Deutsche Welt (Die)   w   1889-1890?
    MoHi: Apr 26, 1889. In Ayer 1890.

Franklin County Democrat   w   1871-1882
    Washington Museum Society: May 24, 31, 1878;
        Jly 11, 18, Sep 19, Oct 3, 17-31, Nov 21, 1879;
        Dec 12, 1879-Jan 6, Feb 27, Mar 19, Apr 2-May
        14, Jun 4-25, Jly 9-Oct 15, Nov 5-Dec 24, 1880;
        Jan 7-Feb 25, Mar 11-25, Jun 3-Sep 30, Oct 14-
        Nov 25, 1881; Jan 6-Mar 3, 17, 31, Apr 28, May
        19, 26, 1882.

Franklin County Journal   w   1892-1900?
    In Rowell 1900-1901, Ayer 1900; under Journal
        Ayer 1895-1896.

Franklin County Observer   w   1861-1926
    MoHi: 1913-Jly 26, 1926; Jun 18, 1869; May 26,
        Jun 2, 1876; Oct 31, 1884; Jan 1, 1904; Oct
        13-27, 1905.

Franklin County Times   w   1884-1886?
    In Dauchy 1884, Rowell 1885-1887, Ayer 1887.

Free Press   w   1868
    Hammond says short-lived. G-AN&P says Die
        Freie Presse possibly was published from 1865 to
        1868.

WASHINGTON (continued)

Gazette   w   1860-1861
See Franklin County Gazette, title of Jan 5,
1860 copy at MoSHi.

Herald   w   1875
In Rowell 1875, founding date of 1875.

Journal   w,d   1892-1899?
In Rowell 1893-1899, Ayer 1895-1898. See
Franklin County Journal. Daily had shorter
career.

Missourian   w   1861+
MoHi: May 25, 1939-1944. Film, 1945+.

Post   w   1869-1910?
MoHi: Oct 24, 1890. Also known as Washingtoner
Post. German.
DLC: Nov 17-Dec 1870; 1871-1877; Jan-Nov
14, 1878; Nov-Dec 1895; Jan-Oct 23, 1896.
ICHi: Aug 24, 1876.

Republican   w   1888-1890
MoHi: Oct 24, 1890. In Rowell-Ayer 1889-1890.

Spitzbub (Der)
Mentioned in G-AN&P as scandal sheet, no dates.

Times   w   1884-1887?
Mentioned by Hammond.

Union   w   1861
In American Newspaper Directory 1861.

WASHINGTON, D. C.

Army Times
MoHi: 1946-Aug 1948.

Columbian Star
MoHi: 1827-Nov 29, 1828.

National Intelligencer
MoHi: Feb 7, 1846-Sep 11, 1852.

WATERLOO (Clark County)

Clark County Press   w   1869?-1871?
MoHi: Jun 17, 1869. In Rowell 1869-1871.

Patriot   w   1861
In American Newspaper Directory 1861.

WATSON (Atchison County)

Atchison County Democrat   w   1897
Listed in Ayer 1898.

Atchison County Independent   w   1937-1950?
Listed in Ayer 1942-1951.

WATSON (continued)

Times   w   1876
County history says Times lasted few months.

Watsonian   w   1906-1908?
In Ayer 1909, founding date 1906.

WAVERLY (Lafayette County)

Express   w   1870-1872?
MoHi: May 7, 1870. In Rowell 1871-1872.

Gazette   w   1905-1907
In Rowell 1906-1908, Ayer 1907.

Herald   w   1929-1943?
In Ayer 1931-1944.

Lafayette County Sentinel   w   1876-1878
MoHi: Film, Aug 18, 1876-Aug 2, 1878. Moved to
Lexington Aug 16, 1878.

Monitor   w   1889
Listed in Ayer 1890.

News   w   1909-1917? 1921-1922?
In Ayer 1910-1918, 1922-1923. Second listing
has starting date of 1921.

Saturday Morning Visitor   w   1858-1861?
MoHi: Nov 13, 1858-Dec 15, 1860. Also under
St. Thomas (Cole County), MoHi: Nov 13,
1858-Jan 14, 1860. In American Newspaper
Directory 1861 under Waverly.

Times   w   1887-1900, 1926+
MoHi: Oct 16, Nov 6, 1890. Film, 1951+.

Watchman   w   1901?-1906?
In Rowell 1902-1907, with two founding dates--
1900 and 1887. In Ayer 1902 with founding date
1901.

WAYLAND (Clark County)

Hustler   w   1907-1909?
In Ayer 1910, founding date 1907.

New Homestead   w   1912-1913
Listed in Ayer 1913-1914.

News   w   1914-1916?
In Ayer 1917, founding date 1914.

Old Homestead   w   1899-1907?
In Rowell 1904-1908, Ayer 1902.

Times   w   1899-1908
In Rowell 1908, Ayer 1908-1909.

WAYNESVILLE (Pulaski County)

Fort Gateway Guide   w   1962+

Gasconade Valley Plain-Dealer   w   1876
   ICHi: Jun 9, 1876. In Rowell 1876, founding date
   1876.

Pulaski County Democrat   w   1882+
   MoHi: 1902-1914; 1916-Sep 1917; Oct 10, 1940-
   1941; Mar 1942-1944; Jly 10, 1903; Dec 1915.
   Film, 1945+.

Messenger   w   1883-1885
   In Rowell 1885, Dauchy 1883.

Pulaski County News   w   1882-1885
   In Rowell-Ayer 1886. See Dixon News.

Pulaski County Signal   w   1872
   In Rowell 1873. Hammond says followed by
   Gasconade Valley Plain Dealer.

Tribune   w   1879-1881
   In Rowell-Ayer 1880-1882. Also known as
   Pulaski County Tribune.

WEATHERBY   (DeKalb County)

DeKalb County Populist   w   1898
   In Rowell 1898-1899, Ayer 1899.

Magnet   w   1892-1895?
   In Ayer 1896, founding date 1892.

News   w   1893
   Death noted in National Printer-Journalist,
   Dec 1893.

Populist   w   1898
   Apparently same as DeKalb County Populist.
   Start reported in Country Editor, May 1898.

Post   w   1896-1897, 1913-1917?
   In Rowell 1897, Ayer 1897-1898 for first News,
   Ayer 1917-1918 for second.

WEAUBLEAU   (Hickory County)

Bazoo   w   1898
   In Rowell 1898-1899.

Hickory County Courier   w   1908-1909
   In Ayer 1909-1910.

Leader   w   1903
   In Ayer 1904.

Old Hickory   w   1913-1915?
   In Ayer 1915-1916.

Standard   w   1898-1902?
   In Rowell 1898-1903, Ayer 1899-1900.

WEAUBLEAU (continued)

Tri-County News   w   1934-1936?
   In Ayer 1937.

WEBB CITY   (Jasper County)

Chief   w   1891
   In Ayer 1892.

Commoner   d   1895-1900?
   In Rowell 1900-1901.

Crusher   d   1889
   In Rowell-Ayer 1890.

Enterprise   w   1877?
   Mentioned by Hammond.

Express   w   1900?
   In Ayer 1901, no founding date.

Graphic Review   w   1932+
   Shopper, free circulation.

Jasper County Republican   w   1893-1895
   Rowell 1894 lists one, founded 1893. Ayer 1896
   lists one, founded 1895.

Leader   d   1927-1946?
   In Ayer 1929-1947.

Mining Enterprise   w   1877-1878
   In Rowell 1878-1879.

Mining Record   w   1893-1895?
   In Ayer 1896, founding date 1893.

New Century   w   1877?
   In Pettengill 1877.

Register   d, w   1891-1917
   MoHi: Sep 18, 1903; Aug 17, 1905; Feb 21, 1906.
   Film, Nov 2, 1903-Sep 1910; 1914-Jan 1917.
   For several years had w edition.

Republican   d   1890
   MoHi: Oct 25, 1890. In Rowell 1891.

Sentinel   w, sw   1879+   d, sw   1890-1961
   MoHi: Aug 8, 1901-Apr 1906; Dec 22, 23, 1902.
   Film, 1920-Jun 1929; 1951+.
   KHi: Dec 14, 1925. Irregular listing. Rowell 1896
   lists d, founded 1890, w 1895. Ayer 1922
   lists w, founded 1921, and in 1929 has 1922
   for founding date. D ended, sw began Mar 3,
   1961.

Southwestern   w   1936-1961
   MoHi: Film, Mar 27-Oct 2, 1961. Formerly in
   Joplin. Ceased Oct 2, 1961.

Star   d   1890
   In Ayer 1890, founding date 1890.

WEBB CITY (continued)

Sunday Journal w 1892-1893
    In Rowell 1893-1894.

Times w 1879-1895 d 1890-1895?
    MoHi: Nov 19, 1891.

Topic d 1896?
    Missouri Editor, Oct 1896, says "Daily Topic
    has been revived." Rowell 1896-1899 lists Morning
    Topic, founded 1895. Ayer 1898 notes Evening
    Topic.

Topic and Mining Journal w 1896-1897?
    In Ayer 1898, w edition Evening Topic.

WEBSTER GROVES (St. Louis County)

Advertiser w 1954+
    See News-Times. Free distribution.

Leader w 1905?-1907?
    MoSHi: Aug 26, Sep 2, 1905; Jan 26, 1907.

Messenger w ?
    MoSHi: Oct 4, 11, Nov 8, 22, 1923; Mar 8, 1931.

News w 1910-1914
    MoHi: May 17, 1912-1913.
    MoSHi: Dec 10, 1910; May 5, 1911; Jun 7, 21,
    Jly 5, 19, Aug 2-Oct 17, Nov 7-Dec 12, 26,
    1913. Merged with Times Jan 1914.

News-Times w 1910-1961
    MoHi: Jan 23, 1914-1944. Film, 1945-1961.
    MoSHi: scattered issues, 1914-1919, 1921-1925.
    Acquired by Advertiser 1961.

Record w 1889-1890
    In Rowell 1890, Ayer 1890-1891.

St. Louis County Sentinel w 1904-1909?
    MoSHi: Sep 28, 1907. In Ayer 1908-1910.

Times w 1896-1899? 1908-1914
    MoHi: Jan 9, 16, 1914. See News.
    MoSHi: scattered issues, 1898, 1909-1913.

Webster and Kirkwood News w 1899-1900
    MoSHi: Sep 23, 30, 1899. In Rowell 1900-1901.

Webster News w 1910-1945
    Also listed as News-Times.

Ye Olde Towne Crier w 1932-1933
    MoSHi: May 18, 25, Jun 1, Aug 10, 17, Sep 7,
    1933.

WELLINGTON (Lafayette County)

Globe w 1894
    In Ayer 1895.

WELLINGTON (Lafayette County)

News w 1904-1922
    MoHi: 1919-Sep 1920. Film, Aug 3, 1916-1918.

Qui Vive w 1894-1898
    In Rowell 1895-1899, Ayer 1897-1898.

Review w 1923-1927
    In Ayer 1925-1928.

World w 1912-1914
    In Ayer 1915, founding date 1912.

WELLSTON (St. Louis County)

Journal w 1928+
    Merged with Local. Free paper.
    Microfilm Cen: Film, 1950-1959.

Local w 1914-1929?
    MoSHi: Sep 6, 1917. Last in Ayer 1930.

News w 1926
    In Ayer 1927.

St. Louis County Herald m 1903-1930
    MoHi: 1903-1924. Family publication.

Tribune w 1909
    In Ayer 1910.

WELLSVILLE (Montgomery County)

Advertiser w 1879-1882, 1894-1895
    First in Rowell 1880-1882, Ayer 1880. Missouri
    Editor, Dec 1894, tells of start of second; Apr
    1895 tells of suspension.

Bazoo w 1876-1878
    ICHi: Jly 6, 1876. In Rowell 1877-1879.

Club w 1892
    Populist paper, according to Ashcraft.

Courier w 1886
    In Ayer 1886, founding date 1886.

Democrat w 1883-1885?
    In Rowell 1884-1885.

Dispatch w 1898-1899?
    In Rowell 1898-1899, Ayer 1899.

News w 1886-1890?
    In Rowell-Ayer 1888-1890. Optic-News in
    Rowell 1891.

Optic-News w 1877+
    MoHi: Jly 18, Nov 18, 1902; Jly 17, 1903-Jly
    1904; 1914-Sep 1921. Film, Aug 29, 1958+.

WELLSVILLE (continued)

Record   w   1879-1906?
    MoHi: Film, Aug 1901-1903. Rowell 1900-1908
    uses 1891 founding date. Ayer, first listing
    Record 1899, uses 1879 date.

Star   w   1907-1952?
    Last in Ayer 1953.

Wide Awake   w   1880-1898
    Last in Ayer 1898, Rowell 1899.

WENTWORTH (Newton County)

Miner   w   1891-1893
    In Rowell 1892-1893, Ayer 1892-1894.

Mining Journal   w   1893-1897
    In Rowell 1894-1898, Ayer 1895-1898.

WENTZVILLE (St. Charles County)

Leader   w   1886-1887?
    In Ayer 1887, Rowell 1888.

News   w   1866-1869?
    In Rowell 1869-1870.

St. Charles News   w   1863-1870
    Organ says started in Wentzville 1863, moved
    to St. Charles 1870.

Union   w   1891+
    MoHi: 1920-1944. Film, 1914-1919; 1945+.

WESTBORO (Atchison County)

Atchison County Democrat   w   1898
    In Rowell 1898-1899. Rowell 1900 refers to
    Democrat-Wave.

Chief   w   1881-1882
    In Rowell 1883, founding date 1881.

Democrat   w   1898
    Apparently same as first listing. Start noted in
    Country Editor, Mar 1898.

Democrat-Wave   w   1898-1902?
    In Ayer 1900, Rowell 1900-1903.

Enterprise   w   1901-1922?
    MoHi: May 4, 1906-1907; May 1914-1921.

Sun   w   1876-1882?
    In Dauchy 1883, founding date 1876.

Wave   w   1892-1897
    MoSHi: Feb 8, 1896-Feb 13, 1897. In Rowell 1893-
    1897, Ayer 1892-1897.

WEST LINE (Cass County)

News   w   1898-1899
    In Ayer 1899-1900.

WEST ST. LOUIS (St. Louis County)

Western Star   w   1878?-1881?
    In Pettengill 1878. R.B. Grossman was press
    association member 1881.

WESTON (Platte County)

Border Times   w   1864-1871
    MoHi: Feb 13, 1864-Aug 9, 1867; Feb 28, 1868-
    Feb 18, 1870.
    WHi: Feb 13-Mar 26, Jun 10-17, Jly 22-Aug 12,
    Nov 4, 1864; Feb 10-Mar 17, 1865; Mar 15,
    1867.

Chronicle, Platte County Chronicle   w   1872+
    MoHi: Oct 1929-1944. Film, May 1886-Feb
    1930; 1945+.

Commercial   w   1872-1882
    Union List says name used for Chronicle during
    these years. Rowell 1883 lists same data under
    Missouri Commercial.

Democrat   w   1845
    Organ says one of three "insignificant and
    ephemeral papers that everted but little influence
    in the newspaper world" in 1845.

Forest Rose   w   1857-1858
    Organ says "literary paper devoted to dis-
    semination of polite literature, wit, humor and
    poetic gems."

Frontier Journal   w   1845-1849
    Renamed Reporter 1849, Organ says.

Herald   w   1847-1848, 1915-1917?
    Organ notes first Herald, merged into Frontier
    Journal 1848. Ayer 1916-1918 lists second.

Journal   w   1892-1893?   1906-1907
    MoSHi: Jan 4-Feb 15, Mar 1-Apr 19, 1845 as
    continuation of Independence Journal. Ayer
    1892 and Rowell 1893-1894, Ayer 1908 list
    other Journals.

Key City Commercial   w   1844-1858
    Formerly Frontier Journal and Reporter, notes
    Organ. Says name changed to Key City Com-
    mercial 1857, soon stopped.

Landmark   w   1865-1871
    Founded in Weston, to Platte City 1871.

Ledger   w   1904-1905
    In Rowell-Ayer 1906.

WESTON (continued)

Mail w 1859-1862?
    MoHi: Jan 4, 1862 as Western Mail. Sources
        disagree on founding, 1859, 1860.
    WHi: Jan 21, 1862 as Western Mail.

Platform w 1871
    In Rowell 1872 as Missouri Platform. Hammond
    says equipment formerly used on Border Times
    which suspended 1871.

Platte Argus w 1844-?
    DLC: Oct 31-Dec 1856.
    KHi: Aug 18, 1855 (Vol 12, No 14). Organ says
        replaced Eagle and moved back to Platte
        City 1844.

Platte County Argus w 1884-1929
    MoHi: 1926-Sep 26, 1929. Sold to Chronicle
        Sep 1929.

Platte County Landmark w 1865-1871
    MoHi: Jan 5, Feb 2, 23, Mar 16, 23, Apr 6, May 11,
        25, Jun 1, 15, Aug 10-31, Sep 8, 29-Oct 20, Nov
        3-Dec 8, 1866; Feb 8, Jly 5, Aug 30, Sep 13,
        Oct 18, 1867. To Platte City 1871.

Platte County Sentinel w 1861-1864
    MoSHi: May 14, 1863. To Platte City 1864.

Platte County World w 1896-1901
    MoHi: Film, Aug 19, 1900-Nov 28, 1901.

Platte Eagle and Weston Commercial Gazette
w 1842-1844
    Moved to Platte City as Argus 1844.

Progress w 1900?
    In Rowell 1901, founding date 1882.

Reporter w 1849-1856
    Formerly Frontier Journal.

Times d 1867
    MoHi: Sep 18, 1867. Also Border Times, w.
    WHi: w, Nov 27, 1863.

True Democrat w 1860
    Missouri Republican, Aug 23, 1860, tells of start
    by "Democratic Club of Weston."

Western Mail w 1862?
    See Mail.

World w 1896-1900
    MoHi: Film, Feb 18, 1898-Jly 19, 1900. "The
    World will stand up for Weston just as long as
    Weston stands up for the World," said editor in
    first issue.

WESTPHALIA (Osage County)

Osage County Volksblatt w 1896-1917
    MoHi: Aug 13-Dec 1903; 1905-1917.

WEST PLAINS (Howell County)

Champion-Gazette w 1881-1897
    In Rowell 1897-1898, Ayer 1898.

Howell County Gazette w 1881-1945
    MoHi: Nov 25, 1898-1944. Film, 1906-1907; Jan-
    Jun 21, 1945; Jan-Nov 1947. Merged with
    Journal as Journal-Gazette Jun 28, 1945. D at
    different times.

Journal w 1870-1945
    MoHi: Mar 11, 18, Apr 1-Jun 24, 1897; Dec 1898-
        Jun 21, 1945; Sep 7, 8, 1904; Jun 8, 22, Jly 6-
        Aug 31, Oct 26, Dec 14-28, 1905; Jan 1-25, 1906.
        Film, 1896-1898; Oct 24-Dec 30, 1946; Jan 9-
        Nov 13, 1947 (As Journal-Gazette for later
        years.)
    ICHi: Jun 23, 1876.
    KHi: Feb 25, 1926. As South Missouri Journal several
        years.

Journal-Gazette w 1870-1953 d 1894-1896?
    MoHi: Film, Jun 28, 1945-1946; 1948-1952. Sus-
        pended Mar 1953.

News w 1895-1907
    MoHi: Nov 25, 1898-1907; Mar 26, Apr 2, 1896.
    MoSHi: Jly 4, 1895-1907. Also called Howell
        County News.

People's Searchlight w 1912-1917?
    Last listed in Ayer 1918.

Quill w, sw 1885-1949 d 1903+
    MoHi: d, Jly 5, 1949-1950; Dec 2, 15, 1954. Film,
        1951+ w, sw 1914-1944. Film, Jun 14, 1907-
        Aug 1908; 1945-Jly 1, 1949. Changed from sw
        to d, Jly 5, 1949.
    KHi: d, Aug 28, Nov 13, 1922.

Type of the Times
    MoHi: Oct 2, 1869.

WEST POINT (Bates County)

Banner w 1856-1861
    Organ says this was second in county; destroyed by
    Kansas raiders 1861.

WESTPORT (Jackson County)

Border Star w 1855-1868
    MoHi: Film, Dec 31, 1858-Nov 10, 1860.
    MoKc: Film, Dec 31, 1858; Jan 28, Feb 11, 25, Apr
        8, 22, 29, May 13-Jun 10, Jly 15-Sep 16, Oct 1-
        29, 1859; Nov 12, 1859-Apr 14, 1860; Apr 21-
        May 26, Jun 9-Sep 29, Oct 6-Nov 10, Dec 8-22,
        1860. See Kansas City for several Westport
        papers.

WESTPORT (continued)

Border Star (continued)
KHi: Film, Dec 31, 1858-Dec 22, 1860.
NjR: Mar 15, 1855.

Border Times w 1855-1868
MoKc: Apr 5, 12, 1856, photostats.

Enquirer w 1893-1894?
Start noted in National Printer-Journalist,
Oct 1893. In Ayer 1894.

Examiner w 1893-1894?
In Rowell 1894. Rowell 1895 noted as combined
with Sentinel.

Frontier News w 1855
KHi: Oct 6, 1855.

Index w 1888-1891
In Rowell 1890-1892, Ayer 1891.

Leader w 1885-1899?
Listed in Ayer 1897-1900.

Record w 1888-1889?
Listed in Rowell-Ayer 1889.

Sentinel w,d 1892-1894
MoKc: Film, Aug 19, 1893-Jun 9, 1894. Rowell
1893 lists as d, Rowell 1894 as w. Rowell 1895
refers to Sentinel-Examiner.

Sentinel-Examiner w 1892-1899
MoKc: Film, Jun 16, 1894-Apr 29, 1899. Last
in Rowell 1899. See Examiner, Sentinel.

Star of an Empire w 1856-?
KHi: Jan 17, 24, Mar 21, Sep 5, 1852.

WHEATLAND (Hickory County)

Harpoon w 1887
In Ayer 1887, Rowell 1888.

Headlight w 1888-1889
In Ayer 1889 with 1888 founding date; Rowell
1889-1890 with 1887 founding date.

Hickory County Democrat w 1886
In Ayer 1886, founding date 1886. See Hermitage.

Hickory County Enquirer w 1876-1877?
ICHi: Jly 6, 1876. Listed in Rowell-Pettengill
1877. Hammond says became Star and moved
to Huntsville.

Hickory County Mirror w 1870-1875?
MoHi: Jan 14, 1870. Hammond says moved to
Hermitage as New Era.

Star w 1877-1882
In Rowell 1878-1882, Ayer 1880.

WHEATON (Barry County)

Enterprise w 1918
Listed in Ayer 1919.

Journal w 1910+
First in Ayer 1911.

WHEELING (Livingston County)

Democrat w 1902-1906?
In Ayer 1903, Rowell 1903-1907.

Eureka w 1899-1900
In Ayer 1900, Rowell 1900-1901.

Gazette w 1906
Listed in Rowell-Ayer 1907.

Missing Link w 1898
Listed in Ayer 1899.

News w 1890-1891
In Rowell 1891-1892, Ayer 1892.

Observer w 1892
In Ayer 1892, founding date 1892.

Sun w 1895-1898?
In Ayer 1897-1898 with 1895 founding date; in
Rowell 1896-1899 with 1890 founding date.

WHITESVILLE (Andrew County)

Banner w 1900-1914? 1922-1923
Apparently two. First in Ayer 1901-1915,
second Ayer 1924 with 1922 founding date.

Northwest Missourian w 1900?-1917
First in Ayer 1916, founding date 1900. Last in
Ayer 1918.

Times w 1898-1904?
Listed in Rowell 1900-1905.

WHITEWATER (Cape Girardeau County)

Star w 1895
Populist paper, in Ayer 1896.

Times w 1905-1907?
In Rowell 1906-1907, Ayer 1907.

WILLIAMSTOWN (Lewis County)

Banner w 1887-1888?
In Ayer 1887-1888, Rowell 1888.

WILLIAMSVILLE (Wayne County)

Buzz Saw w 1894-1898?
In Ayer 1896-1897, Rowell 1895-1899.

Echo w 1886-1888?
In Ayer 1886-1887, Rowell 1887.

WILLIAMSVILLE (continued)

Herald w 1910-1913
    Listed in Ayer 1913-1914.

Iron News w 1909-1911
    Listed in Ayer 1910-1912.

Leader w 1892-1893
    Listed in Rowell 1894.

Transcript w 1888-1892
    MoHi: Oct 23, 1890. In Rowell 1889-1893,
    Ayer 1889-1892.

WILLOW SPRINGS (Howell County)

Advocate w 1925-1931
    United with Republican to form News. In Ayer
    1927-1931.

Democrat w 1913-1914
    Listed in Ayer 1915.

Howell County Hummer w 1894
    Start noted in Missouri Editor, Sep 1894.

Index w 1884-1910
    MoHi: Film, 1903. In Ayer 1887-1911.

Independent w 1913
    In Ayer 1914.

News w 1890+
    MoHi: Aug 27, 1931-1944. Film, Aug 27-Dec 31,
    1931; 1945+. Result of merger Republican
    and Advocate Aug 27, 1931.

Republican w 1890-1931
    MoHi: 1920-Aug 13, 1931. Film, Sep 29, 1904-
    Jly 1908; Feb 1913-1919. See Advocate.

WINDSOR (Henry County)

Helmet w 1874-1875
    In Rowell 1874-1875, "only paper in Windsor."

Herald w 1885
    In Rowell 1886.

Journal w 1903
    In Rowell-Ayer 1904.

New Democrat w 1883
    In Rowell 1884.

Republican w 1895-1898
    MoHi: Mar 26, 1897; Jan 7, 28, 1898.

WINDSOR (continued)

Review w 1876+
    MoHi: Dec 29, 1898-Sep 1899; Jan-Oct 1909;
    1914-Nov 1916; Jly 1917-1944; Feb 25, 1909;
    Sep 18, 1952. Film, 1945+.
    MoSHi: Mar 5, 1896-1899; Feb 8, 1900-Jan 31,
    1901.
    ICHi: Jly 21, 1876.

Star w 1919-1936
    First in Ayer 1934, founding date 1919. Mailing
    list sold to Review 1936.

Times w, sw 1881-1891
    Listed as w Rowell 1891, sw Rowell 1892, Times-
    Democrat Rowell 1893.

Times-Democrat w 1881-1897
    Country Editor, Apr 1897, says ended.

4-County Windsorite w 1911-1916
    In Ayer 1913-1917.

WINFIELD (Lincoln County)

Gazette w 1915-1916
    Listed in Ayer 1916-1917.

News w 1907
    Listed in Ayer-Rowell 1908.

Phonograph w 1894
    See Moscow Mills Phonograph

Reflector w 1891
    Listed in Ayer-Rowell 1892.

Times w 1896
    Silver Democrat paper, in Ayer 1897.

WINONA (Shannon County)

Current Wave w 1884-1891
    In Ayer 1891, Rowell 1891-1892.

Magnet w 1896
    Listed in Ayer 1897.

Ozark News w 1895-1898
    In Rowell 1897-1898, Ayer 1897-1899. Union
    List says name used for several years for Shannon
    County Democrat.

Search-Light w 1899
    Start noted in Country Editor, Feb 1899.

Shannon County Democrat w 1895-1962
    MoHi: Aug-Dec 1903; 1911-1916; 1919-Jly 8,
    1943; Nov 17, 1916. Film, 1917-Dec 20,
    1918. Combined with Eminence Current Wave
    1962.

WINONA (continued)

Shannon County Globe   w   1894-1895?
In Rowell 1895, Dauchy 1896.

WINSTON (Daviess County)

Commercial   w   1882?
H. Howard member of press association 1882.

Enterprise   w   1887
Listed in Rowell 1888.

Independent   w   1883-1886?
In Rowell 1885-1887. One reference to Emporia.

Mirror   w   1891-1893
In Rowell 1892-1894 with 1891 founding date; in
Ayer 1894, 1891 with 1888 founding date. Moved
to Gallatin 1893, according to National Printer-
Journalist, Aug 1893.

News   w   1910?
MoHi: Feb 24, Jly 14, 1910.

Sentinel   w   1901-1928
MoHi: Aug 8, 1901-Feb 23, 1928; Aug 24, 1905.
Early copies Ayer give 1888 founding date.
Majority use 1901.
KHi: Feb 21-Apr 17, 1924 inc.

Star   w   1888-1899?
Last in Ayer 1900, Rowell 1903.

WORLAND (Bates County)

Watchman   w   1892
KHi: Apr 15-Aug 26, 1892.

WORTH (Worth County)

Tribune   w   1913-1914
MoHi: Film, Apr 30, 1913-Nov 18, 1914. To
Grant City Dec 9, 1914.

WORTHINGTON (Putnam County)

Press   w   1903-1910
In Rowell 1904-1908, Ayer 1905-1911.

Star   w   1888-1904?
In Rowell 1905, founding date 1888.

WRIGHT CITY (Warren County)

Banner   w   1872?
County history tells of merger of Visitor with
Banner 1872.

Journal   w   1897
Start noted in Country Editor, Apr 1897.

WRIGHT CITY (continued)

News   w   1889, 1904-1917
MoHi: Jan 15, 1909; May 12, 1911. First News
in Ayer 1889, Rowell 1890. Second in
Rowell 1904-1908, Ayer 1905-1918.

Visitor   w   1871
See Banner.

WYACONDA (Clark County)

Blade   w   1890
In Ayer 1891.

Clark County News   w   1888-1924
MoHi: 1904-1924; Apr 21, 1905; Jan 5, 1906.
Ayer 1924 notes News-Herald.

Echo   w   1888-1890
In Rowell-Ayer 1889-1891.

Leader   w   1926-1930
Union List says name used briefly for Reporter-
Leader.

Missouri Coupon   w   1895
In Rowell-Ayer 1896.

News-Herald   w   1888-1924
See Clark County News. Apparently only briefly
under this combined title.

Reporter-Leader   w   1926-1931
MoHi: May 19, 1931-Nov 10, 1932. Formed by
merger Dec 11, 1931.

ZINCITE (Jasper County)

Gazette   w   1891
In Rowell 1892.

Miner's Star   w   1886
In Ayer 1886, founding date 1886.

ZION (Madison County)

Assembly News   w   1904?
Listed by Williams 1904.

School News   1904
Listed by Williams 1904.

Ensign   1904
Listed by Williams 1904 as in Jackson County.
Some question on all three of these listings.